John Ramsay's Catal[ogue]

BRITISH MODEL [TRAINS]

FIRST EDITION

C000300244

'O' Gauge
Hornby Trains, Bassett-Lowke

'OO' Gauge
Hornby Dublo, Wrenn Railways, Tri-ang Railways

SWAPMEET PUBLICATIONS

Swapmeet Publications
PO Box 47, Felixstowe, Suffolk, IP11 7LP
Phone (01394) 670700, Fax: (01394) 670730

Swapmeet Toys and Models Ltd., t/a Swapmeet Publications
Reg. No. 1715966. Reg. Office: 36 Rembrandt Way, Bury St Edmunds, Suffolk. Directors: E. J. Ramsay, S. E. Ramsay, Co. Sec. M. J. Ramsay, BA.

Originator and Editor
John Ramsay

Assistant Editor
John King

1st Edition published 1998

Book designed by John King.
Typeset by Swapmeet Toys and Models Ltd, Felixstowe.
Printed by Crowes of Norwich.

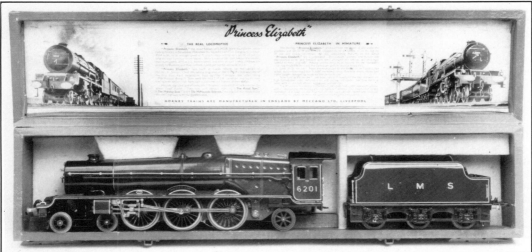
WHEN REPLYING TO ADVERTISEMENTS PLEASE MENTION JOHN RAMSAY'S CATALOGUE

CORGI *Collector*

Join the Corgi Collector Club and share your diecast hobby with fellow Corgi enthusiasts worldwide.

Membership benefits include:-
- 10 issues of the Club magazine each year, giving up to the minute information on new product releases, the background to many Corgi models and where to see the Corgi Roadshow in your area.
- Club membership card giving discount at selected Gold Star retail and leisure outlets.
- Family membership discounts - 1 magazine per family - all living at the same address - plus 1 membership card per member.
- Exciting free gifts when you introduce new members.
- Voucher booklet featuring discounts and value added offers for all the family at museums, transport and leisure related outlets and selected Corgi retailers.
- Competitive insurance facilities
- Participation in all reader offers, Club competitions and prize draws.
- Special invitations to Corgi product previews at the Corgi Heritage Centre and Regional Centres around the UK.

**IN ADDITION,
MEMBERS HAVE THE
OPPORTUNITY TO PURCHASE**
Up to 2 of the exclusive annual Club model
Corgi catalogues, Club Magazine binders and many other items of Corgi branded Club merchandise

HOW TO JOIN   Send the appropriate remittance, made payable to Corgi Collector Club, by cheque (drawn on a British bank), postal order, International Giro or credit card (Visa, Mastercard, Switch) to:

**The Corgi Collector Club,
P O Box 323,
Swansea. SA1 1BJ. UK**
Tel/Fax/Answerphone 01792 476902

SUBSCRIPTION RATES (1998)
Membership runs for one year from the date of application

£14 (UK)
£16 (Europe)
£20 (Rest of World)

We look forward to welcoming you as a Corgi Collector Club Member

Contents

Page

Page

INTRODUCTION 9

ARTICLES and INFORMATION:
Acknowledgements:
   Catalogue contributors 12
   Official Company Acknowledgements 12
Advertisers Index...............................8
Brief history of model manufacturers 26
Catalogue Omissions 12
Classifying the condition of
  models and boxes 11
Development of Model Trains...................27
How to use this Catalogue........................11
Index of Model Manufacturers.................209
Leeds Model Company
Market Price Range Grading system..........10
Milbro 74
Model and box valuation guidelines 10
'O' gauge Introduction 29
Post-war Hornby 'O' gauge 71
Scales and Gauges 28
Selling models to the Trade 12
Tin-Plate Trains.................................190

AUCTION RESULTS SECTIONS:
Reference 'OO' gauge Auction Results....104
'O' and larger gauge Auction Results 75
'OO' and 'HO' gauge Auction Results.....175

MODEL LISTINGS:

Bassett-Lowke 30

Bing for Bassett-Lowke.......................33

Dinky Toys Trains.............................191

Hornby Dublo
  Introduction 87
  Accessories 99
  Catalogues 101
  Coaches 1938 - 1964 90
  Information sources..........................102
  Locomotives 1938 - 1964....................88
  Packaging 102
  Pricing guidelines 101
  Train Sets 96
  Technical information....................103
  Vans and Wagons...........................92

Hornby 'O' gauge 38
  Locomotives 56
  Private-Owner Wagons 60
  Miscellaneous Rolling Stock...................61
  Post-war Hornby 71

Lone Star 193
Master Models 195
Mettoy 198
Playcraft 199

Tri-ang Railways 126
  Locomotives 127
  Military and Novelty items 152
  Rolling Stock – Coaches 134
  Rolling Stock – Vans and Wagons 139
  'Transcontinental' range 140
  Tri-ang 'TT' Table Top Railways...........153

Trix Twin Railways 200
Wells-Brimtoy 206

Wrenn Railways
  Locomotives 165
  Passenger Coaches 170
  Vans and Wagons.........................171

Index to Advertisers

Page

Abbey Models (Nick Powner)..................................209
Acme Toy Co...22
Allsorts...24
John Ayrey (Wholesalers).......................................18
B & B Military...23
Trevor Bannister..156
Biddle & Webb Auctions...15
Bonhams Auctions...........................Inside rear cover
Michael Bowen..14
Capes Dunn Auctions..15
Carr Collectables...156
Cars and Boxes, Germany (Hardy Ristau)........................156
Christie's Auctions...113
Andrew Clark...23
Clark's Collectables..156
G. Cleveland (Wholesalers)......................................5
Collector's Gazette ....Rear cover
Collectors Toy and Model Shop..................................17
Corgi Club..4
Corgi Heritage Centre (Chris Brierley)........................207
Diecast Toy Exchange Auctions, USA............................157
Digby's Miniature Automobiles..................................19
A. E. Dowse Auctions...24
Terry Durrant...155
Euro Antique Toy Auctions, USA (Tim Arthurs)...................21
A. B. Gee (Wholesalers).......................................157
Gloucester Toy Mart..22
GrA's Models...21
Allen Green (Wholesalers)......................................24
Hornby Dublo Wanted...155
David Kerr..209
Lacy, Scott & Knight Auctions 6
Cliff Maddock..22
Bob May...156
The Model Shop, Inverness......................................22
The Model Store...209
Much Ado About Toys..24
MW Collectable Toys..24

New Cavendish Books..13
John Neale...19
John Nicholson's Auctions......................................15
K. H. Norton (Wholesalers).....................................18
Nostalgia Toy Museum...19
Past Present Toys..14
Pentoy (Wholesalers)...21
Phillips Auctioneers...13
Pit Stop...23
Platform 6 Auctions..19
Barry Potter Auctions..20
Railway Mart...22
Remember When (Mike Rooum).....................................22
Romantic Robot..156
Ron's Model Rail and Diecast...................................17
The Shunting Yard...155
Sotheby's Auctions...15
Southampton Model Centre.......................................16
Square Wheels..22
Stamp Insurance Services.......................................24
Kerri Stanley..22
Sue Richardson...24
Swapmeet Publications:
    Catalogue Consultancy Service 208
    Catalogue Users Survey.................................208
    Display Cabinets.......................................212
    7th Edition 'British Diecast Model Toys Catalogue'
    Volume I...210
    7th Edition 'British Diecast Model Toys Catalogue'
    Volume II 211
    1st Edition 'French Meccano Dinky Toys' 208
Trains and Olde Tyme Toys.....................................155
U.K. Toy & Model Auctions......................................23
Unique Collections...14
Vectis Model Auctions...................Inside front cover
Wallis & Wallis Auctions..3
The Warehouse, Dover...25

The advertisers index has been compiled as an extra service for Catalogue users. Whilst every care has been taken in compiling the listing, the publishers cannot accept responsibility for any errors aor omissions. Similarly, the publishers cannot accept responsibility for errors in the advertisements or for unsolicited photographs or illustrations.

Introduction

Welcome to this 1st edition of the 'British Model Trains Catalogue'.

The objective of the catalogue is to provide an accurate price guide for the most collectable 'OO' and 'O' gauge model trains plus comprehensive listings of the auction prices realised.

The major 'Hornby Dublo' and 'Wrenn Railways' listings were formerly included the 'British Diecast Model Toys Catalogue'. However from feedback received from both the trade and collectors alike, it was apparent that the listings required their own individual publication, rather than being included in a book concentrating on Dinky Toys etc.

The decision to publish the above listings in a dedicated model trains catalogue has enabled us to include more 'OO' listings such as Tri-ang plus 'O' gauge listings such as Hornby Trains. In addition we have also been able to underpin the 'Market Price Range' figures shown by the inclusion of hundreds of actual auction results.

Finally it has been possible to include a thirty-two page colour section entirely dedicated to model trains.

The Editor would like to express his appreciation to Hugo Marsh of Christie's of South Kensington for supplying the superb 'OO' gauge pictures. The pictures illustrate the models sold at their recent 'Bianco Hornby Dublo Reference Collection' sale and are truly a unique reference in their own right.

Similarly the Editor would like to thank Barry Potter of Barry Potter Auctions for kindly supplying many of the superb 'O' gauge and 'Wrenn Railways' pictures.

We believe the information contained in the listings provides an accurate guide to market prices of collectable models.

The Editor is indebted for the assistance provided by Terry Durrant, Dick Fawcett, Mark Hewitt and Rob Smith of Southampton Model Centre without whose help the 'OO' listings could not have been completed.

The objective of the section devoted to providing 'O' gauge Auction Results and catalogue pictures is to provide collectors and the trade with a comprehensive coverage of the prices achieved over the past two years. The aim of the listings has been to include examples of all those manufacturers who produced models with British railway company liveries – quite a formidable task.

Overall, with high prices fine model trains it is crucial that the price guidance given is as accurate as possible. Consequently the 'Market Price Range' information has been based on actual market prices achieved on both a current and an historical basis. In addition, to firmly underpin the price guidance given, a comprehensive range of actual auction results has been listed.

We do not believe it is sensible to give too much credence to any one auction result. However, the constant support provided by auction results does help to stabilise market price levels. Nevertheless, collectors would do well to understand that the price guidance given is simply a guide – no more, no less. There cannot of course be any guarantees that prices achieved in the past will be repeated in the future.

As with all forms of collecting, condition is of paramount importance. Consequently whenever the information is available the auction results contain full details of the condition of both the model and its box.

Model collecting is an international hobby and many of the fine models sold in the UK are purchased by overseas buyers. This international influence has undoubtedly helped to maintain the firm price levels for top quality models.

As always the success of the Catalogue is due to the splendid level of support provided by both collectors and the trade.

In conclusion we trust that this 1st Edition of the 'British Model Trains Catalogue' will assist collectors to enjoy their hobby all the more. It is our intention to include extra model listings in future editions. If you feel you can help in any way do please contact us.

Market Price Range Grading System

Based on the findings of the Market Surveys undertaken since 1995 virtually all the 'OO' gauge models have been given a 'Market Price Range'.

The price gap between the lower and higher figures indicates the likely price range a collector should expect to pay for an item which is in top-class condition for its age and type, e.g., 'Mint Boxed' or 'Mint' for post-war locomotives and rolling stock. Pre-war items would be described as 'Excellent' or 'Good' for early items.

PRICES FOR MODELS IN LESS THAN MINT BOXED CONDITION

Many boxed models seen for sale fail to match up to the exacting standards on which the Market Price Range has been based, having slight model or box damage. In these instances models may be priced at 50% to 60% of the Market Price Range shown, and this is particularly relevant when a model is common. Boxed models with considerable damage or unboxed models will be priced at much lower level.

Note: It cannot be over-emphasised that irrespective of the price guidance provided by this Catalogue, collectors should not always expect to see prices asked within the price ranges shown. Traders will ask a price based on their trading requirements and will NOT be governed by any figures shown in this Catalogue, nor could they be reasonably expected to do so.

MODELS NOT GIVEN A 'MARKET PRICE RANGE'

It has not been possible to give every model a price range and these exceptions are as follows:

NPP   No Price Possible

This is shown alongside models never encountered in the survey and about which there is doubt as to their actual issue, even though a model may have been pictured in a catalogue.

Readers will appreciate that unlike postage stamps or coins, no birth records are available in respect of all the die-cast models designed or issued.

NGPP   No Grading Possible at Present

Where a model or set is particularly rare and no price information whatsoever is possible, no price grading has been shown as the Compiler believes that this is carrying rarity and value assessment into the realms of pure guesswork. As and when information becomes available concerning these rarities it will be included in the Catalogue.

DESCRIPTION OF MODEL COLOURS

The descriptions of the various colours used to describe model colour variations have been derived from the following sources:
i) Manufacturers colour descriptions.
ii) Colours commonly used and known to refer to certain models over a period of many years.
iii) Colours which we in consultation with the trade or specialist collectors decide most closely describes a previously unrecorded genuine colour variation.
iv) Colours given a model by an bonafide auction house. If this model is a previously unrecorded colour variation we will include the variation in future catalogue listings provided that:
   a) The auctioneers are themselves satisfied that the model is genuine and not a repaint
   b) Specialist dealers and collectors who view the model at an auction sale and are satisifed that the colour variation is genuine and is not a repaint.

SCARCE COLOURS AND VARIATIONS

Collectors or traders who know of other variations which they believe warrant a separate listing are invited to forward this information to the Editor together with any supporting evidence.

Model and Box Valuation Guidelines

The research has produced the following comparative price information concerning the values of both unboxed models and separate boxes in the various condition classifications.
 The guidelines have been based on the 'General Condition' grading system as described in the previous section. The percentage value ranges are designed to reflect the relatively higher values of the rarer models and boxes.

'OO' gauge

UNBOXED MODEL CLASSIFICATION	% VALUE OF MINT BOXED MODEL
Mint	50% - 60%
Excellent	40% - 50%
Good	20% - 40%
Fair	10% - 20%
Poor	0% - 10%

BOX CLASSIFICATION	%VALUE OF MINT BOXED MODEL
Mint	40% - 50%
Excellent	30% - 40%
Good	20% - 30%
Fair	10% - 20%
Poor	0% - 10%

'O' and larger gauges

Pre-war and post-war issues
Single models are usually priced on an unboxed basis. If a box does exist use the above 'OO' basis as a guide.

Classifying the condition of models and boxes

The condition of a model and its accompanying box does of course have a direct bearing on its value which makes accurate condition grading a matter of key importance.

Unlike other collecting hobbies such as stamps or coins, no one universal grading system is used to classify the condition of models and boxes. Nevertheless, whilst several versions exist, there are really two main systems of condition classification in the UK as follows:

The 'Specific Condition' Grading System
The following example is fairly typical of the types of descriptions and gradings seen on Mail Order lists.

M	Mint	AM	Almost Mint
VSC	Very Slightly Chipped	SC	Slightly Chipped
C	Chipped	VC	Very Chipped

If a model is described as Mint Boxed, the condition of its box is not normally separately described. However, it is expected to be in first class and as near original condition as is possible, bearing in mind the age of the model concerned.

If a box is damaged the flaws are usually separately described. This method has always seemed to work out quite well in practice, for all reputable dealers automatically offer a 'Sale or Return if not satisfied' deal to their clients, which provides the necessary safeguard against the misrepresentation of the model's condition. The Compiler would stress that the foregoing is only an example of a mail order condition grading system and stricter box grading definitions are known to exist.

The 'General Condition' Grading System
This method is often used by auctioneers to describe the condition of locomotives and rolling stock.

(M)	Mint	The item is in perfect condition.
(NM)	Near Mint	Almost perfect, any imperfections will be extremely minor
(E)	Excellent	The item will have had very careful use, with only small imperfections
(G)	Good	The item will have had more use, showing obvious imperfections
(F)	Fair	The item will have heavy signs of wear, showing major imperfections
(P)	Poor	The item will be in a very distressed condition, with many faults

In addition to these gradings, many auctioneers separately describe the condition of models and boxes.

Box Condition Gradings
1. MINT (M)
The box must be complete both inside and out and contain all the original packing materials, manufacturer's leaflet and box labels. It should look as fresh, new and original in appearance as when first received from the manufacturers.

2. EXCELLENT (E)
The box is in almost mint condition but is only barred from that classification by just the odd minor blemish, e.g., there may be slight damage to the display labels caused by bad storage. The original shop price label may have been carelessly removed and caused slight damage. The cover of a bubble pack may be cracked or there may be very slight soiling etc.

3. GOOD (G)
The box is complete both inside and out, and retains an overall attractive collectable appearance. Furthermore, despite showing a few signs of wear and tear, it does not appear 'tired'.

4. FAIR (F)
The box will have a 'tired' appearance and show definite signs of wear and tear. It may be incomplete and not contain the original packing materials or leaflets. In addition it may not display all the exterior identification labels or they may be torn or soiled or a box-end flap may be missing or otherwise be slightly damaged. In this condition, unless the model is particularly rare, it will not add much to the model's value.

5. POOR (P)
The box will show considerable signs of wear and tear. It will almost certainly be badly damaged, torn, incomplete or heavily soiled and in this condition, unless it is very rare, is of little value to a collector.

Auction Results Sections
See the Auction Results sections for details of model and box condition descriptions used by individual auction houses.

How to use the Catalogue

Identifying models from their lettering
All lettering shown in CAPITAL LETTERS indicates the actual lettering on the model itself. It may appear in either the Model name (vehicle) or Model Features (description) column. Similarly *lettering in Italics* indicates that it is shown on the actual model.

Abbreviations
In this Edition dependence on abbreviations has been reduced to a minimum but where necessary they are used to include information concisely.

Selling models to the Trade

The model value figures produced by the Price Grading system always refer to the likely *asking prices* for models.

They have been prepared solely to give collectors an idea of the amount they might reasonably expect to pay for a particular model.

The figures given are *not* intended to represent the price which will be placed on a model when it is offered for sale to a dealer. This is hardly surprising bearing in mind that the dealer is carrying all the expense of offering his customers a collecting service which costs money to maintain.

Collectors should not therefore be surprised when selling models to the trade to receive offers which may appear somewhat low in comparison with the figures shown in the Catalogue.

Dealers are always keen to replenish their stocks with quality items and will as a result normally make perfectly fair and reasonable offers for models. Indeed, depending on the particular models offered to them, the actual offer made may well at times exceed the levels indicated in the Catalogue which are only *guidelines* and not firm figures.

One last point when selling models to the trade do get quotations from two or three dealers especially if you have rare models to be sold.

Catalogue omissions

Accurate birth records do not exist in respect of all the models issued. Therefore whilst every effort has been made to provide comprehensive information it is inevitable that collectors will have knowledge of models which have not been included. Consequently the Compiler will be pleased to receive details of these models in order that they may be included in future editions. Naturally, supporting evidence regarding authenticity will be required.

This Catalogue has been prepared solely for use as a reference book and guide to the rarity and asking prices of model and toys.

Whilst every care has been taken in compiling the Catalogue, neither the Compiler nor the publishers can accept any responsibility whatsoever for any financial loss which may occur as a result of its use.

Catalogue contributors

The Editor would like to express his personal thanks to the following contributors without whose help the Catalogue would not have been produced.

Terry Durrant of Norfolk

Dick Fawcett of Suffolk

Dave Jowett, Stewart Bean and Harry Walker for assistance with the Wrenn Railways listing

Brian Secker of Trains and Olde Tyme Toys, Norwich

Rob Smith of Southampton Model Centre

Mark Hewitt of Kent for the Tri-ang listings

David Leach of the Collectors Model Shop, Margate

Roy Chambers of Kent for a major contribution to the Hornby 'O' Gauge listings

Barry Potter of Barry Potter Auctions

Hugo Marsh of Christie's, South Kensington

Sue Duffield of Sotheby's, Sussex

Glen Butler of Wallis & Wallis, Lewes

Leigh Gotch of Bonham's Chelsea

John Morgan of Vectis Model Auctions, Thornaby

Brian Leigh of Romsey Model Auctions

Kegan Harrison of Phillips, Bayswater

Albert Chaplin of Lacy, Scott & Knight, Bury St Edmunds

Official Company Acknowledgements

It is acknowledged that the name 'Meccano' is the registered trademark of Meccano SA, Calais, France.
It is acknowledged that the name 'Dinky Toys' is a registered trademark of the Mattel group of companies.
It is acknowledged that the names 'Hornby Series', 'Hornby Trains', Hornby Dublo', 'Tri-ang', 'Tri-ang-Hornby', 'Hornby Railways' and 'The Hornby Book of Trains' are all trademarks or trade names of Hornby Hobbies Ltd., Margate, Kent.
It is acknowledged that the name 'Wrenn Railways' is the registered trademark of G & R Wrenn Ltd, Bowlers Croft, Basildon, Essex.
It is acknowledged that the name 'Bassett-Lowke' is the registered trademark of Bassett-Lowke Ltd, Northampton.

WHEN REPLYING TO ADVERTISEMENTS PLEASE MENTION JOHN RAMSAY'S CATALOGUE

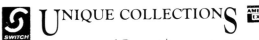

WHEN REPLYING TO ADVERTISEMENTS PLEASE MENTION JOHN RAMSAY'S CATALOGUE

14

WHEN REPLYING TO ADVERTISEMENTS PLEASE MENTION JOHN RAMSAY'S CATALOGUE

WHEN REPLYING TO ADVERTISEMENTS PLEASE MENTION JOHN RAMSAY'S CATALOGUE

WHEN REPLYING TO ADVERTISEMENTS PLEASE MENTION JOHN RAMSAY'S CATALOGUE

WHEN REPLYING TO ADVERTISEMENTS PLEASE MENTION JOHN RAMSAY'S CATALOGUE

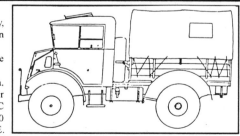
WHEN REPLYING TO ADVERTISEMENTS PLEASE MENTION JOHN RAMSAY'S CATALOGUE

● PURCHASE IN CONFIDENCE

Whether you are interested in locomotives only or complete railways you can be certain that Milbro products will give you the same utterly reliable service that is expected of the great railway groups in this country. Send 6d. for your copy of the 100 page catalogue

THEY look the same, run with identical reliability and are built to the same fine standards as the huge expresses that maintain such efficient schedules throughout the country.

MILBRO TRUE·TO·SCALE replicas for reliability

MILLS BROS. (Model Engineers) Ltd., Dept. M.R., St. Mary's Rd., SHEFFIELD
London Showrooms:
2, Victoria Colonnade, Victoria House, Southampton Row, W.C.1

Above: Vintage 1938 advertisment

MODEL RAILWAYS AND VEHICLES

A good selection of model railways,
especially '0' gauge, is always kept in this antique shop

THE WAREHOUSE
Associated with Elham Antiques

29-30 Queens Gardens, Worthington Street,
Dover, Kent. CT17 9AH. Tel. 01304 242006
Open Tuesday to Saturday 9.30 - 4.30

Brief history of British model train manufacturers, 1902 – 1971

1902   Bassett-Lowke introduced the first range of commercially produced
        British model trains from their Northampton factory.

1920   Meccano Ltd launch Hornby Trains.

1925   Leeds Model Co. (LMC) introduce their first models to special orders.

1930   Bonds O' Euston Rd Ltd introduce their 0-6-2 'Bonzone' electric tank
        locomotive.

1925   Milbro (Mills Brothers) began manufacture of 'O' gauge locomotives.

1936   Bassett-Lowke start manufacturing 'Trix Express' twin track railway,
        i.e., British Trix is formed.

1938   Meccano Ltd introduce Hornby Dublo Trains.

1948   Graham Farish began manufacturing locomotives

1950   Rovex Plastics Ltd introduce their black plastic 'Princess' train set.

1950   Trackmaster introduce some plastic vans and wagons to the market place.

1951   'Rovex' and 'Trackmaster' are incorporated into the Lines Brothers
        Group to form Tri-ang Railways. The Company traded as Rovex
        Scale Models Ltd and operated from a factory in Margate.

1951   Gaiety (Castle Arts / J.V. Murcott & Sons Ltd) introduced their
        pannier tank locomotive.

1952   Tri-ang Railways issue their first products.

1953   'Ever-Ready' batteries introduced their low-voltage train set.

1964   Hornby Dublo Trains taken over by Tri-ang. Hornby 'O' gauge
        trains cease to be supplied.

1965   Tri-ang-Hornby products issued.

1969   Tri-ang Group go into liquidation. The Rovex section of the business
        is taken over by the Dunbee, Combex, Marx organisation, and
        continued to operate as Hornby Railways.

1971   The Tri-ang subsidiary G & R Wrenn became an independent firm, and
        possessing some of the Hornby Dublo tools, began to produce
        the original Hornby Dublo models under the name of Wrenn Railways.

Development of Model Trains

Model trains commenced soon after the first real train ran from Euston to Birmingham in 1838, but these were professionally built replicas, only within the pockets of the wealthy.

The idea of quantity production started at the end of the 19th Century in Nuremburg, the centre of the German clock-making industry. It was the home of the Marklin Brothers, Carette, the Bing Brothers and Bub - now famous names associated with tinplate trains, especially in the period 1900-1930.

Early models in large scales were fired by methylated spirits and driven by steam – leaving water on carpets and causing minor fires; naturally, these 'piddlers' were hated by house-wives! They are now sought only by a few specialist collectors.

British trains proliferated in Edwardian times when W.J. Bassett-Lowke designed British models, manufactured for him by the German firms. After the First World War, Bassett-Lowke employed other makers to produce a magnificent range of models of varying degrees of realism. The more sophisticated ones now fetch high figures.

In 1920, Frank Hornby produced his first train and by the mid-1930s Hornby had become a household name. The majority are brightly coloured pieces of tinplate, not prototypical, in gauge 'O' (7mm = 1ft) but later in the 30s truer to scale models were produced, culminating in the 'Princess Elizabeth' at 5gns - at a time when a good weekly wage was £3! Due to popular demand, Hornby models are now rather inflated in price, however, the common ones are still fairly cheap. The value of model railway items – as with most collecting – is governed by rarity, condition and original box.

During the 1920s and 1930s there were many lesser firms producing excellent scale models, such as Leeds Model Company and Milbro; whilst the 'Woolworths' side of 'O' gauge was catered for by Mettoy and Wells. In America, Lionel and American Flyer Lines were the best-known makers.

The scales directly reflect social history; big Edwardian houses had gauge '1' (10mm = 1ft) and larger on their carpets. Small houses of the 20s accommodated 'O' gauge, although a small table-top railway was produced by Bing, it was not until the late 1930s that 'OO' (4mm = 1ft) by Trix and Hornby Dublo really commenced.

Improved technical ability has also made smaller units possible and in today's modern world of flats; sophisticated plastic mouldings, pioneered by Tri-ang in the 1950s, now covers mechanics in 'N' (2mm = 1ft) and 'Z' (1mm = 1ft) gauges. These scales are an optician's delight!

This article first appeared in the June 1992 'Antiques and Collectables Magazine' headed 'Little Trains to Get Steamed Up About' (Copyright Roy Chambers).

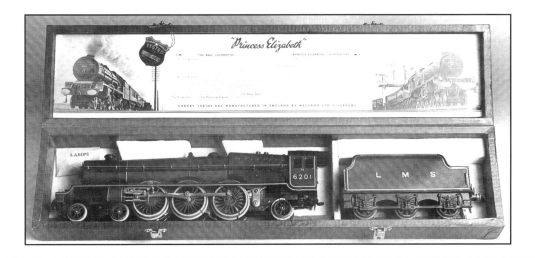

Scales and Gauges

Scale refers to the linear scale of the model, for example 4mm to 1 foot – the 'OO' scale measurement.

Gauge refers to the distance between the running rails of the track.

Gauge name	Scale	Gauge distance
'N'	1:148 or 1:60	9 mm
'OOO'	2 mm to 1 foot	9.5 mm
'TT'	3 mm to 1 foot	12 mm
'HO'	3.5 mm to 1 foot	16.5 mm
'OO'	4 mm to 1 foot	16.5 mm
'EM'	4 mm to 1 foot	18 mm
'O'	7 mm to 1 foot	32 mm (1-1/4 inches)
'No.1'	10 mm to 1 foot	45 mm (1-3/4inches)
'No.2'	7/16 inch to 1 foot	51 mm (2 inches)
'No.3'	17/32", 1/2" or 14 mm to 1 foot!	72 mm (3-13/16")

The illustrations below are only approximately to scale but serve to give some idea of the difference in size between the various gauges.

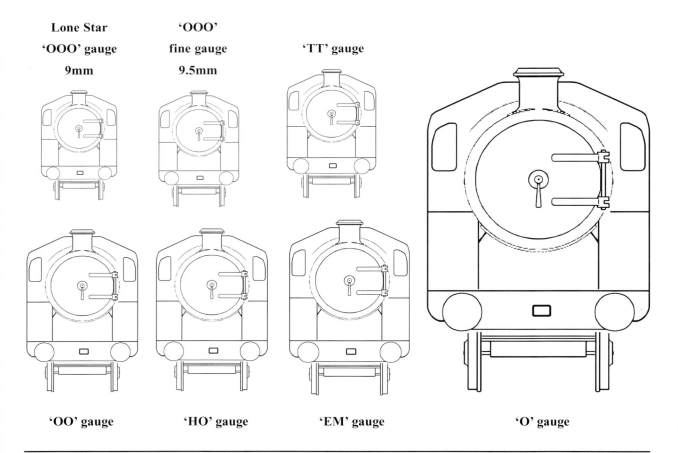

Lone Star 'OOO' gauge 9mm	'OOO' fine gauge 9.5mm	'TT' gauge	
'OO' gauge	**'HO' gauge**	**'EM' gauge**	**'O' gauge**

'O' gauge Model Railways

The scale of 'O' gauge is 7mm to 1 foot and was available early in the 20th century, reaching its height of popularity between the two World Wars. Its manufacture almost died out in the late 1950s because of the rapid development of 'OO' gauge (4mm to 1 foot) and the compactness of modern housing. Its resurrection is seen today in the form of 'O' gauge Fine Scale, highly detailed and realistic models usually with very efficient modern 12 volt electric 'can' motors (an area not covered in this guide).

Propulsion of the coarse scale models is by live steam (usually meths fed to a burner under the boiler) or by clockwork or electric motor of 4, 6, 8, 12 or 20 volts. Products vary from simple toy trains to more sophisticated scale models in a variety of sizes, all running on 32mm gauge track.

The locomotives and rolling stock were backed up by a large range of accessories, some of which now command disproportionately high prices. This is because they are less common, being destroyed by well-meaning spring-cleaning parents who retained the more imposing looking locomotives and coaches.

One difference between model train collectors and most other model collectors is that approximately 85% of the former use their possessions on railway layouts. They receive encouragement in this activity through very good societies who provide a back-up of literature, spares and insurance. The majority of the models are made of tinplate with some cast parts and they are either tinplate printed or enamelled. Special ones are sometimes made of brass.

Packaging does not seem to have played a very important part in selling the models, most of which cannot be seen when in their boxes. They are not as attractive as the boxes provided for model cars which were produced in a later, more advertising conscious period. The exception here of course is the boxes made for the Hornby train sets. These are covered by attractive, imaginative pictures of speeding locomotives. Single models are normally packed in plain card boxes with a single colour printing giving the information.

In the following price guide the figures given are for Very Good to Excellent unboxed examples except in the case of the Hornby 'Princess Elizabeth' which has a rather special pack. Prices for sets assume a pristine box is included. Prices are only an average guide; mint boxed items will be rather more and scruffy examples much less.

At the end of the day it depends on what you are prepared to give and for what the other chap is prepared to sell!

BASSETT-LOWKE

Wenman Joseph Lowke was born in 1877 into a boiler making family trading as J.T. Lowke & Co. Ltd. On starting his own business in 1901 W.J. Lowke combined his fathers name with his mothers maiden name of Bassett and so the famous Bassett-Lowke Company name was formed.

In 1903 Bassett-Lowke produced their first locomotive which was a Gauge 1 LNWR steam powered model of the 'Lady of the Lake'. It was soon to be followed by the famous 'Black Prince' locomotive which was produced in LNWR livery although other liveries were available to special order. This locomotive was available in a range of gauges O, 1, 2 and 3.

Several other locomotives were manufactured and by the outbreak of the first world war nineteen models were available.

In the period 1920-39 many locomotives were produced (see the reproduced catalogue). Among the best known were 'Moguls' in the LNER, LMS, GWR and Southern liveries of which the LMS is the common version. Other famous locomotives included the LNER 'Flying Scotsman', the LMS 'Royal Scot', the 4–4–0 'Duke of York' and 'Princess Elizabeth'. After the war the same locomotive became 'Prince Charles'. The last Model Railway Catalogue was issued in 1963.

BING FOR BASSETT-LOWKE

In 1902 Bassett-Lowke contracted the famous Bing Brothers firm in Nuremberg, Germany to manufacture British outline locomotives. (A similar arrangement existed with Carette). The locomotives were to be to the design of the Bassett-Lowke designer Henry Greenly. In 1925 Bassett-Lowke manufactured the first 'OO' Gauge system – the Bing Table Top Railway.

BASSETT-LOWKE AND TRIX

In 1935 Bassett-Lowke introduced into Britain 'The Bassett-Lowke Twin Table Railway' which had been produced by the German firm of Trix and known as the 'Trix Express' range.

Soon the models were beng made in Britain by the British Trix Company and had die-cast locomotive bodies. After the war the model range was known as the Trix Twin Railway (TTR).

BASSETT-LOWKE LTD.
6D NORTHAMPTON
LONDON AND MANCHESTER

Bassett-Lowke

Wenman Joseph Bassett-Lowke commenced his business in 1899 in Northampton, where his family already had a successful agricultural engineering firm. He is the father of model railways in Great Britain and as early as 1902 was importing models made in Nuremburg, to his own British outline designs.

He travelled widely and made many friends on the continent, taking photographs in the process in order to give lectures on his return.

In Northampton he was a very energetic councillor, being responsible for the new public swimming baths, however, he declined the position of Mayor, probably because of his very active business life and travels. W.J. Bassett-Lowke was a socialist and a Fabian and seems to have been popular with people from all walks of life.

He was a keen patron of the modern arts and became a friend of Charles Rennie Mackintosh, the art Nouveau architect, who redesigned 78 Derngate for Bassett-Lowke, complete with furniture.

Later, the continental architect of modern cubic shaped buildings, Peter Behrens, was commissioned to design a new house at 'New Ways', Northampton. Strangely although he was amongst the first to introduce modern architecture to this country, Bassett-Lowke did not build a modern factory but continued work in series of small, old buildings.

Further examples of Bassett-Lowke's interest in the arts can be seen in the firm's catalogues and Christmas cards, where various designers and draughtsmen exploited the styles of the period.

The firm's railways products covered many scales and were propelled by clockwork, electricity or live steam. Their main policy was in providing for the more serious model railway enthusiast and although many items were made in Bavaria, the anti-German atmosphere after the First World War, caused Bassett-Lowke to use local manufacturing subsidiaries.

One subsidiary, Winteringham's, built some very attractive models in 'O' gauge in 1929 including the 'Royal Scot' and 'Flying Scotsman', £3/15/- (£3.75) clockwork and £4/4/- (£4.20) electric. Obviously the products were not cheap when many were receiving a weekly wage of £1.50!

A different approach to marketing was made in the late 1920's through Godfrey Phillips B.D.V. cigarettes, when sons were encouraged to get their fathers to smoke themselves to death to collect enough tokens for a model of the 'Duke of York'! Other products aimed at the lower, popular market were the 'Princess Elizabeth' in the 1920's and 'Prince Charles' in the 1950's. All were freelance design 4–4–0's.

Bassett-Lowke's chief sales outlet and famous shop was at 112 High Holborn. Shops in Edinburgh and Manchester were less successful and retail generally was through a few special model shops and high quality toy shops in the main towns.

The largest railway products were of 15" gauge for such places as seaside piers and private estates. On the other hand, Bassett-Lowke was a prime mover of 'OO' scale in this country through the Bing table-top railway and later through Trix Twin, which pressurised Hornby into introducing their Dublo. Trix Twin was very popular in the late '30s' but has a limited following of collectors today.

Bassett-Lowke made many model ships, industrial and architectural models, including in 1941 a model of Coventry redevelopment, as Churchill wished to boost wartime morale. Model kits of Bailey Bridges for training and a model of Mulberry Harbour for planning the invasion of France were also famous products.

Wenman Joseph Bassett-Lowke died in 1953 aged 76.

This introduction first appeared as an article by Roy Chambers in the August 1992 'Antiques and Collectables Magazine'.
(Copyright Roy Chambers).

Bassett-Lowke

The models listed represent a cross-section of locomotives sold at auction between 1995 and 1997.
The Market Price Range figures assume that the model is in a reasonable collectable condition for its age.

Clockwork Locomotives

c.1925	Mogul 2-6-0 Locomotive and Tender	'G.W.R.'	3410	Green	£300-400	❑
c.1925	Mogul 2-6-0 Locomotive and Tender	'L.N.E.R.'	33	Lined Apple Green	£300-400	❑
c.1928	Midland 4-4-0 Compound Loco and Tender	'L.M.S.'	1190	Maroon	£300-400	❑
c.1928	Midland 4-4-0 Compound Loco and Tender	'L.M.S.'	1982	Maroon	£300-400	❑
c.1933	'Flying Scotsman' 4-6-2	'L.N.E.R'	4472	Green	£900-1,200	❑
c.1933	Standard Tank Locomotive 0-6-0 T	'L.M.S.'	78	Black with Red lining	£250-350	❑
c.1934	Stanier Mogul 2-6-0	'L.M.S.'	2945	Black	£350-450	❑
c.1936	Goods Locomotive 0-6-0	'L.M.S.'	4256	Black	£250-350	❑
c.1937	'Princess Elizabeth' 4-6-2	'L.M.S.'	6201	Lined Maroon	£2,000-2,500	❑
c.1937	'Royal Scot' 4-6-0	'L.M.S.'	6100	Lined Lake	£500-750	❑
c.1951	'Prince Charles' 4-4-0	'B.R.'	62453	Lined Blue	£300-400	❑
c.1952	'Prince Charles' Passenger Set				£500-600	❑
c.1952	'Prince Charles' Goods Set				£500-600	❑

Electric 'O' gauge Locomotives

c.1957	Mogul 2-6-0 Locomotive and Tender	'L.N.E.R.'	33	Green	£700-900	❑
c.1927	0-6-0 Locomotive and Tender	'L.M.S'	1063	Black 4F (3-rail)	£400-500	❑
c.1928-35	Midland 4-4-0 Compound Loco and Tender	'L.M.S.'	1063	Brown (3-rail)	£350-450	❑
c.1931	'Royal Scot' 4-6-0 Loco and Tender	'L.M.S.	6100		£500-750	❑
c.1935	'Lord Nelson' 4-6-0	'S.R'	850	Green	£500-750	❑
c.1936	Arsenal / Melton Hall 4-6-0	'L.N.E.R'	2848	Green	£2,000-2,500	❑
c.1937	'Flying Scotsman' 4-6-2	'L.N.E.R.'	4472	Lined Apple Green	£900-1,200	❑
c.1937	Tank Locomotive 0-6-0 T	'SOUTHERN'	947	Black	£400-600	❑
c.1937	'Princess Elizabeth' 4-6-2 Loco and Tender	'L.M.S.'	6201	Lined Maroon	£2,500-3,500	❑
c.1939	Tank Locomotive 0-6-0 T	'L.M.S.'	78	Lined Black	£250-350	❑
c.1940	Tank Locomotive 2-6-2	'L.M.S.'	94	Black (3-rail AC)	£1,750-2,250	❑
c.1940	4-6-0 Locomotive and Tender	'L.M.S.'	5294	Black '5'	£1,750-2,250	❑
c.1948	King Edward VII 4-6-0	'GREAT WESTERN'	6001	Lined Green	£2,500-3,500	❑
c.1948	Tank Locomotive 0-6-0 T	'L.M.S.	70	Lined Black	£250-350	❑
c.1948	4-4-0 Compound Locomotive and Tender	'L.M.S.	1036	Lined Lake	£250-350	❑
c.1948	4-4-0 Compound Locomotive and Tender	'L.M.S.	1082	Lined Lake	£250-350	❑
c.1948	4-4-0 Compound Locomotive and Tender	'L.M.S.	1108	Lined Lake	£250-350	❑
c.1950	'Flying Scotsman' 4-6-2	'L.N.E.R'		Green with Black and White lining (200)	£1,500-2,000	❑
c.1954	'Prince Charles' 4-4-0	'B.R.'	62453	Lined Green	£350-450	❑
c.1959	'Duchess of Montrose' 4-6-2	'B.R.'	46232	Lined Green	£800-1,200	❑
c.1960	4-4-0 Compound Locomotive	'B.R.'	41109	Lined Black	£300-400	❑

Bassett-Lowke manufactured many other locomotives and it is intended to include more variations in the next edition.

Bassett-Lowke

The models listed represent a cross-section of locomotives sold at auction between 1995 and 1997.
The Market Price Range figures assume that the model is in a reasonable collectable condition for its age.

Bassett-Lowke 'O' gauge Rolling Stock

Wagons and Tankers

Well Wagon with Boiler Load ....'Bassett-Lowke Ltd Boiler Makers' ....**£400-500** ❑
Flatrol Wagon with 'Callender' Cable Load...**£400-500** ❑
Oil Tanker 'PRATTS SPIRIT' ....**£400-500** ❑
Oil Tanker 'MOBILOIL' ....**£400-500** ❑
Milk Tanker 'UNITED DAIRIES ....**£400-500** ❑

Pre-war Coaches

1931	1931 Series (G.W.R.) ....Either All 1st or Brake/3rd...	**£100-125**	❑
1931	1931 Series (L.N.E.R) Teak Coaches ....All 1st or Brake/3rd	**£100-125**	❑
c.1925	LMS 12 Wheeled Dining Car...........................Maroon	**£200-300**	❑

Post-war Coach

B.R. Coach...Red and Cream, either 2nd Class or Brake/2nd ....**£75-100** ❑

Bing for Bassett-Lowke

The models listed represent a cross-section of locomotives sold at auction between 1995 and 1997.
The Market Price Range figures assume that the model is in a reasonable collectable condition for its age.

Clockwork lithographed 'O' gauge Locomotives

Made in Germany by Bing and sold by Bassett-Lowke in Britain during the period 1904-1925.

c.1914	'Dunalastair' 4-4-0	'C.R.'	142	Caledonian Blue	**£500-750**	❑
c.1914	Bowen-Cooke 4-6-2 Tank Locomotive	'L.N.W.R.'	2670	Lined Black	**£750-1,000**	❑
c.1914	Wainwright class 'D' 4-4-0 Loco and Tender	'S.E. & C.R'		Fully Lined Green livery	**£1,800-2,500**	❑
c.1914	'City of Bath' 4-4-0	'G.W.R'	3433	Lined Green	**£600-800**	❑
c.1921	4-4-0 Tank Locomotive	'L & N.W.R'	44	Lined Black	**£300-400**	❑
c.1923	4-4-0 Tank Locomotive	'L.N.E.R.'	3611	Lined Black	**£300-400**	❑
c.1927	'Duke of York' 4-4-0	'L.N.E.R.'	1927	Green	**£300-400**	❑

N.B. Bassett-Lowke also sold locomotives manufactured by Carette and Marklin. It is intended to include more details in the next edition.
E.g., Marklin issue c.1935 Schools Class Locomotive 'Merchant Taylors' and Tender No. 910.......**£1,000-1,500**.

BASSETT-LOWKE LTD

G.W.R. Castle Class Locomotive

This fine G.W.R. prototype is familiar to railway enthusiasts throughout the world. It is renowned, not only for its excellent standard of performance, but also for its fine proportions in the best G.W.R. tradition. This model faithfully reproduces the characteristics of the prototype and is an excellent model that will appeal to all admirers of Swindon design. This model incorporates all the features of the Prairie Tank Locomotive described opposite.

Specification (applies to all four locomotives)

Frames. Hard brass. **Wheels.** Cast-iron.

Bogies. Cast-iron wheels with brass frames.

Movement. Standard 12-volt D.C. Permanent Magnet Motor and Gearing, mounted in brass mainframes with bushed bearings for driving axles. The chassis is removable in one unit with cylinders and motion. 2 Rail or 3 Rail.

Tender. Standard 4000-gallon type with the bodywork constructed throughout in hard brass, wheels in cast-iron, fitted to steel axles.

Finish. Hand built and hand painted throughout and finished in any style of livery to customer's individual instructions.

This model reproduces the characteristic powerful appearance of the famous prototype, which is such a worthy member of the handsome and successful series of 4-6-0 locomotives on the G.W. system. It is the latest addition to our standard range and carries the distinctive 'G.W. Look' as successfully as the Castle.

G.W.R. King Class Locomotive

Picture taken form a post-war Bassett-Lowke Ltd catalogue

BASSETT-LOWKE LTD

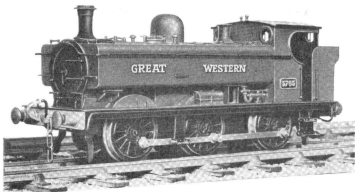

W.R. 0-6-0 Pannier Tank. 57XX Class

This neat little shunting tank locomotive was first built at Swindon in 1929 from the designs of Mr. G. B. Collett, and became the standard G.W.R. shunting tank and short distance freight engine, although they may be seen on passenger trains, except those numbered between 6,700 and 6,779, which are not vacuum fitted. Built in large numbers, these engines are seen all over the Western Region.

Prices

CASTLE CLASS LOCOMOTIVE
Length: 18¼ in.   Weight 4¾ lb.   .. .. £65. 0. 0.

KING CLASS LOCOMOTIVE
Length: 19 in.   Weight: 5¼ lb.   .. .. £75. 0. 0.

PANNIER TANK LOCOMOTIVE
Length: 8½ in.   Weight: 2½ lb.   .. .. £55. 0. 0.

PRAIRIE TANK LOCOMOTIVE
Length: 11¼ in.   Weight: 3 lb.   .. .. £54. 0. 0.

These locomotives are produced in an endeavour to satisfy the demand for locomotives superior to the standard range of quantity produced models listed on later pages but without the costly fine detail of the exhibition model. In each case the designs are made with special mechanisms so that there is "daylight" below the boiler and the mechanisms are made removable in one unit complete with cylinders and motion, thus facilitating all servicing. We believe that these models carry with them the atmosphere of the prototype and will have a considerable appeal to followers of the Great Western Railway.

G.W.R. Prairie Tank Locomotive

MODELS BY
BASSETT-LOWKE

Page Seventeen

Picture taken form a post-war Bassett-Lowke Ltd catalogue

BASSETT-LOWKE SCALE MODELS
PRESENTATION SETS

Scale Model Express Train in Presentation Cabinet: Comprising:—

4-6-2 "Pacific" type Locomotive and Tender ;
1st class Corridor Coach ;
2 Bogie Coaches, 3rd Class and Van ;
Super Controller ;
Plugs, Wire and Instruction Book ;

all packed in Presentation Cabinet described below.

L.M.S. No. 2/344 £6 6 0
L.N.E.R. No. 4/344 £6 6 0

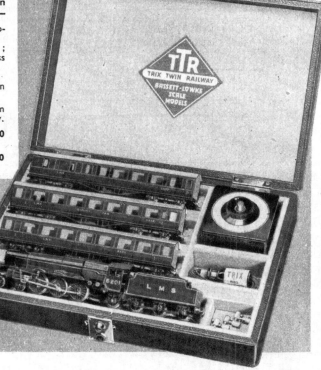

Jewels are not usually packed in match boxes, nor pearls wrapped in old newspapers. Old masters are the better for their rich frames.

All things of beauty and of value must have their fitting receptacles, and so we have prepared a really handsome Presentation Cabinet, fitted with plated spring hasp and lock, to contain the models of the "PRINCESS" Class and the "FLYING SCOTSMAN" Locomotives with their Scale Model Coaches as detailed above. These Cabinets make a magnificent present for any Model Railway enthusiast.

The illustration above shows the "FLYING SCOTSMAN" Express Train as set up on the line. For full individual specifications see pages 5 and 6 (Locomotives) and 7 (Coaches).

Rails, etc., are packed separately—see page 13.

8

Page from the 1938 – 1939 Trix Twin Railway Catalogue

Models manufactured by Meccano Ltd at their Binns Road, Liverpool factory from 1920 until they ceased supplying the trade in 1964-1965.

The following short history of the development of Hornby 'O' Gauge trains is designed to help collectors understand the model listings and auction results.

1920-23 Meccano Ltd introduced the first Hornby clockwork locomotives in 1920-21. The engines were sold as constructional toys and had a 0–4–0 wheel arrangement. The models were held together by standard Meccano nuts and bolts and had buffers fitted between the engine and tender. The engines had a brass dome plus a brass plate on the cab sides with the number '2710'. The first wagons had 'clip-on' lettering 'M Ltd C' on the chassis. Train sets packed in a leatherette type box. By 1923 the constructional element had been superseded by a tab ended construction which led to the introduction of several models as follows:

1923-25 No.1 Locomotive (0–4–0) introduced. This was basically the same as the first issue without the buffers between the engine and tender. Model number '2710'. No.2 Locomotive introduced (4–4–0) with model number '2711' Pullman Coaches introduced in a cream and green finish.

A 4–4–4 Tank engine introduced. This model is thought to be the first Hornby Series engine to be finished in the actual liveries of the railway companies which had formed in 1923. At this stage only the L.M.S and L.N.E.R liveries were used. The engine number shown on the side tanks was '4–4–4' which matched the wheel arrangement.

'Zulu" train sets in an all - black livery introduced, and the first items of rolling stock were produced – wagons and vans followed by special issues such as tankers.

The first accessories introduced and these included a station called 'Windsor'.

1925 The first Hornby electric train introduced – The Metropolitan Railway.

1926 The Riviera 'Blue' Train introduced – a 4–4–2 locomotive plus two blue continental coaches. 'M' Series introduced; a series comprised of cheaper sets designed to compete against cheaper imported sets. Sets numbers used include M0, M1 and M2.

1928 No.3 locomotives (4–4–2) were introduced with famous names such as 'Flying Scotsman' and 'Royal Scot'.

1929 No.2 Specials were introduced as follows: L.M.S. Compound, G.W.R. County Class, L.N.E.R Shire Class and 'Southern' L1 Class.

1930-31 No.1 Special locomotive (0–4–0) introduced. No.2 Special Tank locomotive introduced a 4–4–2 updated version of the 4–4–4 Tank. Original No.2 Tank engine and tender withdrawn. The new engines have squat chimneys and domes. The early brass domes are now painted. Pullman Coaches are now in their correct maroon and cream livery.

1935 The 1935 Hornby Book of Trains shows electric train sets with changed reference numbers e.g. No. 3E Riviera 'Blue' Train is now shown as E36.

1937 No.4 'Southern Schools' class locomotive introduced. L.M.S. 'Princess Elizabeth' locomotive introduced.

1938 Hornby-Dublo trains ('OO' gauge) introduced (See Hornby Dublo listing).

1939-45 No production possible.

1954 'BR' appears on locomotives.

1957 'Saxa Salt' wagon introduced.

1964-65 End of the line – Meccano Ltd ceases to produce Hornby 'O' gauge items.

Hornby Trains

Frank Hornby was a shipping clerk in his native Liverpool but a keen engineer at heart, who also obtained much pleasure from the use of the camera. His spare time was filled in trying to perfect his various inventions and the success of one, 'Mechanics Made Easy', enabled him to form a company in 1908 – Meccano Ltd. This new constructional toy was very successful and after World War I Frank Hornby turned his attention to model railways, encouraged by the government policy to buy British, not German toys.

Production started in 1920 when two different sets were introduced. One, the litho printed King George V set was based on a product of the German firm Bing, in fact there is opinion that it was made by Bing.

This little four-wheeled train was unsuccessful but the first true Hornby locomotive was of nut and bolt construction on the same principle as Meccano.

It did not come in kit form and was the successful beginning to a long line of 'O' gauge locomotives; Hornby did not make any larger scale, nor was there any marketing of foreign firms products.

The nut and bolt construction was replaced by tabbed tinplate and in addition to 0–4–0's, 4–4–0 tender locos and 4–4–4 tank locomotives were made; well constructed and beautifully finished they were powered by clockwork or electricity. Hornby did not make any live steam locomotives.

These products were not meant to look like any prototypes; turned out in different railway colours they were meant to capture the spirit of the real thing in toy form. After earlier unsuccessful attempts with electric motors, the Metropolitan locomotive of 1925 was the first electric Hornby to go on general sale. It was also the first true-to-type representation, although it still had only four wheels tucked underneath its skirts.

At 125 volts it could make your eyes light up if mis-used! This model lasted only a year then motors became 4 volt for a short time, then 6 volt and 20 volt.

Frank Hornby was well thought of in Liverpool and he was encouraged to stand for Parliament, as the Unionist Candidate for Everton in the General Election of 1931.

He successfully defeated the Labour member and a previous Unionist representative which meant that much of his working week was now spent in London. He still continued to chair the Hornby board of Directors, which included his two sons, but illness forced him to hand over responsibilities and he died aged 73 in 1936.

Hornby continued to produce small tinplate trains, the 'M' series until the 1950's and the middle range of 0–4–0 locomotives and accessories lasted over the same period However, the entry into the more scale model market was not continued after World War 2. The fine 4–4–0 series such as the Compound, 'Yorkshire', 'Schools' class, etc., and 'Princess Elizabeth' belonged to the late '20's and '30's. Even the ungainly 4–4–2, 3c series 'Lord Nelson', 'Royal Scot', etc., finished in 1940.

The same period saw the production of the very collectable private owner vans and tankers, supported by colourful stations, bridges, signals and many other lineside features. Special models were made for overseas markets and in the 1920's a factory was established in Paris. A very extensive network of dealers and agents was set up in this country and overseas as far away as New Zealand and Buenos Aires.

Additionally, in the '1930's boys were fascinated to see a new realism in very small trains, the Hornby Dublo range, which was further developed after World War 2. Although Hornby's products did not cover such a wide field as Bassett-Lowke's, the Liverpool factory manufactured excellent Meccano car and aeroplane construction kits, some fine speed boats and the famous Dinky Toy cars.

This introduction first appeared as an article by Roy Chambers in the August 1992 'Antiques and Collectables Magazine'.
(Copyright Roy Chambers).

Hornby Trains

Hornby – the best known manufacturer of toy trains (as opposed to models) in this country, indeed, a household word.

Started by Frank Hornby (1863 - 1936) of Liverpool, the inventor of Meccano, in 1920 and launched during the high point of the anti-German-made toys campaign. Although marked 'Made in England', the first cheap tinplate LNWR 0–4–0 tender locomotive and coaches were based on German designs. However, the backbone of the new Hornby range was the more expensive, better made, nut and bolt constructed series of 0–4–0's in LNWR, GN and MR company colours. These set a standard of quality which was to remain until the demise of Hornby 'O' gauge in the late 1960's.

Most of the locomotives were freelance in design and although all were beautifully made and finished, some, like the No.3's and the 4–4–2's, were peculiar in character. The products of more prototypical appearance were the No.2 special tender locomotive 4–4–0, the No.4 'Eton' 'Schools' class 4–4–0 and the top of the range 'Princess Elizabeth' 4–6–2. The latter was introduced in 1937, packed in a very attractive wooden box, at a cost of five guineas when the average weekly working wage was about £2.

At the other end of the scale, the 'Woolworths' type market was catered for by the 'M' series, still very nicely made but much more basic.

The locomotives were supported by a large and colourful range of rolling stock, buildings and accessories, the private-owner wagons being especially attractive.

After the Second World War the products, which changed from 'Hornby Series' to 'Hornby Trains', were far less embracing with only four-wheeled engines, little bogie stock, and fewer accessories being made. Sadly, around 1967 these famous toys capitulated in the face of the opposition of the modern 'OO' gauge model railway.

For detailed reading the unbeatable bible is 'The Hornby Gauge 'O' System' by Chris and Julie Graebe, whilst the Hornby Railway Collectors' Association is a 'must join' for anyone interested in these remarkable products.

> Hornby Railway Collectors Association (H.R.C.A.)
> Membership Secretary: Bob Field, 2 Ravensmore Road,
> Sherwood, Nottingham, NG5 2AH.

Hornby Boxes 1921–56. A quick guide to box types.

1921	Buff coloured 'shoebox type' with white end labels with English text. Soon they change to show text in English, French and Spanish.
1923	The No.1 and No.2 locomotives were packed in strong boxes covered with a leatherette type of paper. Similar coloured box with tuck in end flaps sealed by a white label.
1924	As above but pink end labels now in use and only printed with an English text. The box now included a picture.
1925	A red card box introduced with 'Hornby Series' on three sides plus a dotted border. Red labels now used to seal the end flaps. The 'Hornby Series' text remained in use until 1940 when it was replaced by 'Hornby Trains'.
1927	The standard glossy red box introduced which eliminates the need for end labels by being specially printed for each individual item.
1930	The Hornby code numbers first appeared on boxes. These simply referred to the type of model in the box. For example, Train Sets were numbered from TS 401, Locomotives from L 452, Tenders from TE50l, Coaches from C551 and Open Wagons from W601.
1930	The 'M' Series for the Woolworths end of the market were packed in blue boxes.
1937	Box printers codes introduced e.g. 5M 4-38. The 5M refers to number of boxes printed i.e. 5000 and 4-38 to the date of production, i.e. April 1938.
1940-48	A wartime cheaper buff coloured cardboard used.
1940	'Hornby Trains' now replaced 'Hornby Series' on the box sides.
1948	The glossy red box was re-introduced.
1956	The orange-red coloured box came into use. Some type '50' wagons packed in green boxes.

Early Locomotives and Tenders

0-4-0 No '0' Locomotive c 1921 – 23. Note the brass dome, stovepipe type chimney, and early trademarks including brass 2710 plaque on cabside.

4-4-0 No '2' Locomotive circa 1921 – 23.
Note the brass dome, stovepipe chimney and early trademark.

Early Chassis Types

Type 1 brass buffers and hook coupling plus early round trademark clip on lettering.

Type 1 with drop link coupling.

Early Chassis Types

Type 2 open chassis 1923 – 32 with drop link coupling.

Type 3 closed chassis 1933 – 62 with automatic couplings which were introduced in 1931.

1   1920 – 1921 trademark

1a   1922 – 1923 trademark

2   1923 – 1925 trademark

3   1926 – 1929 trademark

4   1929 – 1934 trademark (with red outer line)

4a   1929 – 1934 trademark (without red outer line)

5   1934 – 40 trademark (with red outer line)

5a   1934 – 1940 trademark (without red outer line)

5b   1934 – 1940 trademark (as 5 but line under MECCANO)

6   1929 – 1940 footplate trademark

Picture taken from the 1927/28 'Hornby Book of Trains'.

Gauge O, 1¼ in.

HORNBY TRAINS

MO CLOCKWORK GOODS TRAIN SET

Locomotive (non reversing) and Tender, available in red or green, two Wagons, five M9 Curved Rails and an MB9 Curved Brake Rail.   Space required—2ft. square.   Price **4/11**

MO CLOCKWORK PASSENGER TRAIN SET

Locomotive (non-reversing) and Tender, available in red or green, two Pullman Coaches, five M9 Curved Rails and an MB9 Curved Brake Rail.   Space required—2ft. square.   Price **5/6**

MO CLOCKWORK MIXED GOODS TRAIN SET

Locomotive (non-reversing) and Tender, available in either red or green, Side Tipping Wagon, Rotary Tipping Wagon, Petrol Tank Wagon, five M9 Curved Rails, two BM Straight Rails and an MB9 Curved Brake Rail.   Space required—2ft. 9in. by 2ft.   ...   ...   Price **6/11**

The components of the above Train Sets can be purchased separately at the following prices :—

MO Locomotive, non-reversing (without Tender)	Price **2/9**	MO Tender	... Price **6d.**	MO Petrol Tank Wagon	... Price **1/-**
MO Pullman Coach	... Price **9d.**	MO Wagon	... Price **6d.**	MO Rotary Tipping Wagon	... Price **1/-**
MO Side Tipping Wagon	... Price **1/-**	For prices of MO Rails and Points (9 in. radius) see page 51			

19

Picture taken from the Hamleys 'Toys of Quality' catalogue of 1938/39.

HORNBY TRAINS

HORNBY E120 SPECIAL ELECTRIC and No. 1 SPECIAL CLOCKWORK PASSENGER TRAIN SETS

"QUEEN OF SCOTS" (L.N.E.R.) "BOURNEMOUTH BELLE" (S.R.) "THE COMET" (L.M.S.R.) "TORBAY EXPRESS" (G.W.R.)

Gauge O, 1¼in.

E120 Special Electric Passenger Train Set, L.N.E.R.

20-VOLT ELECTRIC—AUTOMATIC REVERSING

E120 Special (20-volt). Locomotive (automatic reversing) with electric headlamp, No. 1 Special Tender, two No. 2 Pullman Coaches and one No. 1 Pullman Composite Coach for L.N.E.R. and S.R., or two No. 1 Passenger Coaches and a Guard's Van for L.M.S.R. and G.W.R., twelve EA2 Curved Rails, two EB1 Straight Rails and a Terminal Connecting Plate. Space required—5ft. 4in. by 4ft. 6in. ... ... Price 45/-

CLOCKWORK

No. 1 Special (Clockwork). Locomotive (reversing), No. 1 Special Tender, two No. 1 Pullman Coaches and one No. 1 Pullman Composite Coach for L.N.E.R. and S.R., or two No. 1 Passenger Coaches and Guard's Van for L.M.S.R. and G.W.R., twelve A2 Curved Rails, one B1 Straight Rail and one BBR1 Straight Brake and Reverse Rail by means of which the Train can be either braked or reversed from the track. Space required—5ft. 4in. by 4ft. 6in. ... ... Price 31/-

The components of the above Train Sets are obtainable separately at the following prices :—

Hornby E120 Special Locomotive (20-volt) automatic reversing (without tender) ... Price 27/6   Hornby No. 1 Special Clockwork Locomotive, reversing (without tender) ... Price 15/9
No. 1 Special Tender ... Price 3/3   No. 1 Pullman Composite Coach ... Price 2/6   No. 1 Passenger Coach...Price 2/6   No. 1 Pullman Composite Coach ... Price 2/6   Guard's Van ... Price 2/6

HORNBY E220 ELECTRIC TANK and No. 2 CLOCKWORK TANK MIXED GOODS TRAIN SETS

E220 Electric Tank Mixed Goods Train Set

20-VOLT ELECTRIC—AUTOMATIC REVERSING

E220 (20-volt). Tank Locomotive (automatic reversing) with electric headlamp, No. 1 Wagon, No. 1 Cattle Truck, Oil Tank Wagon, Brake Van, twelve EA2 Curved Rails, two EB1 Straight Rails and a Terminal Connecting Plate. Space required—5ft. 4in. by 4ft. 6in. The Set is supplied in L.M.S.R., L.N.E.R., G.W.R., or S.R. colours ... ... Price 45/-

CLOCKWORK

No. 2 (Clockwork). Tank Locomotive (reversing), No. 1 Wagon, No. 1 Cattle Truck, Oil Tank Wagon, Brake Van, twelve A2 Curved Rails, one B1 Straight Rail and a BBR1 Straight Brake and Reverse Rail by means of which the Train can be either braked or reversed from the track. Space required—5ft. 4in. by 4ft. 6in. The Set is supplied in L.M.S.R., L.N.E.R., G.W.R., or S.R. colours ... ... Price 32/6

The components of the above Train Sets are obtainable separately at the following prices :—

Hornby E220 Special Electric Tank Locomotive (20-volt) automatic reversing ... Price 30/-   Hornby No. 2 Special Clockwork Tank Locomotive, reversing ... ... Price 19/6
No. 1 Wagon ... Price 1/6   No. 1 Cattle Truck ... Price 2/3   Oil Tank Wagon ... Price 1/11   Brake Van ... Price 2/9
The prices of Hornby Rails, Points and Crossings are given in pages 50, 51 and 52. For particulars and prices of Transformers see page 34.

27

Picture taken from the Hamleys 'Toys of Quality' catalogue of 1938/39.

HORNBY TRAINS

Gauge O, 1¼in.

HORNBY E220 SPECIAL ELECTRIC and No. 2 SPECIAL CLOCKWORK PASSENGER TRAIN SETS

Famous Trains hauled by famous Locomotives.

"THE YORKSHIREMAN" (L.M.S.R.), hauled by the "Standard Compound" Class Locomotive No. 1185. "THE SCARBOROUGH FLIER" (L.N.E.R.), hauled by the "Hunt" Class Locomotive "The Bramham Moor." "THE BRISTOLIAN" (G.W.R.), hauled by the "County" Class Locomotive "County of Bedford." "FOLKESTONE FLYER" hauled by the "L1" Class Locomotive No. 1759.

No. 2 Special Clockwork Passenger Train Set "The Yorkshireman" (L.M.S.R.)

20-VOLT ELECTRIC—AUTOMATIC REVERSING

E220 Special (20-volt). True-to-type Locomotive (automatic reversing) with electric headlamp, one No. 2 Special Tender, two No. 2 Corridor Coaches, one No. 2 Corridor Composite Coach, twelve EA2 Curved Rails, two EB1 Straight Rails and a Terminal Connecting Plate. Space required—5ft. 4in. by 4ft. 6in. ... ... Price **72/-**.

CLOCKWORK

No. 2 Special (Clockwork). True-to-type Locomotive (reversing), one No. 2 Special Tender, one No. 2 Corridor Coach, one No. 2 Corridor Composite Coach, twelve A2 Curved Rails, one B1 Straight Rail and one BBR1 Straight Brake and Reverse Rail by means of which the Train can be either braked or reversed from the track. Space required—5ft. 4in. by 4ft. 6in. ... ... Price **52/-**

The components of the above Train Sets are obtainable separately at the following prices :—

Hornby E220 Special Electric Locomotive (20-volt) automatic reversing (without Tender) Price **37/6** Hornby No. 2 Special Clockwork Locomotive, reversing (without Tender) Price **27/6**
No. 2 Special Tender Price **6/-** No. 2 Corridor Coach Price **7/6** No. 2 Special Tender Price **6/-** No. 2 Corridor Composite Coach Price **7/6**
The prices of Hornby Rails are given in pages 50, 51 and 52. For particulars and prices of Transformers see page 34

If you are interested in Deferred Payment Terms turn to page iii of cover.

HORNBY MODEL OF THE "SCHOOLS" CLASS LOCOMOTIVE "ETON"

This is a fine scale model of the famous "Schools" class, perhaps the most popular series of locomotives ever produced by the Southern Railway Company.

All who are interested in scale-model locomotives, and especially "Southern" enthusiasts, will welcome the "ETON" both for its beauty and its fine performance.

E420
20-VOLT ELECTRIC AUTOMATIC REVERSING
Locomotive.
Price **42/6**
Tender.
Price **6/-**

No. 4C CLOCKWORK
Locomotive.
Price **35/-**
Tender.
Price **6/-**

29

Picture taken from the Hamleys 'Toys of Quality' catalogue of 1938/39.

HORNBY TRAINS
BRITISH AND GUARANTEED

HORNBY No. 2 PULLMAN SET, L.N.E.R.

This set is identical in every way with the No. 2 Pullman Sets described on the opposite page, except that in this case the lettering and colouring are representative of the London and North Eastern Locos and rolling stock. Gauge 0.

Hornby No. 2 Pullman Set, L.N.E.R., complete, well boxed, Price 50/-
*Hornby No. 2 Pullman Set, L.N.E.R., complete, well boxed, fitted for Hornby Control, Price 55/-

HORNBY No. 2 GOODS SET, L.N.E.R.

The Loco, Tender, and Rails in this set are similar to those in the No. 2 Pullman Sets, but two Wagons take the place of the Pullman Coaches. The set is supplied with either green or black loco and tender and the colour required should be stated when ordering. Gauge 0.

Hornby No. 2 Goods Set, L.N.E.R., complete, well boxed, Price 32 6
*Hornby No. 2 Goods Set, L.N.E.R., complete, well boxed, fitted for Hornby Control, Price 37 6

No. 2 Goods Set is also supplied with G.W. lettering. In this set the loco is coloured G.W. green only. The contents are the same as those of the L.M.S. and L.N.E.R. No. 2 Goods Sets. Gauge 0.

Hornby No. 2 Goods Set, G.W., complete, well boxed, Price 32 6
*Hornby No. 2 Goods Set, G.W., complete, well boxed, fitted for Hornby Control, Price 37 6

The Locos, Tenders, Pullman Coaches and Wagons of the above train sets may also be purchased separately if required. Prices are as follows :—

Hornby No. 2 Loco ... ... Price 20/- Hornby Wagon ... ... Price 2 6
Hornby Pullman Car ... ... " 12 6 Hornby No. 2 Tender ... ... " 3 6
*Hornby No. 2 Loco, fitted for Hornby Control, Price 22 6

* For particulars of the Hornby Control System, see page 26.

49

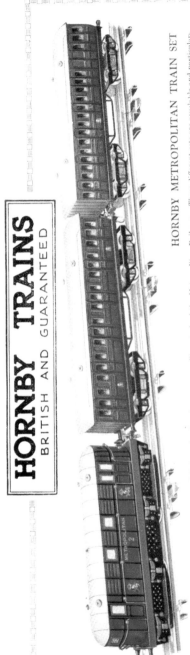

HORNBY TRAINS
BRITISH AND GUARANTEED

HORNBY METROPOLITAN TRAIN SET

The Locos and Coaches in these train sets are modelled on the electric passenger rolling stock of the Metropolitan Railway. Three different sets are available and particulars of the motive power and contents of each are given below.

HORNBY METROPOLITAN TRAIN SET No. 1 contains Electric Loco, two Coaches and Electrical Rails for a 4-ft. diameter circle. The motor in the Loco is designed to run from the main supply, either alternating or direct, of 100-250 volts, connection being made by an adaptor that will fit in a lamp socket of the house supply. A suitable rheostat is included for speed regulating. The train is electrically lighted. Gauge 0.

Hornby Metropolitan Electric Train, Set No. 1, complete, well boxed, Price 110 -
Metropolitan Electric Loco No. 1 ... Price 52 6   Metropolitan Coach No. 1 ... Price 18 -   Rheostat ... Price 18 6

HORNBY METROPOLITAN TRAIN SET No. 2 contains Electric Loco, two Coaches, Resistance Controller, and Electrical Rails. The Loco is fitted with an electric motor which is operated from a 4-volt Accumulator or from a suitable transformer connected to the main (alternating current only). Gauge 0.

Hornby Metropolitan Electric Train Set No. 2, complete, well boxed, Price 95 -
Metropolitan Electric Loco No. 2 ... Price 47 6   Hornby Metropolitan Coach No. 2 ... Price 18 -   Resistance Controller ... Price 3 6

*HORNBY METROPOLITAN TRAIN SET No. 3 contains a powerful Clockwork Loco, two Coaches, and set of Rails including a Control Rail. The Loco is fitted for Control.

Hornby Metropolitan Train Set No. 3, complete, well boxed, Price 55 -
Hornby Metropolitan Clockwork Loco No. 3 ... Price 22 6   Hornby Metropolitan Coach No. 3 ... Price 13 6

THE RIVIERA "BLUE" TRAIN SET

This splendid train set is a model of the famous express that runs regularly between Calais and the Mediterranean Coast. It is beautifully finished and is available with either Clockwork or Electric Loco. Gauge 0.

RIVIERA "BLUE" TRAIN SET No. 1 contains Electric Loco, Tender, two Coaches, Resistance Controller and Electrical Rails. The Loco is fitted with an electric motor which is operated from a 4 volt Accumulator or from a suitable transformer connected to the main (alternating current only). Gauge 0.

Riviera "Blue" Train Set No. 1, complete, well boxed, Price 85 -

*RIVIERA "BLUE" TRAIN SET No. 2 contains a powerful Clockwork Loco, Tender, two Coaches and set of Rails including a Control Rail. The Loco is fitted for Control.
Riviera "Blue" Train Set No. 2, complete, well boxed, Price 70 -

The components of the Riviera "Blue" Train Sets may also be purchased separately if required. Prices are as follows:
Riviera "Blue" Train Loco No. 1 ... Price 37 6   Riviera "Blue" Train Tender ... Price 4 6
Riviera "Blue" Train Coach ... ... 16 6   Riviera "Blue" Train Loco No. 2 ... ,, 27 6
Resistance Controller ... ... Price 3 6

* For particulars of the Hornby Control System, see page 26

PAGE TWENTY THREE

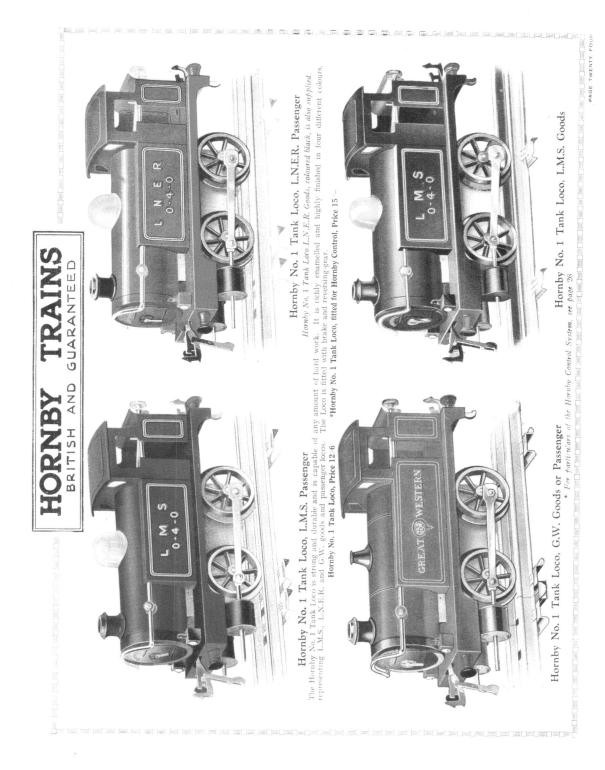

HORNBY TRAINS
BRITISH AND GUARANTEED

Hornby No. 1 Tank Loco, L.N.E.R. Passenger

Hornby No. 1 Tank Loco L.N.E.R. Goods, coloured black, is also supplied and highly finished in four different colours.

Hornby No. 1 Tank Loco, fitted for Hornby Control, Price 15 -

Hornby No. 1 Tank Loco, L.M.S. Passenger

The Hornby No. 1 Tank Loco is strong and durable and is capable of any amount of hard work. It is richly enamelled and highly finished in four different colours. The Loco is fitted with brake and reversing-gear.
representing L.M.S., L.N.E.R. and G.W. goods and passenger locos.

Hornby No. 1 Tank Loco, Price 12 6

*Hornby No. 1 Tank Loco, fitted for Hornby Control, Price 15 -

Hornby No. 1 Tank Loco, L.M.S. Goods

Hornby No. 1 Tank Loco, G.W. Goods or Passenger

* For particulars of the Hornby Control System, see page 26

PAGE TWENTY FOUR

51

HORNBY TRAINS
BRITISH AND GUARANTEED

BRAKE VAN, FRENCH TYPE
Lettered Nord. Modelled on type of Brake Van used in France. Beautifully finished in colours. Opening doors.
Price 4/-

CARR'S BISCUIT VAN
Finished in dark blue. The doors open.
Price 3/6

MOTOR SPIRIT TANK WAGON, "NATIONAL BENZOLE"
Realistic in design and appropriately coloured.
Price 2/6

BRAKE VAN G.W.
Enamelled in grey and black with white roof. Opening doors.
Price 3/6

The Brake Van is also available with L.M.S. lettering.

CRAWFORD'S BISCUIT VAN
Finished in red. The doors open.
Price 3/6

PETROL TANK WAGON, "PRATTS"
Realistic in design and appropriately coloured.
Price 2/6

BRAKE VAN L.N.E.R.
Finished in colours with opening doors; a very realistic model.
Price 3/6

JACOB'S BISCUIT VAN
Finished in crimson lake. The doors open.
Price 3/6

PETROL TANK WAGON, "SHELL"
Realistic in design and appropriately coloured.
Price 2/6

WAGON, FRENCH TYPE
Lettered Nord. Modelled on type of Goods Wagon used in France. Highly finished in colours.
Price 3/3

"SECCOTINE" WAGON
Finished in blue. The doors open.
Price 4/-

MOTOR SPIRIT TANK WAGON "B.P."
Realistic in design and appropriately coloured.
Price 2/6

HORNBY CLOCKWORK LOCOMOTIVES

Hornby Clockwork Locomotives are the longest-running spring-driven locomotives of their respective types in the world. The motors fitted are perfect mechanisms with accurately-cut gears that ensure smooth and steady running.

M0 LOCOMOTIVE WITH TENDER
(Non-reversing)

Locomotive	...	...	Price **2 9**
M0 Tender	...	...	Price **6d.**

Red or Green.

*No. 0 LOCOMOTIVE WITH TENDER
(Reversing)

Locomotive	...	...	Price **8 11**
No. 0/1 Tender	...	...	Price **2 -**

*No. 1 SPECIAL TANK LOCOMOTIVE
(Reversing)

Price **15 9**

No. 0 "SILVER LINK" LOCOMOTIVE WITH TENDER
(Non-reversing)

Locomotive	...	...	Price **3 6**
No. 0 "Silver Link" Tender	...	Price **1 -**

No. 0 STREAMLINE LOCOMOTIVE WITH TENDER
Locomotive Price **3 6** No. 0 Streamline Tender Price **1 -**
Maroon/cream or light green/dark green.

*No. 1 LOCOMOTIVE WITH TENDER
(Reversing)

Locomotive	...	...	Price **11 6**
No. 0/1 Tender	...	...	Price **2 -**

*No. 2 SPECIAL TANK LOCOMOTIVE
(Reversing)

Price **19 6**

New Hornby Locomotives for old!
See page 35 for full details.

M1/2 LOCOMOTIVE WITH TENDER
(Reversing)

Locomotive	...	...	Price **4 6**
M1/2 Tender	...	...	Price **9d.**

Red or green.

*No. 1 TANK LOCOMOTIVE
(Reversing)

Price **11 6**

No. 2 SPECIAL LOCOMOTIVE WITH TENDER
(Reversing)

L.M.S.R. No. 1185 ("Standard Compound" class), G.W.R. "County of Bedford" ("County" class), L.N.E.R. "The Bramham Moor" ("Hunt" class), S.R. No. 1759 ("L1" class)

Locomotive	...	Price **27 6**
No. 2 Special Tender	...	Price **6 -**

*M3 TANK LOCOMOTIVE
(Reversing)

Price **7 6**

*No. 1 SPECIAL LOCOMOTIVE WITH TENDER
(Reversing)

Locomotive	...	...	Price **15 9**
No. 1 Special Tender	...	Price **3 3**

No. 3C LOCOMOTIVE WITH TENDER
(Reversing)

"Caerphilly Castle" (G.W.R.), "Flying Scotsman" (L.N.E.R.), "Royal Scot" (L.M.S.R.), "Lord Nelson" (S.R.).

Locomotive	...	...	Price **22 6**
No. 2 Special Tender	...	Price **6 -**
No. 3C Riviera "Blue" Locomotive		Price **22 6**
No. 3 Riviera "Blue" Tender	...	Price **4 6**

*Lettered and coloured to represent L.M.S.R., G.W.R., L.N.E.R. or S.R. Locomotives.

Picture taken from the 1938/39 Hamleys 'Toys of Quality' catalogue.

33

HORNBY ELECTRIC LOCOMOTIVES

Hornby 20-volt Locomotives are designed to run from the mains supply (Alternating Current) through a 20-volt Transformer capable of supplying 1 amp. at 20 volts. The 6-volt Locomotives may be operated either from a 6-volt accumulator, or (with the exception of the EPM16 Special Tank) through a Transformer capable of supplying 2.5 amps. at 9 volts direct from the mains supply (Alternating Current).

EM120 (20-volt) or EM16 (6-volt) ELECTRIC LOCOMOTIVE, WITH TENDER (non-reversing)

Locomotive (20-volt or 6-volt) ... Price **8 6**
M1/2 Tender ... Red or green ... Price **9d.**

*E120 (20-volt) ELECTRIC LOCOMOTIVE, WITH TENDER (reversing)

Locomotive ... ... Price **20 -**
... ... Price **2 -**

E320 (20-volt) ELECTRIC LOCOMOTIVE, WITH TENDER (Automatic reversing)

L.N.E.R. "Flying Scotsman," L.M.S.R. "Royal Scot," G.W.R. "Caerphilly Castle," S.R. "Lord Nelson"
Locomotive ... ... Price **32 6**
No. 2 Special Tender ... ... Price **6 -**

*EM320 (20-volt) or EM36 (6-volt) ELECTRIC TANK LOCOMOTIVE (Reversing)

Price (20-volt or 6-volt) ... **16 6**

*E120 (20-volt) SPECIAL ELECTRIC LOCOMOTIVE, WITH TENDER (Automatic reversing)

Locomotive ... ... Price **27 6**
No. 1 Special Tender ... ... Price **3 3**

E36 (6-volt) METROPOLITAN LOCOMOTIVE ... Price 30 -

E320 (20-volt) RIVIERA "BLUE" ELECTRIC LOCOMOTIVE, WITH TENDER (Automatic reversing)

Locomotive ... ... Price **32 6**
Riviera "Blue" Tender ... ... Price **4 6**

If you are interested in Deferred Payment Terms turn to page iii of cover

*EO20 (20-volt) ELECTRIC LOCOMOTIVE, WITH TENDER (Reversing)

Locomotive ... ... Price **19 -**
No. O/1 Tender ... ... Price **2 -**

*E120 (20-volt) SPECIAL ELECTRIC TANK LOCOMOTIVE (Automatic reversing) ... Price **27 6**

E220 (20-volt) SPECIAL ELECTRIC LOCOMOTIVE, WITH TENDER (Automatic reversing)

L.N.E.R. "Hunt," L.M.S.R. "Compound," G.W.R. "County," S.R. "L1" Class.
Locomotive ... ... Price **37 6**
No. 2 Special Tender ... ... Price **6 -**

*E120 (20-volt) ELECTRIC TANK LOCOMOTIVE (Reversing) ... Price **20 -**

*E220 (20-volt) SPECIAL ELECTRIC TANK LOCOMOTIVE (Automatic reversing) ... Price **30 -**

*E26 (6-volt) SPECIAL ELECTRIC TANK LOCOMOTIVE Reversing ... Price **27 6**

*EPM16 (6-volt) SPECIAL ELECTRIC TANK LOCOMOTIVE (Reversing) ... Price **33 6**

(6-volt Permanent Magnet Type). Can be run from a 6-volt accumulator, or from the mains through the Transformer-Rectifier listed on page 34

Full details of the new Hornby scale model Locomotives "Princess Elizabeth" and "Eton" are given on pages 31 and 29 respectively.
* Lettered and coloured to represent L.M.S.R., G.W.R., L.N.E.R. or S.R. Locomotives.

32

Picture taken from the 1938/39 Hamleys 'Toys of Quality' catalogue.

HORNBY TRAINS
"Princess Elizabeth"

Gauge O, 1¼in.

20-VOLT ELECTRIC LOCOMOTIVE WITH TENDER—AUTOMATIC REVERSING

This is a magnificent Hornby scale model of the L.M.S.R. 4-6-2 "Princess Elizabeth" locomotive that made a world record for non-stop steam travel in covering the 401.4 miles from Glasgow to London at an average speed of 70 m.p.h. It includes all the main features of the actual engine—massive six-coupled driving wheels, outside cylinders and motion, tapered boiler and fire-box, oval-headed buffers at the front, accurate internal details of cab and tender and Royal nameplate. The boiler fittings are characteristic; the sturdy chimney and squat dome, the top-feed apparatus, the dwarf safety valve columns and horizontal hooter all follow the real ones very closely.

The new Hornby 20-volt automatic reversing motor that is fitted ensures abundant power and makes "Princess Elizabeth" the ideal engine for the

fastest and heaviest trains. The remarkable efficiency and fine appearance of the model appeal to all who see it. Driver Clarke of the real "Princess Elizabeth" has seen the Hornby model and says "It's fine !"

The enamelling and lining follows L.M.S.R. practice faithfully, and the general finish is of the highest Hornby quality.

Price, complete with tender, in special presentation box, **£5 5 0**

"Princess Elizabeth" will run on the standard Hornby 2ft. radius tinplate track, but in order to allow this splendid locomotive to run at its highest speed, and to show the immense loads it will pull, the new Hornby solid steel track should be used. For details see page 52.

To make up a suitable train for the "Princess Elizabeth" Locomotive the No. 2 Corridor Coaches L.M.S.R., featured on page 39, should be used.

For particulars of Deferred Payment Terms, see page III of Cover

QUALITY FEATURES OF "PRINCESS ELIZABETH" MOTOR

1. FIELD.—Constructed of electrical steel laminations, and scientifically designed to obtain maximum power.
2. DRIVING WHEELS.—Accurately pressure diecast to give maximum adhesion and smooth running.
3. GEARS.—All gears machine cut.
4. BEARINGS.—All bearings are of phosphor bronze.
5. ARMATURE.—Of laminated electrical steel mounted on a shaft machined from specially selected high grade steel.
6. SIDEPLATES.—Hard rolled brass, rigidly connected by turned pillars.
7. COMMUTATOR.—Constructed with hard copper segments moulded into a Bakelite body.
8. BRUSH HOLDERS.—Of brass, rigidly mounted on Bakelite moulded brackets.
9. BRUSHES.—Of self-lubricating Morganite Carbon.
10. REVERSING SWITCH.—Bakelite moulded switch barrel with bronze contact springs. Working parts of the automatic mechanism are case hardened.

31

Picture taken from the 1938/39 Hamleys 'Toys of Quality' catalogue.

Hornby 'O' Gauge Locomotives

Model M3 Tank Locomotive

0-4-0 locomotive without cylinders and connecting rods until 1936. Earlier locos repaired by factory were often fitted with rods. Tinprinted body, no hand-rail knobs.   Clockwork 1931-41, Electric LSTM3/20 (20 volt) 1932-34, EM320 (20 volt) and EM36 (6 volt) 1934-41.

1931-41.....LMS .....2270 ....Red (Red wheels).........1931-32, 8-spoke wheels,
1932-36, 12-spoke wheels,
1936-41, 8-spoke wheels,
1936 on, cylinders and rods...............................CW **£50-70** ❏
6v **£120-140** ❏
20v **£140-180** ❏

1931-41.....LNER ...460 ....Green (Red wheels) ....CW **£50-70** ❏
6v **£120-140** ❏
20v **£140-160** ❏

1931-41.....GW ....6600 ....Green (Red wheels) ....CW **£60-80** ❏
6v **£140-160** ❏
20v **£150-170** ❏

1931-41.....SR........E126 ....Dark Green (Red wheels) ....CW **£70-90** ❏
6v **£160-180** ❏
20v **£180-200** ❏

Model No.0 Locomotive

0-4-0 outside cylinder Locomotive with coal rail tender. Clockwork drive mechanism.
Note: In most production runs of Hornby models there were fewer black locomotives so they normally sell for 25% to 35% more. Rare numbers such as 1504, add further value.

1923-24...................'Zulu' ....Black ....Name on splashers in Red / Gold......................... **£120-140** ❏
1924-29.....LMS..2710...Black or Red .....Company on splashers, name on tender................. **£80-110** ❏
1924-29.....LNER..2710...Black or Green..Lined 1925 on, Red wheels 1928 on...................... **£90-120** ❏
1924-29.....GW...2710...Green .... **£110-140** ❏
1929-31.....Numbers 8327, 600, 5097, 5096, 8324, 2449 used on locos with Company on tender.. **£120-140** ❏

1928-31.....SR...E509 ..Black, lined Green, 'Southern' and number on tender, Red wheels. **£150-200** ❏
1928-31.....SR...E759 ..Green, lined White, 'Southern' and number on tender, Red wheels **£140-180** ❏

1931-41.....Redesigned body with long splashers and tender with solid side rails. 6 volt (EO6) and 20 volt (EO20) AC introduced.
All locos lined out but made without cylinders until 1937 when outside cylinders were re-introduced to the range.
LMS .....600, 8324, 500, 551, 5600.........Black or Red ....CW **£75-100** ❏
6v **£150-160** ❏
20v **£180-200** ❏
LNER ...6380, 5508, 2810, 5508, 4797....Black or Green ....CW **£75-100** ❏
6v **£150-160** ❏
20v **£180-200** ❏
GW ....2251, 5399 ....Green ....CW **£85-110** ❏
6v **£160-180** ❏
20v **£190-240** ❏
SR........A504, 1504, E793, A759...........Black or Green ....CW **£110-130** ❏
6v **£180-210** ❏
20v **£230-260** ❏

Model No.1 Tender Locomotive

0-4-0 locomotive with cylinders and connecting rods.
Similar to No.0 locomotive but with brass hand-rail knobs instead of diecast ones and cylinders on all variations. Enamelled body.
Mechanism: Clockwork 1920-41, E16 (6 volt) 1934-35, E120 (20 volt) 1934-41.
General guide price ....CW **£100-150** ❏
6v **£175-275** ❏
20v **£175-275** ❏

Model No.1 Tank Locomotive

0-4-0 tender locomotives with cylinders and connecting rods. Brass dome until 1928 (except Zulu). Wire hand-rails on smoke-box with brass knob each side. Enamelled body. Mechanisms: Clockwork 1922-41, 6 volt DC 1929-34, E16 (6 volt) 1934-36, LST1/20 (20 volt) 1932-34, E120 (20 volt) 1934-41.

1922-23	'Zulu'		Black	Red edge to spectacles, name on tank in Red/Gold.	CW	£130-160	❏
1923-24	LMS		Black	'Zulu' on front of smoke-box	CW	£130-160	❏
1924-26	LMS	'0-4-0'	Black or Red	Letters on tank	CW	£70-90	❏
1926-31	623, 326		Black	Wheels now Black or Red	6vDC	£120-140	❏
1924-26	LNER	'0-4-0'	Black or Green		CW	£70-90	❏
1926-31	LNER	623, 326, 463	Black or Green		CW	£70-90	❏
					6vDC	£120-140	❏
1926-31	GW	no number	Green	'Great Western' and crest on tender.			
				Crest on some 1930-31	CW	£90-110	❏
					6vDC	£140-160	❏
1928-31	SR	A600, B667	Black or Green	'Southern' and number on tank	CW	£100-120	❏
					6vDC	£160-180	❏

1931-41.....Revised design, heavier looking with lower chimney, dome, cab and flared bunker. Control rods above bunker (not through its bunker plate as previously).

LMS	7140, 623, 326, 2115	Black or Red	Black bodies finished 1936, Red wheels now general	CW	£80-100	❏
				6v	£130-150	❏
				20v	£180-200	❏
1931-41.....LNER	826, 2900	Black or Red	Darker Green 1936-41	CW	£80-100	❏
				6v	£130-150	❏
				20v	£180-200	❏
1931-41.....GW	4560	Green	1931-35 'Great Western', 1935-41 'GWR' monogram	CW	£90-110	❏
				6v	£130-150	❏
				20v	£180-240	❏
1931-41.....SR	E111, 111, E29, 29	Black or Green		CW	£100-120	❏
				6v	£140-160	❏
				20v	£200-250	❏

Model No.1 Special Tank Locomotive

Heavy 0–4–0 locomotive with cylinders and connecting rods. Larger than other 0–4–0 tanks with more powerful mechanism, Mechanisms: Clockwork 1929-41, EPM16 (6volt) 1934-39, and E120 (20volt) 1934-41. Finished in the four railway company colours, also black liveries except for GWR.

General guide price	CW	£150-275	❏
	6v	£250-400	❏
	20v	£250-400	❏

Model No.1 Special Tender Locomotive

Similar to the previous model but with splashers over the wheels instead of side tanks, it connects to a larger four-wheeled tender than the other 0–4–0 models. Other details are those for the No.1 Special Tank Loco, however, 6 volt mechanisms were not fitted to this model.

General guide price	CW	£200-300	❏
	20v	£275-450	❏

Model No.2 Tank Locomotive

The only 4–4–4 locomotive made by Hornby. It was produced with a clockwork mechanism only in the years 1923-29. Early engines were in LMS and LNER liveries. GWR was introduced in 1926 and SR in 1928. Many had brass domes and LMS, LNER and SR locos were available in black.

General guide price	CW	£125-200	❏

N.B. Details and prices of Models No.1 Tender Locomotives, No.1 Special Tank and Tender Locomotives, and No.2 Special Tank Locomotives, along with further models will be expanded and detailed in our next issue.

'O' Gauge Locomotives

Model No.2 Tender Locomotive

An elegant 4–4–0 of early 20th century character, powered by clockwork only, except for a very few special orders. These exceptionally rare examples were Hornby's first venture into electric mechanisms. Produced from 1921 until 1929 they have a six-wheeled tender with a coal rail, usually carrying the number '2711', although there are other variations. For the first two years, the locos were made in pre-grouping colours: GN – green, MR – red, CR – blue. After this the colours of the four grouped companies were introduced; black engines available again for all except GWR. The driving wheels were covered by one long splasher and the domes were mainly brass. ....CW **£150-225** ❏

Model No.2 Special Tank Locomotive

The revised No.2 Tank Locomotive produced from 1929-41 with a 4–4–2 wheel arrangement. Powered by clockwork, 6volts and 20volts. A heavier looking engine thatn the No.2 with higher boiler, lower chimney, dome and cab. Made in LMS red or black, LNER green or black, GWR green and SR green or black...CW **£125-275** ❏
  6v **£225-375** ❏
  20v **£225-375** ❏

Model No.2 Special Locomotive

4-4-0 tender locomotives. Hornby's first real venture into true-to-type models. A very attractive range embodying the character of the prototypes. Mechanisms: Clockwork 1929-41, E220 (20 volt) 1934-41.

1929-41.....LMS .....Compound ....1185...Red (Maroon)....1929-30 Red drivers. Unlined tender with sans-serif 'LMS'. Red running plate................CW **£250-300** ❏

1929-41.....LMS .....Compound ....1185...Red (Maroon)....1929-30 Red drivers. Unlined tender with
  sans-serif 'LMS'. Red running plate................CW **£250-300** ❏
  1931- serif letters on lined tender and
  Black running plate ....CW **£325-375** ❏
  20v **£400-500** ❏

1929-35.....LNER ...'Shire' Class, 'Yorkshire' ....234.....Green.................1929-30 'LNER' on tender, Green running plate
  CW **£550-650** ❏
  1930-31 Green running plate, '234' on cab,
  Black running plate after this............................20v **£950-1,050** ❏

1935-41.....LNER ...'Hunt' Class, 'Bramham Moor' .201 .....Green.................Fitted steam pipes from smoke box to running plate
  Darker Green 1936-41 ....CW **£475-575** ❏
  20v **£850-950** ❏

1929-41.....GW ....'County' Class, 'County of Bedford' ....Green.................1929-30 Green running plate,
  'Great Western' and crest on tender
  1930-36 Black running plate, tender as above,
  1936-41 Black running plate,
  'GWR' on tender ....CW **£475-575** ❏
  20v **£800-900** ❏

1929-35.....SR.........'L1' Class ....A759..Green.................'Southern' and number on tender
1935-41.....SR.........'L1' Class ....1759...Green.................'Southern' and number on tender ....CW **£900-1,200** ❏
  20v **£1,500-1,800** ❏

Model No.3 Locomotive

4-4-2 tender locomotive. Mechanisms: Clockwork or 4volt, 6 volt or 20 volt electric from 1931/34. Market prices shown are for locomotives plus tender, all in very good collectable condition for the age.

The Riviera 'Blue Train' Locomotive.

1926-41 'NORD', 31240 / 31801 / 31290
  Brown (black wheels: c/w, red 1931/32) Early issues have two brass
  domes. Bulbholders fitted from 1933. Smoke deflectors from 1934,
  first black, then brown from 1936. All models have 8-wheeled bogie
  tender, pattern of bogies changed in 1937. Engine and tender numbers
  do not match before 1930 ....CW **£200-250** ❏
  20v **£300-375** ❏

1927-41.....LMS 'ROYAL SCOT', 6100..................Maroon body, smoke deflectors fitted 1936-40......................................CW **£200-250** ❏
  20v **£300-350** ❏

1927-35.....LNER, 'FLYING SCOTSMAN', 4472....Green body (Darker Green from 1936) ....CW **£225-275** ❏
  20v **£325-375** ❏

1927-36.....GW, 'CAERPHILLY CASTLE', 4073 ....Green body, 'Great Western' and crest shown on tender,

1936-41.....GW, 'CAERPHILLY CASTLE', 4073 ....Green body, GWR monogram shown on tender......................................CW **£250-300** ❑
                                                                                                                            20v **£350-425** ❑

1928-41.....SR, 'LORD NELSON', E850 / 850........Green body, smoke deflectors fitted from 1936 ....CW **£250-300** ❑
                                                                                                                            20v **£350-450** ❑

1937.........LNER, Special order, 1368 ....Black No.3 Locomotive..NGPP   ❑

General identification points:

1927 - 1929 Coal railed tenders with fixed lamps, stovepipe chimney, polished brass dome or safety valve. Clockwork.

1930 - 1938 Smokebox painted black, dome painted as bodywork, squat chimney. Clockwork wheels were red, instead of black, on LMS locomotives and green on SR, GWR and LNER ones. All reverted to black in 1938.

1930 - 1941 All locomotives fitted with No 2 Special tenders.

1934 Automatic reversing mechanisms E320 and manual E36 replaced E3/20 and E3/6. Wheels on electric locomotives now same diameter (larger) as on clockwork locomotives.

Examples of No.3 Locomotive Sets

c1927-29...'ROYAL SCOT' Set ....With 4-4-2 loco and coal railed tender, control clockwork. Two No.2 Pullman coaches, track key connector and control leaflet. Attractive picture box....................**£400-500** ❑

c1936-41...'ROYAL SCOT' Set ....Locomotive with smoke deflectors (20volt), two No.2 Special Pullman Coaches...**£500-600** ❑

c1935 ....'GOLDEN ARROW' Set ....With 4-4-2 'LORD NELSON' 850 locomotive (3-rail, 20 volt), two grey-roofed No.2 Special Pullman coaches ('Loraine' and 'Alberta').........**£600-700** ❑

c1926-29...'RIVIERA BLUE' Set.............................With 4-4-2 locomotive 'NORD', 31240 and tender 31801, control clockwork. Blue Dining and Sleeping Cars, attractive picture box..............**£500-600** ❑

Metropolitan Locomotive

The first Hornby locomotive representing a prototype although it had only four wheels under its skirt, not two bogies, as in the real thing. Also first production electric motored locomotive, with a high voltage mechanism (125v) in 1925-26. Excerising care prevented your eyes lighting up! Mechanisms: 1925-26 HV, 1926-39 clockwork, 1927-29 4v, 1926-39 6v, 1938-39 20v.

1938.........Metropolitan Locomotive........................Body tinprinted maroon, lined black and yellow, with brass handrails and window surrounds, red valances, grey roof held by four brass nuts ....CW **£200-250** ❑
                                                                                                                            6v **£250-300** ❑
                                                                                                                            20v **£350-400** ❑

Model No.4 'Eton' Locomotive

4-4-0 'Schools' class tender locomotive. Hornby's final engine based on a prototype. Drive mechanisms: Clockwork and E240 (20 volt motor).

1937-41.....SR.........'Schools' Class, 'Eton' ....900 .....Dark Green........small cab plate '900', 'Southern 900' on tender side (tender (No.2 special) is incorrect for prototype)
                                                                                                                            CW **£750-850** ❑
                                                                                                                            20v **£900-1,300** ❑

'Princess Elizabeth' Locomotive

4-6-2 'Princess' 'Pacific' class tender locomotive. Hornby's largest and most impressive piece of motive power. However, incorrect proportions on locomotive give a distorted appearance to line of boiler and firebox. Early wooden presentation cases were red with blue lining marked 'Meccano Ltd. Liverpool. Princess Elizabeth' in gold. Middle period boxes were red with cream lining and late ones blue with green lining. Both the latter had a nice printed description and picture inside the lid. Drive mechanism: (20 volt electric motor).

1937-40.....LMS .....'Princess Elizabeth'...................6201...Red ....'37' inside cab - sand, 'LMS' and number - serif.
                                                                                            '38' inside cab - sand, 'LMS' and number - sans serif.
                                                                                            '39-40' inside cab -maroon, 'LMS' and number - sans serif.
                                                                                            boxed..**£1,800-2,300** ❑

Hornby 'O' Gauge Private Owner Wagons

Tinplate Private Owner Wagons manufactured by Hornby are outstandingly colourful and attractive and it was an effective way of advertising. They were toy representations of the privately owned wagons run on the railways by various companies in the 1920's and 1930's.

Hornby usually encouraged the companies to to pay part of the cost of the transfers which ensured them of good advertising in the toy shop windows and in the home. A 1922 'Shell' Tank Wagon was the first Private Owner Wagon made by Hornby and the very early vans were of nut and bolt construction.

Company name	Year(s)	Notes	Market Price Range	
'COLMAN'S MUSTARD'	1923-24	Light Yellow body, Red lettering, Royal Coat of Arms and bull's head, White roof, Black open chassis	£450-550	❑
'SECCOTINE'	1923-30	Blue body, Silver block lettering 'Seccotine Sticks Everything'. Orange roof, Black chassis (open type), fixed doors	£250-300	❑
	1931-33	Orange roof, Black chassis (closed type), sliding doors	£250-300	❑
	1933-34	Red roof, Black chassis (closed type), sliding doors	£250-300	❑
'CARR'S BISCUITS'	1924-24	Blue or Grey-Blue body, serif lettering and Royal Coat of Arms (Gold), White roof, Black chassis (open type), fixed doors	£100-150	❑
	1925-30	Blue or Blue-Grey roof, Black chassis (open type), fixed doors	£100-150	❑
	1930-32	Blue or Blue-Grey roof, Black chassis (closed type), fixed doors	£100-150	❑
	1932-41	Blue or Blue-Grey roof, Black chassis (closed type), sliding doors	£100-150	❑
'CRAWFORD'S BISCUITS'	1924-24	Red body, serif lettering and Royal Coat of Arms (Gold), White roof, Black chassis (open type), fixed doors	£125-175	❑
	1925-31	Red roof, Black chassis (open type), fixed doors	£125-175	❑
	1931-32	Red roof, Black chassis (closed type), fixed doors	£125-175	❑
	1932-41	Red roof, Black chassis (closed type), sliding doors	£125-175	❑
'JACOB & Co.'S BISCUITS'	1924-24	Maroon body, serif lettering (Gold), coloured Royal Coat of Arms, White roof, Black chassis (open type), fixed doors	£120-165	❑
	1925-30	Maroon roof, Black chassis (open type), fixed doors	£120-165	❑
	1930-31	Maroon roof, Black chassis (closed type), fixed doors	£120-165	❑
	1931-41	Maroon roof, Black chassis (closed type), sliding doors	£120-165	❑
'FYFFES BANANAS'	1931-32	Deep Yellow body, Blue block lettering and logotype shaded White, White roof, Green chassis, fixed doors	£70-100	❑
	1932-33	White roof, Green chassis, sliding doors	£70-100	❑
	1933-39	Red roof, Red chassis, sliding doors	£70-100	❑
	1939-41	Red roof, Black chassis, sliding doors	£70-100	❑
'CADBURY'S CHOCOLATE'	1932-33	Blue body, serif lettering (Gold), White roof, Black chassis	£100-150	❑
	1933-35	Blue body, serif lettering (Gold), White roof, Green chassis	£100-150	❑
	1935-38	Blue body, serif lettering (Gold), White roof, Black chassis	£100-150	❑
	1938-41	Blue body, block lettering (Gold), White roof, Black chassis	£100-150	❑
'PALETHORPE'S SAUSAGES'	1938-41	Maroon body, thin Gold lettering 'Palethorpe's Royal Cambridge' with coloured pack of sausages, Grey roof, Black chassis	£150-200	❑

Hornby 'O' Gauge Miscellaneous Rolling Stock

Examples of Market Price Ranges for models in very good collectable condition, boxed where possible. (see also Auction Price Results)

Coaches

Eight different names were given to the coaches:

'ALBERTA', 'ARCADIA', 'GROSVENOR', 'IOLANTHE', 'LORAINE', 'MONTANA', 'VERONA', 'ZENOBIA'.

1921-23 ....No.2 ....'PULLMAN' Coach ....Cream and Green, Gold lining, brass buffers, fixed doors ....**£100-125** ❑

1921-23 ....No.2 ....'PULLMAN DINING SALOON' ....Cream and Green, Gold lining ....**£100-125** ❑

1925-28 ....No.2 ....'PULLMAN' Coach ....Brown and Cream , brass buffers, opening doors ....**£100-125** ❑

1928-41 ....No.2-3 ....'PULLMAN' Coach ....Brown and Cream, Cream roof ....**£75-100** ❑

1928-41 ....No.2 ....Special 'PULLMAN' Coach ....Brown and Cream, Grey roof , (Cream roof 1928-30)................**£125-175** ❑

1928-40 ....No.2 ....Metropolitan Coach ....1st or Brake/3rd coaches, 'woodgrain' finish............................**£150-200** ❑

1928-40 ....No.2 ....Saloon Coach, 'LMS' ....Red body, Grey roof ....**£100-125** ❑
1928-40 ....No.2 ....Saloon Coach, 'LNER' ....Brown body, Grey roof ....**£100-125** ❑

1935-41* .....No.2 ....Passenger Coach, 'LMS' ....1st/3rd or Brake/3rd, Maroon body, Grey roof..........................**£100-150** ❑
1935-41* .....No.2 ....Passenger Coach, 'NE'...........................1st/3rd or Brake/3rd, 'Woodgrain' body, Lighter Grey roof ....**£125-175** ❑
1935-41* .....No.2 ....Passenger Coach, 'GWR'.......................1st/3rd or Brake/3rd, Cream/Brown body, Grey roof.................**£200-250** ❑
1935-41* .....No.2 ....Passenger Coach, 'SR'...........................1st/3rd or Brake/3rd, Dark Green body, Grey roof.....................**£250-300** ❑
(*) Note: These four coaches were also issued in the years 1948-50.

1937-41 ....No.2 ....Corridor Coach, 'LMS' ....All 3rd or 1st/3rd/Brake, Maroon body, Grey roof ....**£100-150** ❑
1937-41 ....No.2 ....Corridor Coach, 'LNER' ....All 3rd or 1st/3rd/Brake, 'Woodgrain', Lighter Grey roof ....**£175-225** ❑
1937-41 ....No.2 ....Corridor Coach, 'GW' ....All 3rd or 1st/3rd/Brake, Cream/Brown body, Grey roof ....**£200-250** ❑
1937-41 ....No.2 ....Corridor Coach, 'SOUTHERN'..............All 3rd or 1st/3rd/Brake, Dark Green body, Grey roof..............**£250-300** ❑

1928-41 ....No.3 ....Riviera Blue Coach ....Dining Car or Sleeping Car ....**£150-200** ❑

1931-41 ....No.3 ....'MITROPA' Coach ....Speisewagen (Dining Car) or Schlafwagen (Sleeper) ....**£1,000-1,250** ❑

Tankers and Wagons

1929-41 ....'COLAS' Bitumen Tank Wagon.................Blue tank, closed chassis after 1930. Red tank 1936-41.............**£300-500** ❑

1927-36 ....'MOTOR BP SPIRIT' Tank Wagon ....Pale Yellow tank, closed chassis after 1930.............................**£100-125** ❑

1929-31 ....'UNITED DAIRIES' Milk Tank Wagon .....Cream tank, Grey open chassis ....**£300-350** ❑
1931-37 ....'UNITED DAIRIES' Milk Tank Wagon .....White tank, Blue closed chassis ....**£325-375** ❑

1936-40 ....'NESTLES MILK' Tanker ....White tank, Green, Blue or Black closed chassis ....**£225-250** ❑

1931-40 ....'MECCANO' Coal Wagon.........................With coal load, Red, Gold letters, closed chassis ....**£75-100** ❑

1928-29 ....Refrigerator Van, 'SR'.............................Pink body, hinged door, large Gold 'SR' ....**£300-400** ❑

1924-30 ....Rotary Snowplough.................................Early issue LNER, Grey with Black base, Green after 1927,
                                                                                                        sliding door, cast lamp...**£100-150** ❑

1929-41 ....'NORD' Covered Wagon...........................Grey body, Gold letters (White 1939-41), canvas tarpaulin,
                                                                                                        closed chassis after 1930 ....**£75-100** ❑

See also the following reprinted 1938–39 catalogue pages which feature the basic models and accessories available at that time.
N.B. The listings above represent but a fraction of the hundreds of variations of rolling stock known to have been issued. As and when more pricing information becomes available, it will be published in future editions of this Catalogue. However, other variations are to be found listed in the Auction Results sections.

HORNBY ROLLING STOCK

The Hornby System includes a complete range of Rolling Stock, Accessories, and Rails, Points and Crossings, with which the most elaborate model railway can be constructed. Every vehicle is suitable for both clockwork and electric railways.

*GUARD'S VAN — Price **2/6**

No. O PULLMAN COACH — Price **1/3**

M1/2 PULLMAN COACH

No. 1 PULLMAN COACH — Price **2/6**

No. 1 PULLMAN COMPOSITE COACH — Price **2/6**

No. O "SILVER JUBILEE" COACH
Articulated. Finished in silver and grey ... ... Price **1/-**

No. O STREAMLINE COACH
Articulated. Available in two colour schemes, maroon and cream and light green and dark green ... Price **1/9**

PULLMAN CAR
American Type (as illustrated). Lettered "Washington" or "Madison." ... Price **1/6**
Continental Type. "Mitropa" No. O Lettered "Mitropa" ... Price **1/6**

No. 2 PULLMAN COACH
Not suitable for 1ft. radius rails ... Price **9/6**

No. 2 SPECIAL PULLMAN COACH
Not suitable for 1ft. radius rails. ... Price **13/-**

METROPOLITAN COACH
Not suitable | Metropolitan Coach E fitted for electric lighting (first-class or brake-third). Not suitable for 1ft. radius rails ... Price **11/6**
Price **7 6**

Metropolitan Coach C (first-class or brake-third). for 1ft. radius rails.

*No. 1 PASSENGER COACH — Price **2/6**

MO PULLMAN COACH — Price **9d.**

No. 2 SALOON COACH
L.M.S.R. or L.N.E.R. Not suitable for 1ft. radius rails ... ... Price **9/6**

*No. 2 PASSENGER COACH
Not suitable for 1ft. radius rails. First-third or Brake-third ... Price **6/6**

No. 2 SPECIAL PULLMAN COMPOSITE COACH
Not suitable for 1ft. radius rails. ... Price **13/-**

RIVERA "BLUE" TRAIN COACH
"Dining Car" or "Sleeping Car." Not suitable for 1ft. radius rails. Price **10/6**

No. 3 "MITROPA" COACH
Similar in design to above. Lettered "Mitropa" ... Price **10/6**

*Available in the colours of the L.M.S., L.N.E., G.W. or S.R. Companies

38

Picture taken from the 1938/39 Hamleys 'Toys of Quality' catalogue.

HORNBY ROLLING STOCK

FITTED WITH AUTOMATIC COUPLINGS

The Hornby No. 2 Corridor Coaches featured below are new models of the latest types now in use on the systems of the four main railway groups.

No. 2 CORRIDOR COACH

L.M.S. First-third. Not suitable for 1 ft. radius rails ... ... Price **7/6**

No. 2 CORRIDOR COACH

L.N.E.R. First-third. Not suitable for 1 ft. radius rails ... ... Price **7/6**

No. 2 CORRIDOR COACH

G.W. First-third. Not suitable for 1 ft. radius rails ... ... Price **7/6**

No. 2 CORRIDOR COACH

S.R. Open-third. Not suitable for 1 ft. radius rails ... ... Price **7/6**

No. 2 CORRIDOR COACH

L.M.S. Brake-composite. Not suitable for 1 ft. radius rails ... ... Price **7/6**

No. 2 CORRIDOR COACH

L.N.E.R. Brake-composite. Not suitable for 1 ft. radius rails ... ... Price **7/6**

No. 2 CORRIDOR COACH

G.W. Brake-composite. Not suitable for 1 ft. radius rails ... ... Price **7/6**

No. 2 CORRIDOR COACH

S.R. Brake-composite. Not suitable for 1 ft. radius rails ... ... Price **7/6**

BRAKE VAN

Opening doors. In N.E. or S.R. lettering ... ... Price **2/9**

No. O BANANA VAN

Lettered L.M.S. only. Price **1/6**

No. O MILK TRAFFIC VAN

Lettered G.W. only. Price **1/6**

No. O REFRIGERATOR VAN

Lettered L.M.S., G.W., N.E. and S.R. ... ... Price **1/6**

BRAKE VAN

Opening doors. In L.M.S. or G.W. lettering ... Price **2/9**

No. 1 BANANA VAN "FYFFES"

Sliding doors ... Price **2/3**

MEAT VAN

Lettered L.M.S., G.W. and N.E. ... ... Price **1/6**

FISH VAN

Lettered L.M.S., G.W. and N.E. ... ... Price **1/6**

39

Picture taken from the 1938/39 Hamleys 'Toys of Quality' catalogue.

HORNBY ROLLING STOCK
FITTED WITH AUTOMATIC COUPLINGS

No. 1 CATTLE TRUCK
Sliding doors ... Price **2/3**

No. 2 CATTLE TRUCK
Opening doors. (Not suitable for 1ft. radius rails) ... Price **4/6**

No. 1 LUGGAGE VAN
Sliding doors ... Price **2/3**

No. 2 LUGGAGE VAN
Opening double doors. (Not Suitable for 1ft. radius rails.) Price **4/6**

No. 1 REFRIGERATOR VAN
Sliding doors ... Price **2/3**

SNOW PLOUGH
Price **3/6**

FIBRE WAGON
As used in France and other Continental countries. Price **1/3**

FLAT TRUCK (L.M.S.R.)
With Furniture Container
Price **2/-**

No. 1 MILK TRAFFIC VAN
Sliding doors. Contains four milk cans ... Price **2/3**
Separate Milk Cans, each **1d.**

GUNPOWDER VAN
Sliding doors ... Price **2/3**

CHOCOLATE VAN "CADBURY'S"
Sliding doors ... Price **2/3**

BREAKDOWN VAN AND CRANE
Sliding doors. (Not suitable for 1ft. radius rails.) Price **5/11**

BOX CAR
A model of the type in use on American railways. Price **2/3**

FLAT TRUCK (S.R.)
With Ventilated Container
Price **2/-**

BISCUIT VAN, "CRAWFORD'S"
Sliding doors ... Price **2/3**

BISCUIT VAN, "JACOB'S"
Sliding doors ... Price **2/3**

BISCUIT VAN, "CARR'S"
Sliding doors ... Price **2/3**

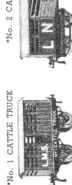

FLAT TRUCK (L.N.E.R.)
With Goods Container
Price **2/-**

FLAT TRUCK (G.W.R.)
With Insulated Container
Price **2/-**

FLAT TRUCK & CONTAINERS

The Flat Truck and Containers shown in the accompanying illustrations can be purchased separately as follows:—Flat Truck, Price **1/6** Containers, L.M.S.R. (Furniture), L.N.E.R. (Goods), G.W.R. (Insulated), S.R. (Ventilated). Price **6d.** each

* Lettered L.M.S., N.E. G.W. or S.R.

40

Picture taken from the 1938/39 Hamleys 'Toys of Quality' catalogue.

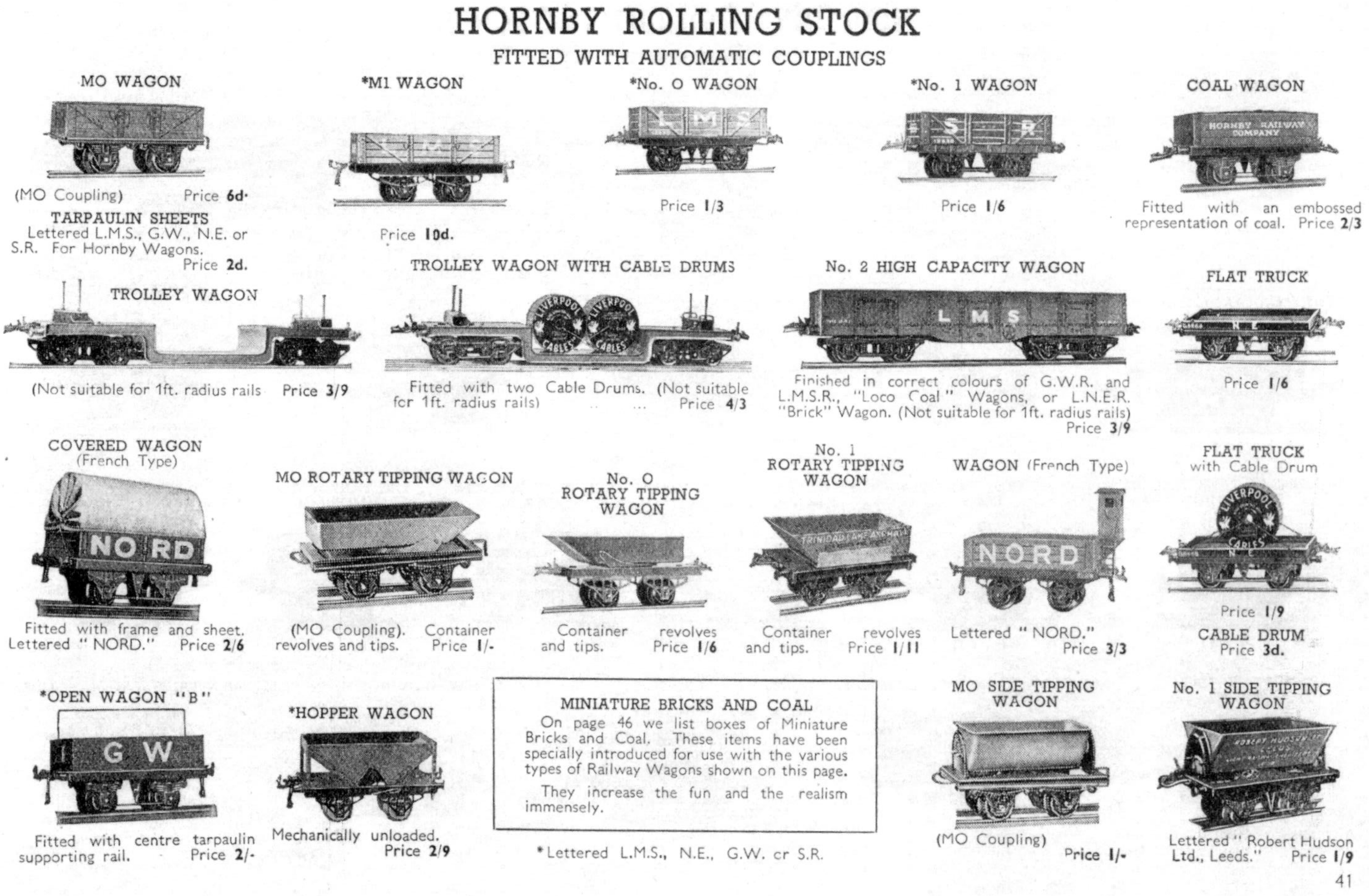

HORNBY ROLLING STOCK
FITTED WITH AUTOMATIC COUPLINGS

COAL WAGON
Fitted with an embossed representation of coal. Price **2/3**

MO WAGON
(MO Coupling) Price **6d.**

TARPAULIN SHEETS
Lettered L.M.S., G.W., N.E. or S.R. For Hornby Wagons. Price **2d.**

*M1 WAGON
Price **10d.**

TROLLEY WAGON
(Not suitable for 1ft. radius rails Price **3/9**

*No. O WAGON
Price **1/3**

*No. 1 WAGON
Price **1/6**

FLAT TRUCK
Price **1/6**

TROLLEY WAGON WITH CABLE DRUMS
Fitted with two Cable Drums. (Not suitable for 1ft. radius rails) Price **4/3**

No. 2 HIGH CAPACITY WAGON
Finished in correct colours of G.W.R. and L.M.S.R., "Loco Coal" Wagons, or L.N.E.R. "Brick" Wagon. (Not suitable for 1ft. radius rails) Price **3/9**

FLAT TRUCK
with Cable Drum
Price **1/9**

CABLE DRUM
Price **3d.**

COVERED WAGON
(French Type)
Fitted with frame and sheet.
Lettered "NORD." Price **2/6**

MO ROTARY TIPPING WAGON
(MO Coupling). Container revolves and tips. Price **1/-**

No. O ROTARY TIPPING WAGON
Container revolves and tips. Price **1/6**

No. 1 ROTARY TIPPING WAGON
Container revolves and tips. Price **1/11**

WAGON (French Type)
Lettered "NORD." Price **3/3**

MO SIDE TIPPING WAGON
(MO Coupling) Price **1/-**

No. 1 SIDE TIPPING WAGON
Lettered "Robert Hudson Ltd., Leeds." Price **1/9**

*"OPEN WAGON "B""
Fitted with centre tarpaulin supporting rail. Price **2/-**

*HOPPER WAGON
Mechanically unloaded. Price **2/9**

MINIATURE BRICKS AND COAL
On page 46 we list boxes of Miniature Bricks and Coal. These items have been specially introduced for use with the various types of Railway Wagons shown on this page. They increase the fun and the realism immensely.

*Lettered L.M.S., N.E., G.W. or S.R.

41

Picture taken from the 1938/39 Hamleys 'Toys of Quality' catalogue.

HORNBY ROLLING STOCK
FITTED WITH AUTOMATIC COUPLINGS

No. 2 TIMBER WAGON

(Not suitable for 1ft. radius rails)   Price **2/6**

MILK TANK WAGON "NESTLE'S MILK"   Price **4/6**

No. 1 PETROL TANK WAGON "REDLINE-GLICO"   Price **1/11**

BITUMEN TANK WAGON "COLAS"
An attractive model with full detail   ...   ...   Price **3/6**

No. 1 TIMBER WAGON   Price **1/3**

MO PETROL TANK WAGON "SHELL-B.P."   (MO Coupling)   Price **1/-**

OIL TANK WAGON "MOBILOIL"   Price **1/11**

BARREL WAGON
With four "Castrol" Barrels.   Price **2/6**

No. 2 LUMBER WAGON
Fitted with bolsters and stanchions.   (Not suitable for 1ft. radius rails.)   Price **2/11**

MO CRANE TRUCK   (MO Coupling)   Price **1/-**

GAS CYLINDER WAGON   Price **1/6**

OIL TANK WAGON "CASTROL"   Price **1/11**

CABOOSE
As used on American railways.   Price **2/-**

No. 1 LUMBER WAGON
Fitted with bolsters and stanchions ...   Price **1/3**

No. 1 CRANE TRUCK
The Crane revolves on its base.   Price **2/3**

No. 1 PETROL TANK WAGON "ESSO"

OIL TANK WAGON "ROYAL DAYLIGHT"   Price **1/11**

WINE WAGON, DOUBLE BARREL
A fine model of a wagon much used in France ...   Price **4/6**

TANK CAR (American Type).
As used in America for the conveyance of oil, etc.   Price **1/9**

No. 1 PETROL TANK WAGON "SHELL-B.P."

CEMENT WAGON "Portland Cement"
An interesting type of wagon with opening door on roof.   Price **1/11**

Price **1/11**

42

Picture taken from the 1938/39 Hamleys 'Toys of Quality' catalogue.

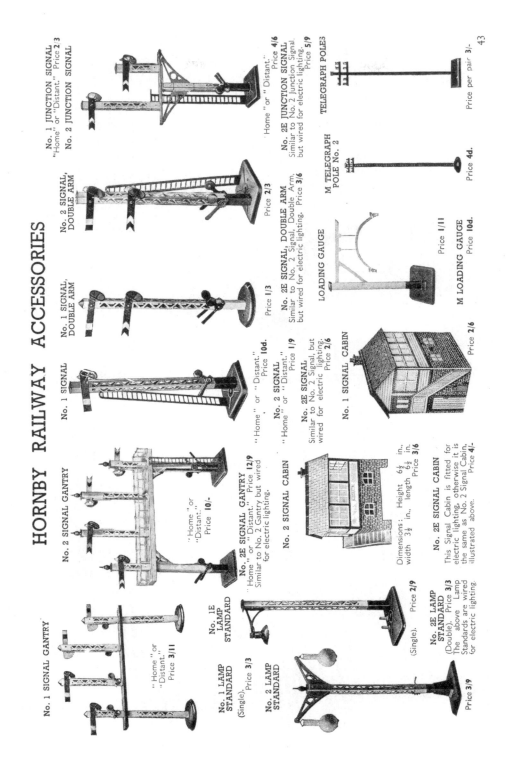

HORNBY RAILWAY ACCESSORIES

No. 1 JUNCTION SIGNAL
"Home" or "Distant." Price 2/3
No. 2 JUNCTION SIGNAL

'Home" or "Distant." Price 4/6
No. 2E JUNCTION SIGNAL
Similar to No. 2 Junction Signal.
but wired for electric lighting.
Price 5/9

TELEGRAPH POLES

Price per pair 3/-

No. 2 SIGNAL, DOUBLE ARM

Price 2/3

No. 2E SIGNAL, DOUBLE ARM
Similar to No. 2 Signal, Double Arm.
but wired for electric lighting. Price 3/6

M TELEGRAPH POLE No. 2

Price 4d.

No. 1 SIGNAL, DOUBLE ARM

Price 1/3

LOADING GAUGE

Price 1/11

M LOADING GAUGE
Price 10d.

No. 1 SIGNAL

No. 2 SIGNAL
"Home" or "Distant."
Price 10d.

"Home " or "Distant."
Price 1/9

No. 2E SIGNAL
Similar to No. 2 Signal, but
wired for electric lighting.
Price 2/6

No. 1 SIGNAL CABIN

Price 2/6

No. 2 SIGNAL GANTRY

"Home " or
"Distant."
Price 10/-

No. 2E SIGNAL GANTRY
"Home" or "Distant." Price 12/9
Similar to No. 2 Gantry but wired
for electric lighting.

No. 2 SIGNAL CABIN

Dimensions: Height 6½ in.,
width 3½ in., length 6½ in.
Price 3/6

No. 2E SIGNAL CABIN
This Signal Cabin is fitted for
electric lighting, otherwise it is
the same as No. 2 Signal Cabin,
illustrated above.   Price 4/-

No. 1 SIGNAL GANTRY

"Home " or
"Distant."
Price 3/11

No. 1 LAMP STANDARD
(Single). Price 3/3

No. 2 LAMP STANDARD

No. 1E LAMP STANDARD
(Single).   Price 2/9

No. 2E LAMP STANDARD
(Double). Price 3/3
The above Lamp
Standards are wired
for electric lighting.

Price 3/9

Picture taken from the 1938/39 Hamleys 'Toys of Quality' catalogue.

43

HORNBY RAILWAY ACCESSORIES

No. 1 STATION

Length 16½ in., width 6 in., height 6 in. ... Price **4/6**

No. 3 STATION

Similar to No. 1 Station for dimensions and style, but of an improved design, more strikingly coloured. Price **5/6**

No. 1A FOOTBRIDGE

Complete with Signals. Price **4/6**

No. 1 FOOTBRIDGE

Without Signals ... Price **2/11**

No. 2 STATION

Built up with three detachable sections. Named "Margate," "Wembley," "Ripon," or "Reading." Length
2 ft. 9 in., breadth 6 in., height 7 in. ... ... Price **8/-**

No. 2E STATION

This Station is fitted for electric lighting, otherwise it is the same as No. 2 Station, illustrated above. Price **9/3**

No. 4 STATION

Similar to No. 2 Station for dimensions and style but of an improved design, more strikingly coloured, and with accessible Booking Hall and Ticket Office Barrier ... ... Price **9/-**

No. 4E STATION

This Station is fitted for electric lighting, otherwise it is the same as No. 4 Station ... ... Price **10/3**

M FOOTBRIDGE

... Price **1/-**

M STATION SET (7 pieces)

Price **2/9**

The components of the M Station Set can be purchased separately as follows : M Signal Box. Price **4d.**

M Signals ... Price **3d.**	M Station ...	price **1/-**
M Telegraph Pole No. 1. Price **3d.**	M Wayside Station.	Price **8d.**

THE HORNBY CONTROL SYSTEM. MORE FUN—MORE THRILLS

There is a certain amount of fascination about even the cheapest and simplest Miniature Railway. For a time we can take a keen interest in a single train running round a plain oval track. Then we add points and crossings and so make possible layouts with branch lines and sidings. Still later, we add further interest by introducing a more or less complete system of signals.

Our thoughts then turn to the Signal Cabin on a real railway, and we wish that, like the signalman, we could control the operation of our railway by means of levers enabling us to manipulate signals and points. The Hornby Control System has been specially devised for the fulfilment of this desire.

The Control System is easy to install on our Hornby Railway, and once it is in operation we are able to control points and signals from one central point, namely, the Signal Cabin. Our railway thus makes a tremendous advance in realism and the possibilities of fun are now unlimited.

Ask your dealer for the free illustrated price list that tells all about the Hornby Control System.

44

Picture taken from the 1938/39 Hamleys 'Toys of Quality' catalogue.

HORNBY RAILWAY ACCESSORIES

No. 1 ENGINE SHED

No. 2 ENGINE SHED

No. E1E ENGINE SHED

This Shed will accommodate any Loco-motive and Tender with an overall length not exceeding 8¼ in. It has double doors at each end. Price **13/9**

Similar to No. 1 Engine Shed but wired for electric lighting. Provided with electrical track. Price **15/-**

No. 1A ENGINE SHED

This Shed is of the same dimensions as the No. 1 Shed described above, but is of simpler design, and has doors at one end only. Price **9/11**

No. E2E ENGINE SHED

This Shed will accommodate any Locomotive and Tender with an overall length not exceeding 17½ in. It has double doors at each end. Price **19/6**

Similar to No. 2 Engine Shed but wired for electric lighting. Provided with electrical track. Price **21/-**

No. 2A ENGINE SHED

This Shed is of the same dimensions as the No. 2 Shed described above, but is of simpler design. Price **16/6**

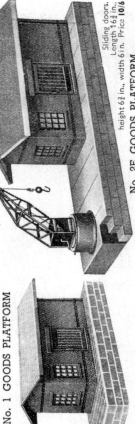

No. 1 GOODS PLATFORM

Length 13 in., height 6¾ in., width 6 in. Price **5/11**

No. 2 GOODS PLATFORM

Sliding doors. Length 16¾ in., height 6¾ in., width 6 in. Price **10/6**

No. 2E GOODS PLATFORM

No. 2E Goods Platform is wired for electric lighting; otherwise it is the same as No. 2 Goods Platform, illustrated here. Price **11/6**

45

ISLAND PLATFORM

Length 32¼ in., height 6¾ in., width 3 in. Price **5/6**

The Ramps can be purchased separately. Price per pair **1/9**

ISLAND PLATFORM E

This platform is suitably wired for electric lighting. Otherwise it is the same as the Island Platform illustrated above. Price **6/3**

PASSENGER PLATFORM

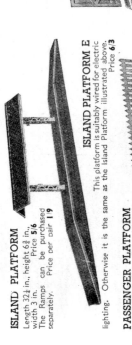

Length 16¾ in., width 3 in. This Platform may be connected to Hornby No. 2 Railway Station or to the Island Platform or used separately ... Price **2/-**

The white Paled Fencing can be purchased separately ... Price per length **6d.**

PLATFORM CRANE

Fitted with a crank handle and ratchet mechanism, also gear for rotating crane. Price **3/3**

No. 1 TURNTABLE

Price **1/11**

No. 2 TURNTABLE

Price **3/9**

No. E2 TURNTABLE (Electrical)

Similar to No. 2 Turntable but fitted with electrical rails. Price **5/6**

Picture taken from the 1938/39 Hamleys 'Toys of Quality' catalogue.

HORNBY TRAINS

Gauge O, 1¼in.

HORNBY E320 ELECTRIC and No. 3C CLOCKWORK PASSENGER TRAIN SETS

These Sets carry the names of famous British Expresses, as follows:—

"THE FLYING SCOTSMAN" (L.N.E.R.), hauled by the "Flying Scotsman" Locomotive. "THE ROYAL SCOT" (L.M.S.R.), hauled by the "Royal Scot" Locomotive. "CORNISH RIVIERA EXPRESS" (G.W.R.), hauled by the "Caerphilly Castle" Locomotive.

No. 3c: "The Flying Scotsman" Train Set (L.N.E.R.).

20-VOLT ELECTRIC—AUTOMATIC REVERSING

E320 (20-volt). Locomotive (automatic reversing) with electric headlamp, No. 2 Special Tender, two No. 2 Corridor Coaches, one No. 2 Corridor Composite Coach, twelve EA2 Curved Rails, four EB1 Straight Rails and a Terminal Connecting Plate. Space required—6ft. 3in. by 4ft. 6in. ... ... Price 67/6

CLOCKWORK

No. 3C (Clockwork). Locomotive (reversing), No. 2 Special Tender, one No. 2 Corridor Coach, one No. 2 Corridor Composite Coach, twelve A2 Curved Rails, three B1 Straight Rails and a BBR1 Straight Brake and Reverse Rail by means of which the Train can be either braked or reversed from the track. Space required—6ft. 3in. by 4ft. 6in. ... Price 47/6

If you are interested in Deferred Payment Terms turn to page iii of cover

HORNBY E320 ELECTRIC and No. 3C CLOCKWORK PULLMAN TRAIN SETS

These Sets carry the name of the following well-known British Express:—

"THE GOLDEN ARROW" (S.R.), hauled by the "Lord Nelson" Locomotive.

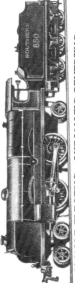

20-VOLT ELECTRIC—AUTOMATIC REVERSING

E320 (20-volt). Locomotive (automatic reversing) with electric headlamp, No. 2 Special Tender, one No. 2 Special Pullman Coach, one No. 2 Special Pullman Coach Composite, twelve EA2 Curved Rails, four EB1 Straight Rails and a Terminal Connecting Plate. Space required—6ft. 3in. by 4ft. 6in. ... ... Price 70/-

CLOCKWORK

No. 3C (Clockwork). Locomotive (reversing), No. 2 Special Tender, one No. 2 Special Pullman Coach Composite, three B1 Straight Rails and one BBR1 Straight Brake and Reverse Rail by means of which the Train can be either braked or reversed from the track. Space required 6ft. 3in. by 4ft. 6in. Price 58/6

The components of the Train Sets shown on this page are obtainable separately at the following prices:—

Hornby E320 Electric Locomotive (20-volt) automatic reversing (without Tender) ... Price 32/6   Hornby No. 3 C Clockwork Locomotive, reversing (without Tender) ... Price 22/6
Hornby No. 2 Special Tender ... Price 6/-   Hornby No. 2 Corridor Coach ... Price 7/6   Hornby No. 2 Special Pullman Coach ... Price 7/6
Hornby No. 2 Special Pullman Coach ... Price 13/-   Hornby No. 2 Corridor Composite Coach ... Price 13/-
The prices of Hornby Rails are given in pages 50, 51 and 52.   For particulars and prices of Transformers, see page 34.

30

Picture taken from the 1938/39 Hamleys 'Toys of Quality' catalogue.

Post-war Hornby 'O' Gauge

Involvement in war work severely curtailed the production of model trains and a heavy wartime tax made further reduction. In the first two years a few items of rolling stock were made and the 'Pool' petrol tanker was introduced but in 1942 the Government banned the manufacture of toy trains.

With the shortages and hardships in post-war Britain Hornby's return to model production was very slow, in fact the company never did regain the pre-war splendour of its 'O' gauge tinplate items. In 1946 the 'M' series (cheap end of the range) was re-introduced with minor differences from its predecessors and the track was modified to have level instead of sloping sleepers. It was as late as 1949 before reasonable model stocks were available and all locomotives were clockwork, 0–4–0 tank or tender variants, in the four railway liveries and finally in BR black or green with lion and wheel emblems. No larger locomotives were made post-war and the few electric 0–4–0's were for export only.

A moderate range of four wheel stock eventually reached the buyers, including No.1 coaches in company and BR colours. For a short period bogie passenger (suburban) coaches were made but the corridor and Pullman versions did not reappear. A little bogie goods stock appeared for a very short time including high capacity wagon (NE, LMS, GW), goods van (NE, LMS). An unlettered breakdown crane, cattle truck, lumber wagon and trolley wagon were made in 1949/50 only.

None of the attractive private owner vans were made after the war, in fact private owner productions were limited to the petrol tankers on which six different company names appeared, excluding 'Pool', a 'Blue Circle' cement wagon and tippers with 'Trinidad Lake Asphalt' and 'McAlpine' on them.

A brand new introduction in the final type 50 range was one of the most attractive post-war wagons 'Saxa Salt', in red on a yellow body.

Initially, the pre-war type chassis was used for wagons but in 1949 simplified embossed spring details were introduced, lasting until 1957 when the type 50 range with a completely re-designed chassis, with separate mock hand brake, took over for the last few years.

The stations, good sheds, bridges, signal boxes and signals were simplified examples of the originals, generally lacking pierced work and fences.

An attempt in 1956 to arrest declining sales by the introduction of the type 30 locomotive in place of the 'M' series, was not successful and the increased public interest in 'OO' scale railways finally brought the great range Hornby 'O' tinplate to a halt around 1962. The old established firm of Tri-ang, run by the Lines Brothers, bought out the Hornby Company and today use that name for their 'OO' productions, but gone are those days of jolly, well built, tinplate trains rattling along between tinplate buildings.

HORNBY CLOCKWORK TRAINS — GAUGE O 1¼ in. (32 mm.)

LONG-RUNNING   STRONG-PULLING

Young boys find endless delight and satisfaction in all that a Hornby Clockwork Railway has to offer. Hornby Locomotives with their long-running clockwork mechanisms are part of a model railway system which includes a fine selection of track, rolling-stock and accessories — all sturdily constructed to last for years.

One of the attractions of a clockwork model railway is being able to start in a small way with a train and track, and add to the equipment from time to time. The choice of Hornby Trains ensures reliable performance, all components being tested and guaranteed.

Boys who run Hornby Trains can look forward to lasting fun managing their own railways.

With the exception of the M1 Sets, Hornby Trains are now finished in British Railways liveries.

HORNBY GOODS TRAIN
SET No. 20 ... 26/6

This set contains Locomotive No. 20 (non-reversing) and Tender No. 20 (finished in B.R. Green), two Wagons No. 20 and 1ft. radius Rails requiring a space 3ft. 3in. by 2ft. 6in.

HORNBY PASSENGER TRAIN
SET No. 21 ... ... 26/6

This set contains Locomotive No. 20 (non-reversing) and Tender No. 20 (finished in B.R. green), two Coaches No. 21 and 1ft. radius Rails requiring a space 3ft. 3in. by 2ft. 6in.

No Hornby Train owner should be without the 'Meccano Magazine'   11

HORNBY CLOCKWORK TRAINS—
GAUGE O
1¼ in. (32 mm.)

HORNBY TANK PASSENGER TRAIN SET No. 41 ... ... 55/-
This set contains Tank Locomotive No. 40 (reversing), two Coaches No. 41, Passenger Brake Van No. 41, and 2ft. radius Rails requiring a space 5ft. 4in. by 4ft. 6in.

HORNBY GOODS TRAIN SET No. 50 ... 67/6
This set contains Locomotive No. 50 (black) (reversible from track), Tender No. 50 (black), Wagon No. I, Flat Truck, Goods Brake **Van** and 2ft. radius Rails requiring a space 5ft. 4in. by 4ft. 6in.

HORNBY PASSENGER TRAIN SET No. 51 ... ... 67/6
This set contains Locomotive No. 51 (green) (reversible from track), Tender No. 51 (green), two Coaches No. 51, Passenger Brake Van No. 51 and 2ft. radius Rails requiring a space 5ft. 4in. by 4ft. 6in.

The 'Meccano Magazine' tells you about Hornby Railways, and real railways, too   13

—HORNBY CLOCKWORK LOCOMOTIVES & TENDERS—

MI Locomotive and MI Tender

Locomotive No. 50 and Tender No. 50 (black)

HORNBY LOCOMOTIVES
Locomotive No. 20 ...	...	12/3
MI Locomotive ...	...	19/6
Tank Locomotive No. 40	...	25/6
Locomotive (black) No. 50	...	34/-
Locomotive (green) No. 51 ...	...	34/-

HORNBY TENDERS
Tender No. 20	...	...	2/-
MI Tender ...	...	...	2/6
Tender (black) No. 50	...	4/9
Tender (green) No. 51	...	4/9

The Hornby Clockwork Locomotive No. 20 cannot be reversed, but like all other Hornby engines it has a brake that can be applied by hand, or from the track by means of a Brake Rail.
Locomotives MI, Nos. 40, 50 and 51 have reversing mechanisms, and the Locomotives Nos. 50 and 51 can also be reversed from the track as well as from the cab.

Tank Locomotive No. 40

Locomotive No. 20 and Tender No. 20

HORNBY GAUGE 'O' TRACK

Train Sets Nos. 20, 21 and MI contain 1ft. radius track, and additional Rails should be of the same radius, otherwise the extended layout may not fit together very well. Although intended for 1ft. track, Locomotives Nos. 20 and MI will run on 2ft. radius track. Locomotives Nos. 40, 50 and 51 must have 2ft. radius track; they will not run on 1ft. radius curves or points.

STRAIGHT RAILS
BI	Straight Rail (length 10¾in.)	...	11d.
B½	Straight Half Rail (length 5⅜in.)		8d.
B¼	Straight Quarter Rail (length 2⅞ in.)		7d.
BBR	Straight Brake and Reverse Rail		1/2

CURVED RAILS
AI	Curved Rail (1ft. radius)	...	11d.
AI½	Curved Half Rail (1ft. radius)		8d.
A2	Curved Rail (2ft. radius)	...	11d.
A2½	Curved Half Rail (2ft. radius)	...	8d.
RCP	Rail Connecting Plates (pkt. of 6)		7d.

CROSSINGS
CAI	Acute-angle Crossing (for 1ft. radius track)	...	5/3
CA2	Acute-angle Crossing (for 2ft. radius track)	...	4/1
CRI	Right-angle Crossing (for 1ft. radius track)	...	5/6
CR2	Right-angle Crossing (for 2ft. radius track)	...	4/4

POINTS
PRI	Right-hand Points (1ft. radius)		5/-
PLI	Left-hand Points (1ft. radius)		5/-
PR2	Right-hand Points (2ft. radius)		5/-
PL2	Left-hand Points (2ft. radius)		5/-
PCC	Points Connecting Clip	...	3½d.

1ft. radius Curves, Points and Crossings cannot be used in the same layout with those of 2ft. radius. The BBR rail is not suitable for Locomotive No. 20.

14   *News of Hornby Railway developments appears in the 'Meccano Magazine'*

Picture taken from the 1955/6 Meccano catalogue.

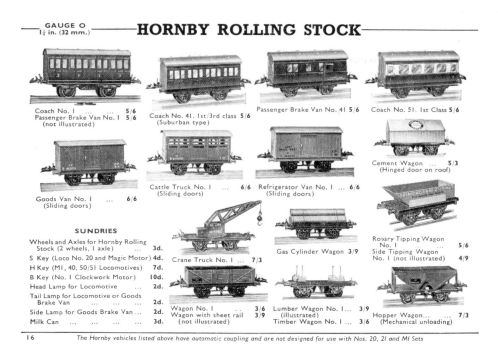

GAUGE O
1¼ in. (32 mm.)

HORNBY ROLLING STOCK

Coach No. 1 ... ... 5/6
Passenger Brake Van No. 1 5/6
(not illustrated)

Coach No. 41. 1st/3rd class 5/6
(Suburban type)

Passenger Brake Van No. 41 5/6

Coach No. 51. 1st Class 5/6

Goods Van No. 1 ... 6/6
(Sliding doors)

Cattle Truck No. 1 ... 6/6
(Sliding doors)

Refrigerator Van No. 1 ... 6/6
(Sliding doors)

Cement Wagon ... 5/3
(Hinged door on roof)

SUNDRIES

Wheels and Axles for Hornby Rolling
Stock (2 wheels, 1 axle) ... 3d.
S Key (Loco No. 20 and Magic Motor) 4d.
H Key (M1, 40, 50/51 Locomotives) 7d.
B Key (No. 1 Clockwork Motor) 10d.
Head Lamp for Locomotive ... 2d.
Tail Lamp for Locomotive or Goods
Brake Van ... ... 2d.
Side Lamp for Goods Brake Van ... 2d.
Milk Can ... ... 3d.

Crane Truck No. 1 ... 7/3

Wagon No. 1 ... ... 3/6
Wagon with sheet rail 3/9
(not illustrated)

Gas Cylinder Wagon 3/9

Lumber Wagon No. 1... 3/9
(illustrated)
Timber Wagon No. 1 ... 3/6

Rotary Tipping Wagon
No. 1 ... ... 5/6
Side Tipping Wagon
No. 1 (not illustrated) 4/9

Hopper Wagon... ... 7/3
(Mechanical unloading)

16   *The Hornby vehicles listed above have automatic coupling and are not designed for use with Nos. 20, 21 and M1 Sets*

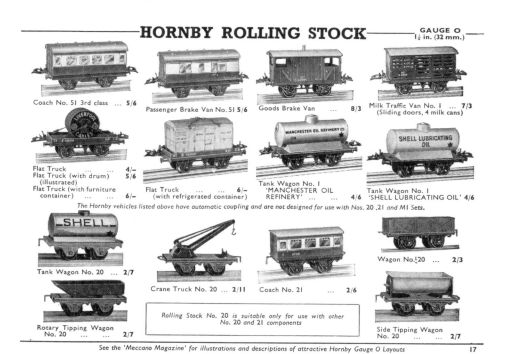

HORNBY ROLLING STOCK

GAUGE O
1¼ in. (32 mm.)

Coach No. 51 3rd class ... 5/6

Passenger Brake Van No. 51 5/6

Goods Brake Van ... 8/3

Milk Traffic Van No. 1 ... 7/3
(Sliding doors, 4 milk cans)

Flat Truck 4/-
Flat Truck (with drum) 5/6
(illustrated)
Flat Truck (with furniture
container) 6/-

Flat Truck 6/-
(with refrigerated container)

Tank Wagon No. 1
'MANCHESTER OIL
REFINERY' 4/6

Tank Wagon No. 1
'SHELL LUBRICATING OIL' 4/6

The Hornby vehicles listed above have automatic coupling and are not designed for use with Nos. 20 ,21 and M1 Sets.

Tank Wagon No. 20 ... 2/7

Crane Truck No. 20 ... 2/11

Coach No. 21 ... 2/6

Wagon No. 20 ... 2/3

Rotary Tipping Wagon
No. 20 ... ... 2/7

*Rolling Stock No. 20 is suitable only for use with other
No. 20 and 21 components*

Side Tipping Wagon
No. 20 ... ... 2/7

See the 'Meccano Magazine' for illustrations and descriptions of attractive Hornby Gauge O Layouts   17

Picture taken from the 1955/6 U.K. Meccano catalogue.

The Leeds Model Company

This firm was established in 1920 by Ralph Stedman, an engineer, who delayed his model building to work on aircraft design and aerial photography at Farnborough during the First World War.

The Company is the third best known British producer of 'O' gauge model railway items and traded under LMC, R F Stedman & Co as well as using its own full name. Initially powered by clockwork, 8/9 volt D.C. motors, with third rail pick up were soon available and some 20 volt AC mechanisms were made for the locomotives. To be competitive in the market a series of freelance tank locomotives, 0–4–0's to 4–6–0's, were made throughout the firm's existence, the character of different railway companies being achieved by the changing of chimneys, domes, safety valves, etc.

In addition, numerous models of scale appearance were produced, the best known being the LNER, 4–4–0, 'Directors'. Other LNER locomotives were 4–6–2 'Flying Scotsman', 4–6–0 'Sir Sam Fay' and 'Cities', 4-4-2, Atlantic type. The GWR was represented by a mogul 2–6–0, 4–6–0 'Castle' and a 4–6–0 'Star' whilst for the LMS a 4–6–0 'Claughton' and an 0–6–0

Pickersgill goods loco were offered. Enthusiasts for the Southern Railway were the cinderellas; other than the standard tank, SR locos were special orders. There were various special orders covering all the companies and the LMC produced a comprehensive range of parts for people to build their own models. Consequently, some badly built models are passed off as 'Leeds'.

The comprehensive range of rolling stock was made of wood or wood with lithographic printed paper stuck on top – the eight private owner wagons are particularly attractive. A completely new introduction to the modelling scene, was the use of bakelite for wagons and coaches by LMC in the second half of the 1930's.

The firm continued production after the last World War with a very restricted range of models, using some of the standard tank range and a freelance version of the 'Director' 4-4-0 in LNER, LMS, SR and BR colours, all fitted with a 12 volt DC mechanism or 20 volt AC to special order.

Sadly, it all came to an end in the 1960's.

Milbro

This is the trade mark for the Sheffield firm of Mills Bros. (Engineers) Ltd initiated in 1919 by three brothers for the production of prototypical model railway items in the 7mm scale and some pieces for larger gauges. Their early catalogues showed coaches, wagons, buildings, all beautifully built of wood, as well as wood and brass track. The LNER teak coaches were particularly impressive.

Following this, locomotives by the Leeds Model Company were shown in the front of the catalogues but these were discontinued as Milbro's own locomotives were produced. These were beautifully built and included for the LMS, 0–6–0 'Jinty' tank, 4–4–0 3P 4–4–0 Compound, 2–6–4 tank, 2–6–0 crab, 4–6–0 Royal Scot, 4–6–0 'Princess Royal', whilst the LNER was represented by 0–6–0 J39, 4–6–2 'Flying Scotsman', 4–6–2 A4 'Silver Link', 2–8–2 'Cock O' The North' and 4–6–4 'Hush-Hush' locomotive. The GW enthusiast was thinly provided for with a 2–4–0 3232 class and a 4–6–0 'King George V', worse still for

the Southern man with only a 4–4–0 'Schools' offered, although it could be had with any name of the class.

These locomotives were expensive – all had 6-8 volt DC motors – the cost of a 'Princess Royal' in 1937 being £21.10.0 (£21.50) which makes a Hornby 'Princess Elizabeth' seem the cheap end of the market at 5gns (£5.25)! Although the 'Royal' is the finer model the 'aura' of the Hornby has reversed their values making the 'Elizabeth' worth about twice as much as the 'Royal'.

In the mid-1930's Milbro introduced a series of freelance 4–4–2 standard tanks, the one design being offered in the livery of the four railway companies. At £2.19.6 (£2.97) this was aimed at the impecunious enthusiast. Like Leeds, Milbro made many parts for the keen builder and it was with these products and some pieces of rolling stock that the firm continued after World War 2, finally coming to a demise in the 1960's.

'O' Gauge and other Auction Results

Bonhams

BONHAMS CHELSEA, 65-69 LOTS ROAD, LONDON

These descriptions of paintwork are used in Bonhams catalogues:

M   Mint toys apparently never taken out of mint original boxes
E   Excellent toys with no apparent paint shipping or defects
G   Good toys with minimum scratches to the paint
F   Fair toys with an acceptable amount of paint damage
P   Poor toys probably suitable for repainting or restoration
Sd   Some damage
Fatigue   Potentially unstable cracking or expansion of metal

These descriptions of boxes are used in Bonhams catalogue:

E   Excellent original box with no damage, complete with
     all interior fittings
G   Good box with normal use wear only, but fittings
     not necessarily complete
F   Fair box, possibly slightly torn or split, but with label intact
P   Poor box, likely to be split or torn, and in need of repair

N.B. Bonhams reserve the right to restrict handling of items described
as mint.

'O' gauge TRAINS and ACCESSORIES

A HORNBY RIVIERA 'BLUE' TRAIN LOCOMOTIVE AND
TENDER. English, circa 1932. The clockwork 4-4-2 locomotive
finished in brown livery with black smokebox and brass domes,
'3801, black wheels with matching tender 'NORD 3180 (G), Minor
touch-ups to paint £120

A HORNBY NO. 3C 'ROYAL SCOT' LOCOMOTIVE AND
TENDER. English, 1934-1935. The clockwork 4-4-2 locomotive
finished in LMS maroon with black smokebox, low mounted buffers,
black wheels, outlined rear splasher lining, No. 6100, with matching
tender with shadowed lettering (G), some minor touch-ups £160

A HORNBY NO. 2 LOCOMOTIVE AND TENDER. English, circa
1928. The clockwork 4-4-0 locomotive finished in maroon LMS
livery, with black smokebox, unlettered splashers, three boiler bands,
and body-colour dome, with matching tender, No. 27 (G), some minor
touch-ups, side of tender has light paint scratching £190

A HORNBY NO. 2 SPECIAL LMS COMPOUND
LOCOMOTIVE AND TENDER. English, circa 1930. The
clockwork 4-4-0 locomotive in maroon LMS livery, No. 85, with
matching tender with lengthways spring anchor to underside (G-E),
repainted to a high standard £140

A HORNBY NO.1 SPECIAL LOCOMOTIVE AND TENDER.
English, 1931-1934. The boxed clockwork 0-4-0 locomotive in LMS
black livery, No. 4525, with 'separate' smokebox door lamp bracket,
red plated wheels, and matching unboxed tender with sans-serif LMS
plain gold lettering, with key envelope containing four lamps and
inner box packaging (G-E, box G), one end of the box base split at
edges £360

A HORNBY NO. 1 SPECIAL TANK LOCOMOTIVE. English,
circa 1929. The clockwork 0-4-0 locomotive finished in black LNER
livery, No. 808, with Hornby logo on smokebox door (G-E). £480

THREE BOXED HORNBY 0-4-0 LOCOMOTIVES. English,
1930s-1950s. Including a post-war clockwork No. 50 locomotive
(reversing), finished in LMS matt red livery, No. 5600, with unboxed
matching tender (G-E, box F-G); a green M1 locomotive with printed
windows and black footplate and cylinders, with unboxed '3435'
tender (G, box G); and a No. 20 locomotive, in BR green livery, with
key and matching boxed tender (G, boxes F-G) £110

HORNBY 0-4-0 LOCOMOTIVES. English, 1959s-1960s.
Including two No. 5 locomotives with tenders, both finished in BR
green, No. 50153, two Type 40 locomotives in black BR livery, No.
82011, one with post-1960 'lion on wheel' transfer, and an M1
locomotive and tender in BR green livery, No. 45746 (G), some slight
touch-ups to paint £170

TWO HORNBY 0-4-0 TANK LOCOMOTIVES. English, 1930s.
Including a clockwork M3 tank locomotive in LNER green livery, No.
460, with green eight-spoke wheels and cylinders (G); and a revised
No. 1 tank locomotive, in SR green, No. 29, in gloss finish (G-E,
some minor touch-ups to paint.....................................£160

A HORNBY 501 LOCOMOTIVE AND TENDER. English, 1950s.
The clockwork loco in maroon LMS livery, '5600', with matching
tender and key (G, box G); together with a boxed flat truck with cable drum
(G, box G); a brown LMS flat truck (G, box G); and a cream
'McAlpine' tipping wagon (F) £50

A HORNBY NO. 1 TANK ENGINE. English, 1924-1926. The
clockwork engine with brass dome finished in LNER green livery and
No. 0-4-0 with gold and red lettering, boxed (F-G, box P), two ends to
box lid missing; together with three small passenger coaches all
lithographed in LNER teak livery; a Bing lithographed railway station
(P), rusted; three open wagons and track £100

A HORNBY CLOCKWORK NO. 2 SPECIAL COMPOUND
LOCOMOTIVE AND TENDER. English, circa 1935. The 4-4-0 No.
1185 locomotive and six-wheel tender finished in LMS maroon livery,
with gold lining. and lettering (G), steps to cab slightly bent
....£180

A HORNBY CLOCKWORK 'COUNTRY OF BEDFORD
LOCOMOTIVE AND TENDER. English, circa 1935. The 4-4-0 No.
3821 engine finished n green GWR livery, with six-wheel tender,
missing dome, cab handrails, one whistle, some paint chips, steps to
cab bent..£240

FOUR HORNBY TANK ENGINES. English, 1930s-1950s.
Including a Hornby 'O' gauge No. 2 special clockwork tank engine
No. 1874 finished in green LNER livery (G), No. 4 transfer scratched;
a Hornby 'O' gauge No. 2 special tank engine No. 6954, finished in
maroon LMS livery (G); a Hornby No. 29 in Southern
green livery (G), repainted; and a Type 40 in black BR livery No.
82011 tank engine £170

A RARE HORNBY LMS FISH VAN WITH WHITE ROOF.
English, 1937. The maroon van with yellow lining and lettering, No.
7674, issued as one of the early batch before the change to grey roof,
post-1937 (G-E)..£150

A HORNBY 'CRAWFORDS BISCUITS PRIVATE OWNERS
VAN. English, 1935-1938. Finish in red with gold lettering and King
George V crest, boxed (G-E, box G)....................................£150

HORNBY PASSENGER COACHES. English, circa 1935.
Including a No. 2 GWR guards composite coach lithographed in
brown and cream; a No. 2 LNER brake/3rd corridor coach,
lithographed in teak livery (G); together with three No. 1 Pullman
coaches 'Ansonia' (F-G)..£320

THREE HORNBY No. 2 SPECIAL PULLMAN COACHES. English, circa 1935. All with hinged doors and finished in brown and cream livery with gold lining, coaches include 'Alberta', 'Montana' and 'Zenobia' (G), 'Montana' missing one set of wheels, celluloid inners warped **£280**

THIRTEEN BOXED HORNBY WAGONS. English, post-war. Including a green LMS hopper wagon, a yellow and green lumber wagon, a yellow and blue 'Robert Hudson Ltd.' side tipping wagon, a brown LMS cable wagon, with strung drum, a yellow 'Portland Cement' wagon, a brown flat truck with maroon BR furniture container, a grey LNER cattle truck, a red and black crane truck, a cream 'Trinidad Lake Asphalt' rotary tipping wagon, a red and blue gas cylinder wagon and three others (G-E, boxes F-G)..............**£130**

TEN BOXED HORNBY WAGONS. English, 1920s-1930s. Including a grey LMS cement wagon with LMS lettering on one side of the base, circa 1924, in a plain lidded box, a grey LNER crane truck, with LNER on both sides of the base, in red lidded box, a pale green LMS No. 1 cattle truck, with dark grey roof with 'No. 1 Cattle Truck' on the base, a brown LNER No. 1 brake van, with open axle guards, unpainted wheels and No. 1 Brake Van on base, a GWR crane truck in blue with brown jib, a cream LMS refrigerator van with black transfers and bolted construction, a red LMS Gas cylinder wagon, with LMS decal on one cylinder and 'Gas Cylinder' on another and more (G-E, boxes R-G) **£320**

TWO HORNBY No. 2 PULLMAN COACHES. English, circa 1936. The brown and cream coaches with small crests and brown 'Pullman' name panels bordered with gold and black lines (G-E, boxes G)..**£280**

THREE HORNBY No. 2 SALOON COACHES. English, 1931-1936. The boxed coaches finished in LMS red livery, with grey roofs and gold window frames and lettering, shadowed in bright red, with diecast round-headed buffers (G-E, boxes P-F), a few small rust spots to roofs of two coaches, one box has lid only **£280**

A HORNBY M3 TANK GOODS SET. English, 1930s. The boxed set with maroon LMS '2270' M3 locomotive, 'Shell Motor Spirit' tank wagon, grey LMS open wagon and timber wagon, with track, 'hints' leaflet and layout leaflet (G-E, box P-F), box lid lacks label, has parts of sides replaced **£100**

A HORNBY M3 TANK GOODS SET. English, 1940s-1960s. The boxed set with maroon LMS M3 tank locomotive, No. 2270, Esso tank wagon, open wagon and timber wagon with track and key, in blue box with inner card packaging (G, box F-G)............................ **£100**

A HORNBY GOODS SET No. 30. English, 1940s-1960s. The boxed set with green M1 '45746' locomotive, open wagon, box van and track in an orange box (G-E, box F-G); together with an MO Pullman passenger set, with green '2595' locomotive and tender (F-G, box F) **£70**

A HORNBY No. 7 WATCHMANS HUT. English, 1932. The boxed miniature in blue and red, with brazier, poker and shovel (G, box F), some slight touch-ups to paint **£35**

ELECTRIC WATER TOWER. With illuminating light, finished yellow/green **£300**

4007 E120 0-4-0 SPECIAL LOCOMOTIVE. English, circa 1935. Finished in green GW livery. with bulb and test label. E............**£500**

50153 CLOCKWORK 0-4-0 LOCOMOTIVE AND TENDER. English, post- war. Green BR livery (boxed). F-G, box G(12)....**£160**

2270 CLOCKWORK 0-4-0 LOCOMOTIVE. English, post-war. Red LMS livery (boxed, lid missing) - F, together with a quantity of rolling stock and track (lot)..**£130**

'RIVIERA' NORD LOCOMOTIVE. English. 1938. The boxed 4-4-2 electric locomotive in brown livery, with smoke deflectors and border bands with gold lining. No. 3 1290 - G, box F **£190**

Barry Potter Auctions

13 YEW TREE LANE, SPRATTON, NORTHAMPTON

SATURDAY 25th JANUARY 1997

'O' GAUGE ROLLING STOCK

Exley. Rake of 3 LMS Maroon Corridor Coaches - Restaurant Car, 2 Brake/3rds, all superbly repainted to perfect original appearance, All Mint **£400-600**

Exley. Rake of 4 BR Red and Cream Corridor Coaches - all 1st, 2 all 3rd, Kitchen car, all superbly repainted to perfect original appearance, All Mint..**£500-800**

Exley. Rake of 3 BR Red and Cream Corridor Coaches - All 1st, all 3rd, Buffet Car, all superbly repainted to perfect original appearance, All Mint..**£400-600**

Exley. 2 early LMS Maroon short bogie Suburban Coaches, each 31cm long, 3rd Brake and 1st/3rd Brake, Both Good Plus ..**£200-250**

Exley early LMS Maroon Suburban Coaches - All 3rd, 1st/3rd, Brake/3rd, one repainted roof, All Good Plus **£180-250**

Exley LMS Maroon Corridor Coaches - All 3rd, Brake/3rd, 1st/3rd Brake, 2 repainted roofs, All Good Plus............................**£180-250**

Exley LMS Maroon Sleeping Car, wrong box label, Good Plus Boxed **£150-200**

Exley LMS Maroon Corridor Coach, 1st/3rd, LMS Maroon Corridor Coach, All 3rd, well repainted, Both Good Plus....**£120-160**

Exley LMS Maroon Corridor Coaches - Dining Car, 2 Brake/3rd, All Good - Good Plus **£160-220**

Phillips

PHILLIPS INTERNATIONAL AUCTIONEERS & VALUERS
10 SALEM ROAD, BAYSWATER, LONDON

These descriptions of condition are used in Phillips catalogues:

E	Excellent	G	Good	F	Fair
P	Poor	SD	Some Damage	AF	As Found

'0' GAUGE

Marklin 4-volt LMS train set consisting of 0-4-0 locomotive (generally G-E, but has significant areas of repainting) and tender 281 (G-E) two lst/3rd 4-wheel coaches 2871, Guards Van 2872 and a small quantity of three rail track (all G-E, marked with Gamages stamp (box G) **£550**

Exley Southern brake/3rd corridor bogie coach 2211 (E-G) **£190**

Exley Southern lst/3rd corridor bogie coach 5050 (E-G)..........**£170**

Exley Southern 1st corridor bogie coach 2121 (E-G) **£360**

Exley Southern Restaurant bogie coach 6166 (E-G)..................**£480**

Exley Southern 3rd bogie coach 6667 (E-G)............................**£190**

Exley Southern brake/3rd bogie coach 4441 (E-G)...................**£200**

Exley LMS 1st corridor bogie coach 8822 (E-G) **£120**

Bowman live steam 4-4-0 locomotive (G-F, scorch damaged, box G) with 6-wheel 'Southern 453' tender (G box G) **£160**

Bing c/w 4-4-0T LMS locomotive 420 (F-G) **£160**

Bing c/w 0-4-0 GWR locomotive 3410 and 6-wheel tender (F-G, cab roof bent and tender missing one pair of wheels and axle) **£100**

OTHER GAUGES

Early English live steam brass 2fi' gauge 2-2-0 'piddler' locomotive 7', 17cm long...**£270**

Brass c.1890 3'-gauge 2-2-2 locomotive 'EDINA' (F-G, denting to boiler, lacks funnel)..**£280**

Gauge 1 brass scratch built electric 4-6-2T Great Central locomotive 26 (G) **£320**

Bassett-Lowke live steam 4-4-0 locomotive 6285 and 6-wheel tender (both F-G)...**£200**

Bassett-Lowke live steam 4-4-0 locomotive 6285 and 6-wheel tender (repainted, boxed) **£100**

HORNBY '0' GAUGE

No 2 SR Mixed goods set contains Electric Southern 4-4-2 TANK LOCOMOTIVE 2091 with contents, original illustrated blue box **£260**

No 1 Passenger set LMS contains LMS 0-4-0 CLOCKWORK LOCOMOTIVE and four-wheel tender 2710 with two lithographed coaches clerestory roofed opening doors, c. 1926, original box (E, box (G)...**£750**

ELECTRIC SET No 3E LMS ROYAL SCOT (6 volt) contains No 6100 4-4-2 locomotive Royal Scot and six-wheel tender, two Pullman coaches Iolanthe and the brake and Acadia, original box (in correct coaches) **£400**

CLOCKWORK No 101 TANK PASSENGER SET in original blue box **£85**

No 4E Lithographed TIN-PLATE STATION fitted for electric lighting 'MARGATE' one lamp broken from bracket, original green box **£190**

No EIE Electrical VIADUCT original green box (a.f.)............**£130**

No 1 GOODS PLATFORM original red box..........................**£70**

CLOCKWORK SOUTHERN 4-4-0 LOCOMOTIVE 'ETON' and matching No 2 Southern 900 special tender, slight wheel fatigue, marked No 900 on buffer board..**£500**

E320 4-4-2 'CAERPHILLY CASTLE' LOCOMOTIVE numbered 4073 and matching No 2 GWR six-wheeled tender, c. 1938(2)..**£240**

CLOCKWORK No 2 SPECIAL 4-4-0 LOCOMOTIVE 'THE BRABHAM MOOR' Numbered 201 with plain LNER No 2 Special tender **£340**

CLOCKWORK No 2 LMS 4-4-0 Standard Compound Locomotive No 1185 with matching No 2 tender, some retouching, maroon. black/yellow lining **£190**

CLOCKWORK No 2 SPECIAL 4-4-0 LOCOMOTIVE 'YORK-SHIRE' numbered 234, early version with green footplate later over painted black, Hornby transfer on the draw bar beam, No 234, Class 049 on buffer bar, matching No 2 LNER Special tender............**£280**

ELECTRIC LMS 4-6-2 LOCO 'PRINCESS ELIZABETH' 6201, maroon, black/gold lining, matching six-wheel tender, original blue coloured wooden case, repair label on one end **£1,700**

LST2/20 ELECTRIC LMS 4-4-2 TANK LOCOMOTIVE numbered 6781, black, red lined, original green box................................**£340**

CLOCKWORK Reversing No. 2 4-4-4 MIDLAND TANK LOCOMOTIVE numbered 2107 in large gold numbers on side tanks, some retouching **£160**

CLOCKWORK Reversing LMS No 2 Special 4-4-2 TANK LOCOMOTIVE No 6781, black, red lined................................**£130**

CLOCKWORK Reversing GWR No 2 Special 4-4-2 TANK LOCOMOTIVE Numbered 4703, green/gold and black lined, end coupling detached...**£170**

CLOCKWORK Reversing LNER No 2 Special 4-4-2 TANK LOCOMOTIVE '1784', green/black, yellow/white lining **£160**

CLOCKWORK No 1 Special 0-4-0 LMS TANK LOCOMOTIVE Numbered 2120, original red lidded box, lacks inserts **£85**

E120 Special 0-4-0 Reversing TANK LOCOMOTIVE Numbered 70, maroon/black, gold lined, wheels repainted (F)....................**£130**

No 1 Special Reversing 0-4-0 GW LOCOMOTIVE Numbered 2301 with four-wheel tender **£90**

No 3E (6 volt) 4-4-2 LOCOMOTIVE 'CAERPHILLY CASTLE' Numbered 4073, original green box (box a.f.)............................**£280**

CLOCKWORK Reversing No 2 LMS 4-4-4 TANK LOCOMOTIVE Numbered on tank side 2107 with LMS cab plate, with red ground contained in original red Hornby series box **£360**

E320 METROPOLITAN LOCOMOTIVE Lithographed maroon, gold/black lined with three Metropolitan carriages 1st, 3rd/brake and 3rd/brake with illuminating switch **£340**

MO PASSENGER TRAIN SET Silver Jubilee LNER Numbered 2503, two interlocking carriages, clockwork LMS No 1 0-4-0 tank locomotive numbered 623 and two other locos (a.f.) (4)............**£240**

LNER SNOW PLOUGH grey, grey roof, black chassis, original lidded plain card box, paper end label **£100**

MILK TANK WAGON 'UNITED DAIRIES' Milk tank wagon in original red box (box tatty) **£100**

No 0 LMS BANANA VAN Lithographed side panels in original box, **No 0 LMS FISH VAN** original red box and **No 0 REFRIGERATOR VAN** original red box (3)..**£240**

LMS GUNPOWDER VAN lacks one door handle (a.f.) **£55**

No 2 CORRIDOR COACH LNER lst/3rd original box and No 2 Corridor Coach, Brake-Composite, orig. box (2) **£260**

GWR No 2 lst/3rd CORRIDOR COACH with another similar, GWR No 2 1st class carriage No 6597 with matching brake end (4) **£260**

No 2 PULLMAN BRAKE END CARRIAGE 'ARCADIA No 2 Pullman coach Iolanthe and another No 2 Pullman coach (3) **£140**

No 2 SOUTHERN 1st Class Coach, No 2 LNER teak, 1st/3rd coach and LNER No 2 3rd/Brake end coach (2)...................................**£260**

TWO No 2 LMS CORRIDOR COACHES brake end/1st/3rd and two other No 2 coaches (both a.f.) **£130**

No 2 LMS SALOON COACH, 1st Class, finished maroon, gold lined windows, opening doors in original red box. ....Not sold - Estimate: **£120-160**

RARE LMS GUNPOWDER VAN finished in red, gold/red lettering in original red box, end flaps missing...**£140**

PRIVATE OWNERS WAGON 'Cadburys Chocolate, type 3 chassis (lacks one buffer) (F)...**£100**

PRIVATE OWNERS WAGON 'Carrs Biscuits, all blue second type chassis, door handle lacking (G)...**£150**

PRIVATE OWNERS COAL WAGON 'Hornby Railway Company', maroon/white lettering and rare LNWR Gunpowder wagon, first type chassis (a.f.) (2) **£120**

PRIVATE OWNERS TANK WAGON Nestle Milk, 3rd type chassis (G) and United Dairies Glass lined milk tank, 2nd type chassis (F) (2) **£240**

BASSET- LOWKE 'O' and '1' GAUGE

ELECTRIC 4-4-0 LOCOMOTIVE PRINCE CHARLES No 62078 and six-wheel tender, blue black and white original green box (G-E, box F one end flap missing)..**£300**

ELECTRIC LNER 4-6-2 LOCOMOTIVE 'FLYING SCOTSMAN' No 4472 and eight-wheel tender, green, black and white lined **£300**

CLOCKWORK 4-4-0 LOCOMOTIVE 'DUKE OF YORK' No 1927 and six-wheeled tender maroon, yellow and black lined, (37cm) **£120**

ELECTRIC LNER 0-6-0 TANK LOCOMOTIVE No 433 buffer board loosed rusting upper section of loco, black (24cm)...........**£140**

LMS ROYAL MAIL SORTING VAN (RARE) lithographed maroon, black/yellow lining and detailing, No.1924 (31.5mm)..**£130**

GAUGE '1' SIGNAL GANTRY with central viewing platform on simulated rock edged based height 42mm. Marklin Island platform with glazed canopy, tow-tone brown and another signal (a.f.) (3) **£700**

MARKLIN 'O' GAUGE

CLOCKWORK LMS 0-4-0 LOCOMOTIVE and (our-wheel tender, No 281, maroon, black, yellow lined (28mm) **£140**

ELECTRIC (4 volt) STEEPLE CAD 0-4-0 Locomotive V3120 Dark green, light green detailing, red lined windows, black chassis. pantographed roof with three Mitropa carriages, dark red, gold lined, grey roofs (24cm)...**£320**

CLOCKWORK DOUBLE PANTOGRAPH 0-4-0 Loco RS 900, mechanism present, one wheel missing but detached **£150**

BING 'O' GAUGE

ELECTRIC LMS 0-4-0 LOCOMOTIVE No 7860 and four wheeled tender, maroon, black and yellow lining (30.5cm) **£140**

CLOCKWORK LNWR 4-4-0 LOCOMOTIVE No 1942 and matching six-wheeled tender black with red/white lining (30cm), lacks buffers from locomotive..**£100**

SPIRIT FIRED 0-4-0 LNWR LOCOMOTIVE 'GEORGE THE FIFTH' black, red lined, unusual cup, oil filter on pistons and four-wheel tender, probably by Bing (20cm).....................................**£220**

CLOCKWORK LNWR 0-4-0 TANK LOCOMOTIVE black, red, white lined, lacks one wheel, a Bing pre-cursor L&NWR clockwork, half cabed locomotive (a.f.) and a small Bing LMS 6-4-0 locomotive, maroon, black and yellow lined (3)...**£150**

CLOCKWORK LMS 4-4-0 LOCOMOTIVE No 1924 with match-ing six-wheeled tender, finished in maroon, black and yellow lined (40.5cm)..**£120**

ELECTRIC SUBURBAN LNER TEAK TRAIN FRONT ENGINE CARRIAGE (RARE) denoted by electric light bulb, four matching lithographed carriages and brake end. length of each carriage (30.5cm)..Not sold - Estimate: **£1,400-1,600**

PRESSED TIN-PLATE SINGLE ROAD ENGINE SHEDS finished with corrugated roof, impressed brickwork walls (each 29cm) (2) ....Not sold - Estimate: **£150-200**

LITHOGRAPHED TIN-PLATE DOUBLE GABLED COUNTRY STATIONS each covered with many integral product advertisements (both discoloured a.f.) length of largest station 66cm ....Not sold - Estimate: **£150-250**

LITHOGRAPHED TIN-PLATE GWR Garter crested 1st class double bogie carriage, highly finished and detailed in maroon, yellow lined (33cm), lacks one buffer, with **Bing double bogie Pullman dining car** Rosemary, opening roof revealing seats and tables inside (32.5cm)...**£140**

GAUGE '1'

Bing for Bassett-Lowke c/w 4-2-2 GNR locomotive 266 and 6-wheel tender (G, lacks lamps and couplings replaced) **£1,250**

Bing c/w 0-4-0T locomotive 112 (G-E) **£400**

Bing live steam 2-2-0 locomotive and 4-wheel tender, marked with early 1863-1901) trade mark (F-G, with scorch damage) **£450**

Marklin c/w LNER 4-4-0 locomotive 'George the Fifth' 2663 and 6-wheel tender (F-G) **£350**

Bing live steam 0-4-0 locomotive 2631 in maroon with black/yellow lining (F, scorch damaged, lacks tender) and a small quantity of Marklin two rail track **£300**

Gunthermann c/w 4-4-0 Grand Central locomotive 1291 (F-G, lacks one wheel, funnel and some small parts) and 8-wheel bogie tender (G) and a quantity of gauge '1' track...............................**£200**

Marklin TH1020 4-6-2T c/w L&NWR locomotive (F-G, lacks con-rods)...**£1,200**

Bing live steam 0-4-0 locomotive 1902 and 6-wheel tender lithographed in black with red/white lining (F, scorch damaged and missing some small parts) **£300**

Bing for Bassett-Lowke c/w 4-4-0 GWR locomotive 'Sydney and 6-wheel tender (G-F, lacks one lamp) **£1,150**

Bing live steam 4-4-2T locomotive in maroon/black (F, scorch damaged) **£820**

Bing c/w 2-4-0 LNWR locomotive 'King George V' 1902 and 4-wheel tender **£400**

Bing c/w 4-6-2 coupe vent black with red lining with 8-wheel bogie tender (E) **£1,600**

Bassett-Lowke LMS bogie post car 1924 (G)........................**£160**
Bassett-Lowke 12-wheel bogie LMS Dining car 13210 (G)....**£140**

Bing through station 'Clapham Junction' (F, incomplete) GN open wagon, Meccano bridge, various signals and a small collection of track **£280**

Bassett-Lowke wooden island station platform 'Sanoy' with central building and sloped roof, with various tin-plate advertising signs 'Wrights coal tar soap', 'Brands Essence', 'Virol', 'OXO' and others (G-E, contained in its original packing case)..............................**£380**

Bing GWR brake/3rd corridor coach 132 ....**£160**
Bing GWR 1st corridor coach 132 (G-F) **£120**
Bing GWR brake/3rd corridor coach 132 ....**£140**
Bing GWR 1st corridor coach 132 (G).................................**£140**
Bing Midland brake/3rd coach (G-F, some retouching)..........**£100**

Bing GWR 1st/3rd coach 1324 with clerestory roof (G-F, some rusting to roof)..**£130**
Bing Midland 1st corridor coach (G-F, but roof separate and some crush damage to coach ends and internal compartments) **£110**

Bing GWR brake bogie coach 1334 with clerestory roof (F-G, some rusting to roof)..**£100**
Bing Midland 1st/3rd coach 1323 with clerestory roof (G-F, bogies detached)..**£110**

Collector's Notes

Auction Results

Wallis and Wallis

WEST STREET AUCTION GALLERIES, LEWES, SUSSEX

Condition grading system used in Wallis and Wallis catalogues:

Mint — Virtually original state

VGC — Very Good Condition – a fine item

GC — Good Condition – a sound item

QGC — Quite Good Condition – some wear and/or damage

FC — Fair Condition – much wear and/or damage, or parts missing

POOR — Items seldom catalogued in this state unless rarity or historical value makes them nevertheless worthy of collection

AF — At Fault or As Found

WO — Working Order – is used to describe functioning items in conjunction with grades of condition, e.g. VGWO&C (Very Good Working Order and Condition), GWO&QGC (Good Working Order and Quite Good Condition), etc.

MONDAY 28TH APRIL 1997

The 'UNDERWOOD COLLECTION' of 'O' gauge Railway

Marx 'O' gauge electric 0-4-0 locomotive and tender, finished in blue/black livery of tin plate construction to represent British outline locomotive, running number 3978 to cabside and Marx Lines logo to tender. 3 four wheel coaches finished in red and named Montclair and Bogata together with Pullman observation coach which has rear light. GC to VGC **£180**

A Bing 'O' gauge station building 13fi" single ramp end platform in plain grey, 2 storey station house to right hand end, stone block litho print, pierced windows, dark blue diamond slate pattern roofs, canopied waiting area to left side of building, white printed fencing to rear, British advertisements, GC **£140**

A scarce Bing 'O' gauge Victoria Station, the smaller 10fi" example fine litho and pressed detailing, colourful British market adverts, double sided style red litho tiled roof, building mounted on low platform, VGC **£100**

Pre War Hornby 'O' gauge Nestles Milk tanker, blue chassis and frame, 4 tinplate wheels, automatic wire couplings, white tank blue painting. GC (wear to a few letters on one side, a few chips) **£120**

Bing 'O' gauge c/w 4-4-0 locomotive and tender 'George the Fifth' finished in black with red/white lining, loco name to front splasher and running number 2663 to cabside. Model is in original condition with signs of age crazing to paint work. GC (footplate flap is detached)..**£210**

Bassett-Lowke 'O' gauge electric 4-4-0 Midland Compound locomotive and tender, finished in maroon with yellow/black lining, running number 1108 to smoke box door and cab side with LMS to tender side. Some minor retouching of paint work otherwise model is in good condition..**£500**

Bassett-Lowke 'O' gauge c/w 4-4-0 Prince Charles locomotive and tender, contained in original box this model is finished in BR blue with white/black lining, running number 62078 to smoke box door and cabside with early BR totem to tender sides. Model is in very good original condition, a fine example. VGC to Mint..............**£700**

Hornby 'O' gauge c/w No 2 4-4-0 locomotive and tender, finished in LNER green with black-white lining, LNER to splasher sides, company crest to cab side and running number 2711 to tender sides which is of nut and bolt construction, locomotive features front lamps, brass steam dome and drop link couplings. Some minor restoration and over painting with matt varnish. QGC to GC **£95**

MODEL RAILWAY

A Mamod steam 0-4-0 locomotive S-14 Princess of Wales, 4 wheel coach in maroon, and brake van in brown together with 8 lengths of straight track. All in original boxes VGC (loco unfired) **£80**

A rare Gauge '1' 0-4-0 Bing live steam tank locomotive approx 10fi" to 11" long, single oscillating cylinder, power drive to flywheel, geared to drive train, nickel plated boiler, brass whistle steam dome and safety valve, single steam control lever to back of cab, spirit fired, removable 3 burner tank, body painted in maroon and black with red and yellow lining. GC to VGC for age..**£350**

'O' gauge c/w 4-4-2 locomotive for Gamages, Made in Germany, (probably by Marklin for Gamages), in British outline finished in mid green with white/black lining with brown edging to footplate sides. Green wheels, sculpted connecting rods, lamps on front footplate, grey cab interior with some painted back head detail. Running number 1422 to cab sides, tender is missing. Model is c 1910 and generally in good condition, paint has usual age crazing **£210**

A fine 'O' gauge 4-4-2 clockwork precursor tank locomotive by Bing, in black L & WR livery, running number 44 red and yellow lining, twin control levers to rear of cab, nickel plated boiler rails, front and rear buffers with original couplings. VGC for age.......**£270**

Bassett-Lowke 'O' gauge bogie coach, finished in red and cream, brake/3rd running number 26233, droplink couplings, corridor connectors, black underframe and cast wheels. Grey roof with pressed ventilators, VGC **£140**

Bassett-Lowke 'O' gauge train set, post war, 4-4-0 'Prince Charles' c/w locomotive and tender in BR green, black/white lining, running number 62453 to cabside and early BR totem to tender side. 4 goods wagons in original yellow and brown box. VGC **£380**

AUCTION RESULTS NOVEMBER 1996

Hornby 'O' gauge No 2 passenger bogie coach, finished in GWR brown/cream livery, all first with GWR button totem. Contained in original box (roof possibly resprayed, orange peel effect) GC **£210**

Hornby 'O' 4-4-0 clockwork locomotive, finished in black with red/gold lining, LNER and running number 444 to tank sides and coat of arms to cab side. Some over painting, cab hand rails missing, sound working order. 6 wagons (5 with early couplings) and track. FC to QGC...**£110**

Wallis and Wallis continued

A fine Hornby pre war Electric double ended twin track engine shed, with fine litho print detailing, brick style walls with green twin opening doors each end, fitted electric lighting, smoke hoods over doors, 8 roof vents, blue green slate style roof, 4 large windows to each side, GC...**£240**

BASSETT-LOWKE LIVE STEAM 4-6-0 LOCOMOTIVE green LNER livery complete with a 6 wheeled tender 6285 to sides. QGC..**£150**

BASSETT-LOWKE ELECTRIC 4-4-0 LOCOMOTIVE 'PRINCE CHARLES' dark green BR livery 62453 to foot-plate sides, complete with a 6 wheeled fender British Railways to sides, original box. VGC **£240**

BASSETT-LOWKE ELECTRIC 0-6-0 LOCOMOTIVE black and red striped LMS livery. 4256 to footplate sides, complete with a 6 wheeled tender, LMS to sides, GC...............................**£250**

WINTERINGHAM LIVE STEAM 2-6-0 LOCOMOTIVE refinished in matt black with red stripes, complete with its 6 wheeled tender. VGC **£155**

WINTERINGHAM LIVE STEAM 2-6-0 LOCOMOTIVE refinished in black, complete with its 6 wheeled tender. GC **£100**

EXLEY 1st Class LMS PASSENGER COACH maroon and black LMS livery, coach No 7666 GC...................................**£210**

HORNBY 20V ELECTRIC 4-6-2 LOCOMOTIVE PRINCESS ELIZABETH maroon and black LMS livery, 7P6201 to footplate sides, complete with its 6 wheeled tender LMS to sides, original wooden box. VGC **£2,100**

HORNBY CLOCKWORK 4-4-0 LOCOMOTIVE 'ETON' dark green Southern livery, 900 to footplate sides, complete with a 6 wheeled tender, Southern 900 to sides, loco in original box, tender unboxed. VGC **£600**

HORNBY SAUSAGE VAN 'PALETHORPES' maroon with grey root and black base, sliding doors to sides. GC **£210**

HORNBY 'REDLINE' TANKER blue chassis and tank with gold lettering in original box. GC-VGC..**£100**

EARLY HORNBY BOX VAN 'SECCOTINE STICKS EVERYTHING' in white with black outline, blue body with orange roof and black base, hinged opening Side doors. QGC to GC **£210**

HORNBY GUN POWDER VAN red with cream roof and black has 'LNER' etc to sides, with hinged opening side doors. QGC.........**£75**

EARLY HORNBY BOX VAN 'SECCOTINE STICKS EVERYTHING' in white with black outline, blue body with orange roof and black base, hinged opening side doors GC **£400**

EARLY HORNBY MILK TANK WAGON 'NESTLES MILD - RICHEST IN CREAM' blue, on cream tank, with blue super-structure and base. GC **£380**

Lacy Scott & Knight

10 RISBYGATE STREET, BURY ST. EDMUNDS, SUFFOLK

Condition grading used in Lacy Scott & Knight's catalogues:

B   BOXED – in the manufacturers original box or container, in appropriate condition

D   DAMAGED – refers to box only

M   MINT – in perfect or near perfect condition

G   GOOD – in good general condition with some chips or scratches of a minor nature

F   FAIR – in fair condition with an average proportion of chips and marks for age

P   POOR – in only moderate condition, perhaps incomplete

R   REPAINTED – has in whole or in part been repainted or has had some touching in.

NOVEMBER 1996

'0' GAUGE

Hornby c/w No 1 Special Tank loco - Southern 828, some connecting rods and valve gear loose in box (BDF) **£120**

A kit built 4-6-0 Finescale Great Central loco with 6 wheel tender 'Immingham' (G) **£250**

A kit built 4-6-0 Finescale LNER loco with 6 wheel tender in green 'Royal Sovereign' 1671 (G) **£250**

A Hornby clw 4-4-2 loco & tender LMS 'Royal Scot' and rear bogie (F) **£320**

A Hornby c/w 2711 loco & tender (P) with 5 various Hornby goods wagons (F) **£110**

A Hornby wagon (French type) 'Nord' (8DM).......................**£120**

Dinky toys Railway Passengers (pre war) No 3(BM)...............**£120**

Hornby No 2E water tank (chain etc loose in box)(BDG) **£340**

Hornby 20V 3R No I Special Tank loco GWR 5500 with instructions (G)..**£360**

A Bonds 'Bonzone' c/w 0-6-0 sadle tank loco - black (G).........**£150**

Hornby No 2 corridor coach LMS - brake/composite with corridor connection (BG) **£160**

Hornby Private Owner Van 'Jacob and Co' (F) **£160**

Hornby Private Owner Van 'Palethorpes' (G-F).......................**£310**

MARCH 1997

Hornby No 2 c/w LMS Tank loco, maroon, 6954 (some R) (F) **£100**

Hornby c/w 4-4-4 GW tank loco 2221 (F) **£110**

Hornby No 1 LMS Gunpowder Van, roof scratched o/w (G) in 'O' milk traffic van box (BG)......................................**£135**

Hornby No 1 Engine Shed with electric 3R track (G)...............**£160**

2 Hornby No 2 Pullmans (F)..**£180**

Hornby No 2 LMS Saloon (F) **£180**

'0' AND No. '1' GAUGE

A Hornby 3R 6 volt No. 2 Special Tank 4-4-2 GWR 2221, smoke box and cab roof. Poor repainted and some other touching in. One buffer missing (F)..**£190**

A Hornby 3R 6 volt 4-4-2 locomotive and tender 'Royal Scot' 6100, smoke box lampholder missing, rear bogie and piston rod loose in box, slide bar broken but in box, tender coupling in box (BDF)..**£170**

A Hornby Snow Plough blue/yellow. Non-opening doors (F) **£30**

A Hornby double arm lamp standard (no bulbs), base has been repaired, one lampshade bent (F) **£80**

A Hornby lamp standard No. 1 (A687) in green box (BDF) ...**£130**

A Hornby double arm signal No. 2E (BDF) **£105**

6 x 18" lengths Hornby fencing (G) **£60**

A Hornby engine shed No. 2E electrical (1 chimney missing) (BDG)...**£340**

A Hornby No. 2E water tank fitted with electric light (hose perished, no operating chain) (BDF) **£360**

A Hornby No. 2 Special Pullman coach, brake end (grey roof, no couplings) 'Montana' (F) **£110**

A Hornby post war island platform with ramps 'Wembley' (BDG)..**£100**

A Hornby No. 3 station complete with ramps 'Ripon' (BG).....**£45**

A Hornby No. 3 station complete with ramps 'Margate' **£160**

A Hornby private owner van: 'Carrs Biscuits' in 'Jacobs' box (BDG)..**£220**

A Hornby No. 2 Special tender LNER: MATT(BDG).............**£160**

A Hornby No. 2 Special Pullman coach, complete, 'Grosvenor' (BDG)..**£190**

Another, brake end 'Verona' (BDG) **£160**

A Hornby clockwork No. 2 engine shed, complete (BDG) **£320**

A Hornby Clockwork No. 2 Special tank locomotive 4-4-2 LNER 1784, green (1 handrail missing) (F) **£150**

A Hornby clockwork 4-4-2 locomotive and tender 'Flying Scotsman' 4472 (Some touching in) (F) **£210**

A Hornby No. 2 wagon lits sleeping car (2644) (G-F) **£150**

2 Hornby LNER No. 2 corridor coaches (1 Bk/End) (F)........**£180**

A Hornby 20V 3R 4—4-0 loco & tender Bramham Moor 201 (cab roof and 1 con rod missing, 2 wheels and toolbox missing from tender, only one name plate) (F) **£460**

A Hornby c/w No. 2 tank loco LNER 1784 complete with key (F) **£105**

STEAM AND SUNDRY RELATED MODELS, RAILWAY MANIA & MARINE MODELS MODEL ENGINEERING TOOLS AND EQUIPMENT

A 3fi" gauge 2-6-2 tank loco to the alternative 'Mountaineer' design '9' by the late Don Young with sprung central buffer couplings, workable sanding gear, forward and reverse, water lifter, large capacity twin displacement cylinder lubrication, working whistle, 2 hand operated emergency boiler feed pumps and removable ball handles to suit. Finished in black livery with appropriate tools, Boiler Certificates etc..**£2,400**

A cast-iron sign 'Station Master', another 'Trespassing is Forbidden' and 'Please do not throw litter on line' **£120**

A 1" scale model of a Minnie single cylinder traction engine finished in a maroon livery **£850**

A 1½" scale Bassett Lowke model Burrell traction engine, partly finished to a very high standard of engineering, complete with drawings and castings etc. **£400**

A 2" scale Burrell Scenic Showmans engine 'Thetford Town compound 3 speed copper boiler. Tested to 160 PSi January 1994. Minus dynamo and canopy, with 4 wheel riding trolley complete with drawings etc. **£2,350**

A 5" gauge loco 'Butch 0-6-0 locomotive, copper boiler tested to 160 PSI. Current Certificate to 4.4.98. outside cylinders. Walschaerts valve gear, hand pump, usual cab fittings, finished in maroon livery **£1,200**

A 5" gauge Polly I freelance 0-4-0 side tank loco, outside cylinders, inside valve gear, usual cab fittings with steam raising blower, firing tools, spares, drawings and plans, on stand finished in black **£650**

A 4½" scale Allchin traction engine, steel boiler, working pressure 120 PSi, hydraulic pressure 300 PSi. Last Boiler Certificate May 1995. Last steamed October 1996. Single cylinder slide valve engine **£8,200**

Christie's South Kensington

85 OLD BROMPTON ROAD, LONDON

Descriptions of paintwork used in Christie's catalogues:

M Toys apparently never taken out of mint original boxes
F Excellent toys with no or very few apparent paint
   chips or defects
G Good toys with minor scratches to the paint
F Fair toys with an acceptable amount of paint damage
P Poor toys probably suitable for repainting or restoration
Sd Some damage

Where to referring to boxes:

E Excellent original box with no or very little damage,
   complete with all interior fittings
G Good box with normal use wear only, but fittings not
   necessarily complete
F Fair box possibly slightly torn or split, but with label intact
P Poor box; likely to be split or torn, and in need of repair

HORNBY 0 GAUGE

Hornby Series clockwork 4-4-2 No. 2 Special Tank Locomotive No.. 6954, painted in lined lake, circa 1938 (G, lamp socket, coupling rods and lever end missing, coupling broken, buffer beams repainted, bogie wheels replaced £253

Hornby Series electric Southern Goods Set, 0-4-0 E120 Special Tank Locomotive A950 painted in lined black, two wagons, track and packing in original set box, circa 1935 (F, some wear and chipping, box P) £977

Hornby Series Locomotive and Rolling Stock: No. 2 Special clockwork 4-4-2 LNER tank No painted in green, seven various goods wagons including No. 2 LMS Cattle, a water tower and signal, mostly in original boxes, including locomotive, 1934-1038 (F-G, boxes P-F) **£402**

Hornby Series E320 20 Volt, Electric 4-4 'Flying Scotsman' Locomotive and No. 2 Special LNER Tender, the latter in original box all painted in lined green, circa 1936 (G, some damage to locomotive buffer beam, cab steps missing)...................................£368

Hornby Series Goods Rolling Stock: Fyffes Banana Van, early GW Gas Cylinder Wagon, Cement, McAlpine Side Tipper and seven others, most in original boxes, 1928-34 (F-E, boxes P-F) £253

Hornby Series clockwork No. 3C 4-4-2 'Flying Scotsman and No. 2 Special LNER Tender, painted in green, in original box, circa 1937 (G-E, some fatigue to driving wheels, boxes F-G, slight damage) £552

Hornby Series clockwork 4-4-0 No. 2 Special GW 'County of Bedford' Locomotive No. 3821, painted in green, in original box, circa 1934 (F-G, one cab side damaged, cab hand rails broken, driving wheels fatigued, box F-G) £402

Hornby Series electric No. 3E 4 volt 4-4-2 'Riviera Blue' locomotive No. 31240, and bogie Nord tender No. 31801, all painted in gold lined brown, a Riviera Blue CIWL dining car and sleeping car, all circa 1927 (P, wear and paint loss to locomotive and coaches) £207

Hornby Series Rolling Stock and Track: blue Cadburys Chocolate Van, in original box, circa 1932 (E, box G), early Rotary Tipper, three other vehicles and small quantity of track and accessories, most in original boxes, 1928-38 (F-E, boxes F-G) £517

Hornby Series clockwork No. 2 Special S.R. 4-4-0 LI Locomotive and Tender No. 1759, painted in lined green, in original boxes and packing with guarantee, circa 1936 (F-G, slight damage to cab, some repainting in cab and tender, coal added, boxes P-F, labels stuck on sides and ends..£920

Hornby Series, No. 2 Engine Shed, with hinged doors, lithographed both sides, circa 1932 (F-G), in original box, lower half with end illustrations (P, lid missing), and an M Station Set in original box, comprising M.Station, M.Wayside Station, M.. Signal Box, two M. Signals and two M. Telegraph Poles, circa 932 (F-G, box F) £402

Hornby Series 'Nestles' Milk Tank Wagon, painted in blue and cream, circa 1938 (F) £253

Hornby Series Electric No. E2P double-track Engine Shed, with green base and hinged doors, lithographed both sides, circa 1935 (G, slight damage to doors) £402

Hornby Series Electric Locomotive and Bogie Coaches, 4-4-2 LMS E220 Special Tank Locomotive No. 6954, painted in lake, and two LMS No. 2 Corridor Bogie Coaches, circa 1938 (F-F, locomotive damaged, front bogie and lampholder missing, some damage and wear to coaches)...£253

Hornby Series clockwork 4-4-0 No. 2 Special LMS Compound Locomotive No. 1185, and Tender painted in lined lake, both in original boxes, circa 1931 (G, Hornby transfer under cab, worn bogie loose pin missing, boxes F)...£414

Hornby Series Electric 0-4-0 No. E120 Special LMS Locomotive No. 2700, and an early unlined No. 1 Special Tender, both painted in lake, 1930 and 1938 (F, some chips and wear) £437

Bassett-Lowke steam 2-6-0 LMS Mogul No. 2945, painted in lined black, fitted twin-double acting cylinders and reverse block and vapor rising spirit lamp, with instructions, circa 1950 (P, worn, locomotive repainted)..£402

A Bassett-Lowke clockwork 4-6-0 LMS 'Royal Scot' Locomotive and Tender No. 6100, lithographed in lined lake, circa 1931 (F-G, some scratches, front coupling broken) £460

A Bassett-Lowke clockwork 4-4-2 L&NWR Precursor Tank Locomotive, painted in black, circa 1925 (P, paint loss, worn), a late HR 4-4-0 Compound body and tender, lithographed in black, in original box (G, box P) and an Exley LMS Non-Corridor 3rd Brake Passenger Coach (P, repainted in lake)......................................£345

Bassett-Lowke lithographed tinplate Advertising Boards, inc. 'Huntley and Palmers', 'Bassett-Lowke', 'Leyland', Wrights Coal Tar Soap', 'Vim', 'OXO', 'News of the World', and others, mounted and framed (G, ten F, Nectar Tea reproductions)..............................£460

A Bassett-Lowke electric 4-6-0 LMS 'Royal Scot' Locomotive and Tender, painted in lined black, in original box (F, paint bloomed, wheel rims and centres painted white, pick-ups changed to outside 3rd rail collection, box P-F)..£862

A Bassett-Lowke Railways two-rail electric 4-4-2 13 LBSC Tank Locomotive No. 39, painted in lined Marsh Umber brown, by D. Barrington Holt, details include rivets, destination disc irons, Westinghouse pump, fillers, vents and hand rail (E).................£483

Auction Results

Bassett-Lowke 4-4-0 LMS 'Duke of York', 1927 (P, sun faded) £161

Bassett-Lowke Electric LMS 4-6-2 'Princess Elizabeth' Locomotive and Tender No. 6201, painted in lake, in a Bassett-Lowke box, circa 1939 (G, some corrosion on boiler and smoke box, Bassett-Lowke box) P-F **£2,990**

Bassett-Lowke Electric BR 4-4-0 Compound Locomotive and Tender No. 41109, lithographed in lined black, in original box, circa 1960 (locomotive and tender G, box F) **£517**

BING FOR BASSETT-LOWKE

Bing for Bassett-Lowke lithographed LNER Teak Corridor bogie Coaches: one Side Corridor 1st/3rd and 3rd Guards Brake, circa 1923 (G-E, some scratches) **£402**

Bing for Bassett-Lowke clockwork 4-4-0 L&NWR Tank Locomotive No. 3611, painted in lined black, circa 1923 (F-G, some damage, two steps loose, one buffer missing) **£437**

Bing for Bassett-Lowke: Corridor Coaches: one side Corridor 1st and 3rd Guards Brake, both lithographed in lake, circa 1923 (G, some slight damage).................(No price available) Estimate: **£180-£220**

Bing for Bassett-Lowke Clockwork 4-4-0 Caledonian Railway 'Dunalastair Locomotive and bogie Tender No. 142, painted in blue and chocolate, circa 1914 (P, paint worn, crazed and part flaking, damage to cab roof, some rust, couplings replaced)..................**£632**

A Bing for Bassett-Lowke Caledonian 0-4-0T 112 Tank Locomotive, Cat. Ref. 21/1, painted in lined blue, circa 1922 (F, dent damage under chimney, some chips and wear, one buffer head missing) **£276**

Gauge '1' Bing for Bassett-Lowke electric 4-4-0 LMS George the Fifth, repainted in unlined black, circa 1924 (P, converted from clockwork, fitted Bassett-Lowke permag mechanism, frames and steps altered, coal rail missing, repainted) **£195**

BING

Bing clockwork 0-4-0 GW Locomotive and six-wheel Tender No. 3410, lithographed in lined green, lake MR bogie Passenger Luggage Full Brake and two lithographed four-wheel LNW Coaches, 1914-25 (F-G) **£195**

Bing clockwork 0-4-0 LNW King Edward VII, lithographed and repainted in lined black, circa 1909, a Marklin LNW lithographed six-wheel tender (P-F, locomotive mainly overpainted, detail added) and a French Hornby No. 10 Station Staff Set with five plastic figures in original red box (G-E, box G-E) ....(NPA) Estimate: **£200-£300**

A Gauge '1' Bing Steam 0-4-0 LNW Locomotive No. 1902 and Six-wheel Tender, painted in black, Joy Valve gear, vapourising spirit lamp and smoke-box lubricator, circa (P-F, burnt and part overpainted) **£483**

CARETTE FOR BASSETT-LOWKE

A Gauge 'III' Carette for Bassett-Lowke 53cm bogie N.E.R. 1st/3rd Coach, hinged doors, lithographed in lined lake, circa 1912 (G, roof repainted)..**£460**

A Gauge 'III' Carette for Bassett-Lowke 53cm bogie N.E.R. Passenger Luggage Full Brake Van, with hinged doors, lithographed in lined lake, circa 1912 (G, roof repainted, slight paint retouching, bogies replaced)...**£463**

A mid-19th Century 31/4 in. Gauge four-wheel First Class Passenger Coach, lined lake and cream painted wood, with hinged doors, external and interior detail, correct leaf springing to axles and buffers (P, some damage, paint dirty and crazed, parts missing - 37cm **£1,092**

THE MARKLIN TRANSPORT SALE

PRICES SHOWN REPRESENT CHRISTIE'S PRE-SALE ESTIMATES

O GAUGE LOCOMOTIVES

A clockwork GNR 4-4-2 'Atlantic' Locomotive and six-wheel Tender, No. 1427, for A W Gamage, circa 1914 (F, blemish to smoke box, some repairs to tender, replaced coal deck and front coal sheet) **£550-700**

A steam spirit-fired MR 0-4-0 Locomotive and lithographed four-wheel Tender No. 281, Cat. Ref. 4030, with twin oscillating cylinders and heat-trough boiler, circa 1924 (F, some scorching and paint flaking to boiler) **£300-400**

A steam spirit-fired GNR 0-4-0 Locomotive and lithographed six-wheel Tender, Cat. Ref 4000, with two double-acting cylinders, lubricators, slip eccentric reverse and heat-trough boiler, circa 1925 (G, some slight scratches).......................................**£400-600**

A steam spirit-fired NBR 4-4-2 Atlantic type Locomotive and six-wheel Tender, Cat. Ref. CE 4020, with twin double acting cylinders, reverse through steam chest and vapourising spirit lamp, circa 1927 (P-F, paint scorched and parts overpainted, tender part worn and overpainted)..**£700-1,000**

A British Market 20 Volt electric LNER 2-8-2 'Cock other North' Locomotive and eight-wheel Tender, Cat. Ref. L70/12920, finished in green livery, in original box, circa 1936 (G-E, slight paint damage to one area of boiler top)..**£8,000-£10,000**

BASSETT-LOWKE AND BING

A Bassett-Lowke electric 4-6-2 'Flying Scotsman' Locomotive No. 4472 and LNER Tender, lithographed on lined green, circa 1939 (G-E, some slight chipping)..**£1,495**

Exley bogie KS GWR Suburban Coaches: two 3rd/Brakes, two 3rds and one 1st (F-G, roofs and some ends repainted, buffer beams redetailed)..**£402**

Bassett-Lowke lithographed bogie Passenger LMS Rolling Stock: twelve-wheel Dining Car and Travelling Post Office Van with track apparatus, both lined in lake, circa 1925 (G, some small scratches, one coupling missing) **£299**

E420 20-VOLT 'ETON' ELECTRIC LOCOMOTIVE and No.2 Special Eton Southern 900 tender - P-F, tender P-F **£75**

RARE HORNBY SERIES printed corrugated card Hornby Trains retailers **advertising three-fold screen,** depicting two keen Hornby Train spotting boys, seated over the central tunnel parapet with Windsor signal box and accessories illustrated on the side wings, c. 1927 - G **£1,210**

HORNBY BOOK OF TRAINS including 1931-2, 1932-3, 1933-4,1934-5, 1937-8, 1938-9, 1939-40 (G), and a Bassett-Lowke Duchess of Montrose box (P)..**£242**

Christie's South (continued)

SERIES No 1 RAILWAY ACCESSORY 'CARLISLE LUGGAGE HAMPER' 1924- 1926 - F-G **£55**

'CRAWFORDS BISCUITS' PRIVATE OWNERS VAN with open axle-guard base, white roof and hinged door, in original box 1924-25 - G, box F-G **£143**
'SECCOTINE' PRIVATE OWNERS VAN with open axle-guard base and orange roof in original box - E, box F **£330**

20-VOLT ELECTRIC GW E220 SPECIAL TANK LOCO-MOTIVE No 2221 in matt finish, 1939-194 1 - F-G **£242**

E220 LMS SPECIAL TANK LOCOMOTIVE No 6954 c.1936 P-F..**£154**
CLOCKWORK No 2 SPECIAL LOCOMOTIVE NO 201 The Brambam Moor and matching No 2 Special Tender, original box, c.1936 - G, tender F, box F.. **£625**

E320 ELECTRIC SOUTHERN 'LORD NELSON' and matching No 2 Special Tender No 850, c.1936 - G..................... **£385**
E320 ELECTRIC Great Western 'CAERPHILLY CASTLE' LOCOMOTIVE and matching early livery No 2 Special Tender, original box, c.1935 - F, tender 0, box G **£308**

CLOCKWORK No 2 SPECIAL LMS COMPOUND LOCO-MOTIVE and matching six- wheeled No. Special Tender c.1935 G-E..**£352**
ELECTRIC LOW VOLTAGE No 2 LMS LAKE 4-4-0 LOCO-MOTIVE c 1924-25 - G.F. and a No 2711 tender - F **£1,100**

GWR No 2 CORRIDOR COACHES two lst/3rd and a 3rd Luggage Brake, c 1938 - P-F **£209**
PULLMAN COACHES: No 2 Special Loraine - G and No 2 Special Composite Arcadia, c. 1932 - G.E **£264**

NESTLES MILK TANK WAGON c. 1938 - F and blue Colas Tank Wagon, early base and link coupling c. 1929 ....**£242**
'COLMANS MUSTARD' Van original box c 1924 - G, box G**£825**

RARE EARLY No 1 MINIATURE LUGGAGE AND PORTERS BARROW SET with hamper marked Carlisle original box, c.1924 E, box G...**£275**

ELECTRIC 20-VOLT 'PRINCESS ELIZABETH' LOCOMO-TIVE and matching six-wheel tender, original blue fitted carrying case with a guarantee, c.1938 - E, case G................. **£1760**
3 LMS No 2 CORRIDOR COACHES and an LMS No 2 Corridor Brake Composite, original boxes, 1938 - E, boxes G.................**£605**

CLOCKWORK No 2 SPECIAL GREAT WESTERN TANK LOCOMOTIVE early version with link coupling and green driving wheels, original box, c. 1930 - E, box F-G **£165**
No 4E ELECTRICALLY-LIT 'READING' STATION with matching ramps, late mottled sand platforms and arched printed window over entrance. red No 2 'Wembley' station box - G.E, box G **£352**

No 1 SPECIAL PASSENGER SET: comprising Great Western 0-4-0 Locomotive and tender 2301. Pullman coaches-Corsair, Cynthia and Ansonia, original box, dated 11.29 - G.....................................**£264**
E220 SPECIAL LNER 20 Volt Tank Locomotive 1784, original green box, 1932-36 -0, box P...**£264**
No 3C ELECTRIC LNER 'FLYING SCOTSMAN' Locomotive and tender 4472, 1933-36 - F-G...**£242**

BASSETT-LOWKE '0' GAUGE

RARE THREE RAIL ELECTRIC BR 4-6-2 'FLYING SCOTS-MAN' LOCOMOTIVE and tender in experimental blue livery, original box, c.1950 - E, box G..............................**£1,320**
CLOCKWORK HAND PAINTED LATE PRE-WAR IM-PROVED LMS MOGUL 2-6-0 Locomotive and matching six wheel tender, c.1939 ....**£528**

ELECTRIC LITHOGRAPHED No 4472 'Flying Scotsman' Locomotive with first series side DC Permag and eight wheeled tender, c.1936 - F-G...**£528**
ELECTRIC PAINTED LNER 2-6-0 Mogul and tender No 33, c.1937 - F..**£308**

ELECTRIC LMS 2-6-4 PANNIER TANK LOCOMOTIVE No 2531, c.1939 - P..**£605**
ELECTRIC LITHOGRAPHED LMS 'ROYAL SCOT' Locomotive and tender No 6100 fitted with standard DC Permag motor P...**£308**
STEAM LMS MOGUL Locomotive type 13000 and six wheeled tender. c.1936 - P...**£308**

EARLY POST WAR ELECTRIC GWR 4-6-0 'Kenilworth Castle' Locomotive and six wheeled tender. in a Royal Scot box, c.1947 - P-F, box P-F **£825**
ELECTRIC LITHOGRAPHED PRE WAR LNER LIVERY No 4472 Flying Scotsman and eight wheeled tender, fitted with Permag mechanism, original box, c.1938 - P. box F **£385**

ELECTRIC PAINTED LNER 0-6-0 Goods Locomotive and tender No 1448 black with red lining, Permag mechanism, original box. c.1932 - P. box P-F **£605**
ELECTRIC HAND PAINTED GWR 2-6-2 PRAIRIE TANK LOCOMOTIVE No 6105, c.1938 - F **£495**

CLOCKWORK BR 'DUCHESS OF MONTROSE' green and matching six wheeled tender. cat ref: 3621/0 original box with wrapping. key and instructions. c. 1958 - G.E. box F-G **£2200**

CLOCKWORK BR 2-6-4 TANK LOCOMOTIVE No 42068 Cat ref 3618/0 original box with key and instructions. c 1958, E, box G..**£990**
CLOCKWORK BR FLYING SCOTSMAN green and matching eight-wheeled tender, Cat ret. 33 10/0 original box with key and instructions. c.1957 - G.E. box F-G **£990**
STEAM BR(M) 2-6-0 MOGUL LOCOMOTIVE and matching six wheel tender. Cat ref 6661/0, original box with instructions, guarantee. c.1957 - G.F. box G **£330**

ELECTRIC LNER 4472 'FLYING SCOTSMAN' and matching eight wheel tender in a post war Flying Scotsman box, c.1938. G, box P-F...**£528**
ELECTRIC LITHOGRAPHED LMS THREE CAR EUSTON-WATFORD SET - G.E; and another LMS Brake End Coach, c.1935. F...**£1,760**

RARE WOODEN 'LONDON TRANSPORT Underground Station Ashfield to complement Tube trains. c.1935. G **£440**

ELECTRIC LITHOGRAPHED BR PRINCE CHARLES 4-4-0 Locomotive and matching six wheel tender, green - E, box G.E, lamp fixed to smoke box door, in original box with instructions, c. 1962. E, box G.E **£198**

ELECTRIC THREE RAIL LMS MOGUL Locomotive No 13000, c.1929 - G..**£264**

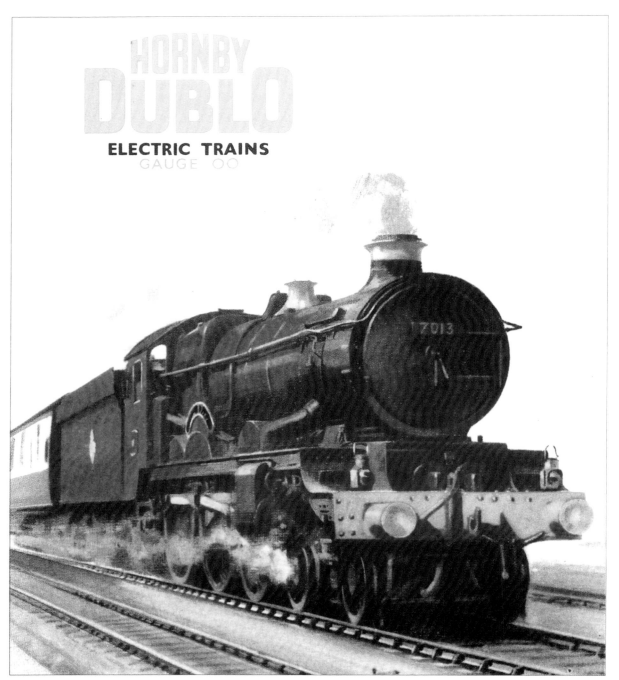

Picture taken from the 1957 Hornby Dublo Catalogue Ref: HD/CF/3 7/857/500

Hornby Dublo Railways, 1938 – 1964

In any chronicle of the Meccano company the middle of the 1930s stands out as the golden years. Frank Hornby's burgeoning enterprise encompassed the famous Liverpool works, a French factory producing its own distinctly Gallic toys and models and a worldwide network of branches and agents with eager customers everywhere for the growing range of Dinky Toys, Meccano sets, and of course the famous Hornby Series gauge 'O' clockwork and electric trains.

Gauge 'O' (scaled at 7 mm. to the foot) had become the paramount model railway scale supplanting the earlier (and bigger) Victorian gauge '1' and Hornby was the premier British manufacturer of gauge 'O' ready-to run trains. However, even smaller (and thus more convenient model railways were being developed, mainly on the Continent, where as far back as 1921 Bing offered their 'table-top' clockwork railway in 'HO' gauge, with an electric version two years later.

'HO' indicates 'half-O' and is 3.5 mm. to the foot. Other 'HO' models appearing in the 1920s included the Trix-Twin sets which were imported from Germany to England by the British Bassett-Lowke company.

As not every Meccano boy lived in a large house capable of accommodating a reasonable size railway, even in gauge 'O', Meccano were doubtless urged by would-be customers and dealers alike to manufacture something a little smaller – a 'OO' railway – and given the Company's superb marketing skills, would have been quite aware of competitors' developments in the smaller scales.

However it was not until 1938 that the first Hornby 'Dublo' models were announced, the decision to produce a 'OO' range having been taken a bare nine months before.

In true Meccano style the new range comprised not merely locomotive models but an extensive choice of goods rolling stock, passenger coaches, railway buildings and signals, as well as the requisite track and controllers.

In 1972 Tri-ang was acquired by the Dunbee-Combex-Marx firm and the Hornby name lives on today as 'Hornby Railways' manufactured by Hornby Hobbies Ltd., of Margate. Study of the present Hornby Railways catalogue reveals a stud of over thirty finely detailed 'OO' locomotives along with a comprehensive range of rolling stock and accessories, tempting railway modellers and collectors alike.

In 1966 Mr G.Wrenn negotiated the purchase of many of the original Dublo tools from Tri-ang, and the firm of G. & R. Wrenn continued to employ these tools in producing diecast 'OO' models until 1992 when production ceased.

A number of the original Hornby Dublo type locomotives (with detail improvements) feature in the Wrenn range and any prizes for 'OO' longevity must surely go to 'N2' tanks and the 'A4 Sir Nigel Gresley', both seeing the first light of day in 1938 and still available in Wrenn form over fifty years later!

The listings have been carefully updated and are now very much enhanced by the results of certain recent auction sales. Christie's 'Bianco Hornby Dublo Reference Collection' Sale in October 1996 presented virtually the complete range of Hornby Dublo ever produced, all in highly collectable condition. Our Reference 'OO' gauge Auction Results (pages 104–112) reports on this sale and helps to underpin the Market Price Range shown in the listings.

We have also included colour and monochrome pictures of virtually all the items in that sale. Sotheby's too, had a highly important sale of Hornby Dublo – in September 1997 and the results are shown on pages 109–112. Much technical information is to be found in these auctions results along with helpful supporting evidence for price guidance.

Readers are also recommended to study the 'OO' and 'HO' Auction Results on pages 175-190 where many more references to Hornby Dublo will be found along with an abundance of facts and figures on other makes of locos, stock and sets.

As always the Editor will be pleased to receive any new information.

Hornby Dublo Locomotives 1938 - 1964

Ref.	Year(s)	Type	Name	Number	Railway	Colours	2/3 rail	Motor	MPR

Steam Outline Locomotives (Clockwork)

DL1	1938-41	4-6-2	'Sir Nigel Gresley'	4498	LNER	Blue		CW	**£750-1000** ❑
DL7	1938-40	0-6-2	Tank	2594	SR	Olive Green		CW	**£700-800** ❑
DL7	1938-40	0-6-2	Tank	6917	LMS	Black		CW	**£400-450** ❑
DL7	1938-40	0-6-2	Tank	2690	LNER	Black		CW	**£450-550** ❑
DL7	1938-40	0-6-2	Tank	6699	GWR	Green		CW	**£700-800** ❑

Steam Outline Locomotives (Electrically powered)

Identification: Early issues have a Gold block with Red line on the rear of the tender with logo 'HORNBY MECCANO LTD, Made in England'. Later issues have a Silver block with Red Line. Pre-war locomotives and very early post-war issues have no model number beneath the running board - later post-war issues do. e.g. EDL7 etc.

EDL1	1938-41	4-6-2	'Sir Nigel Gresley'	4498	LNER	Blue	3	HS	**£600-800** ❑

Note: Pre-war model had full-depth valances over the wheels and simple push rod instead of valve gear.

EDL2	1938	4-6-2	'Duchess of Atholl'	6231	LMS	Maroon	3	HS	NGPP ❑

N.B. Shown in pre-war literature but never issued.

EDL7	1938-41	0-6-2	Tank	2594	SR	Olive Green	3	HS	**£600-700** ❑
EDL7	1938-41	0-6-2	Tank	6917	LMS	Black	3	HS	**£300-400** ❑
EDL7	1938-41	0-6-2	Tank	2690	LNER	Black	3	HS	**£300-400** ❑
EDL7	1938-41	0-6-2	Tank	6699	GWR	Green	3	HS	**£500-600** ❑

EDL1	1947-53	4-6-2	'Sir Nigel Gresley'	7	LNER	Blue	3	HS/HI	**£125-150** ❑

Binns Road Repair, Rare variation with
'EDL11' under cab roof (Silver King body) .... **£250-350** ❑

EDL2	1947-53	4-6-2	'Duchess of Atholl'	6231	LMS	Maroon	3	HS/HI	**£100-150** ❑

Rare variation with Cream nameplate .... 3 .... **£250-400** ❑
Rare variation with projection under the
offside name plate instead of the normal inlet .... 3 .... **£250-400** ❑

EDL2 .... Rare variation with smoke deflectors on either
side of front of boiler ('EDL12' under cab roof) .... 3 .... **£500-800** ❑
Note: This variation occurred when models were repaired at Binns Road and were fitted with
new 'Duchess of Montrose' bodies painted in 'Duchess of Atholl' livery.

EDL2	1952	4-6-2	'Canadian Pacific'	1215		Black		HI	**£600-700** ❑

This model was made for the Canadian market.   Replicas of the Canadian Pacific are currently made using 'Duchess of Atholl' originals.

EDL11	1953-54	4-6-2	'Silver King'	60010	BR	Gloss Green	1	HI	**£200-250** ❑
EDL11	1954-58	4-6-2	'Silver King'	60016	BR	Matt Green	3	HI	**£150-200** ❑
L11/ /3211	1958-63	4-6-2	'Mallard'	60022	BR	Matt Green	3	HI	**£200-250** ❑
L11	1958-63	4-6-2	'Mallard'	60022	BR	Matt Green	3	HI	**£20-250** ❑
3211	1962-63	4-6-2	'Mallard' (nickel plated wheels)	60022	BR	Matt Green	3	HI	**£400-500** ❑
2211	1959-64	4-6-2	'Golden Fleece'	60030	BR	Matt Green	2	HI	**£130-175** ❑
EDL12/	1953-54	4-6-2	'Duchess of Montrose'	46232	BR	Gloss Green	3	HI	£150-175 ❑
/3212	1954-58	4-6-2	'Duchess of Montrose'	46232	BR	Matt Green	3	HI	**£95-125** ❑

Binns Rd repair variation, nickel plated
wheels, plain Brown box .... 46232 .... 3 ...... HI .... **£125-150** ❑

The immediate post-war versions (listed below) were fitted with post-war automatic couplings requiring a chamfer in the front buffer beam:

EDL7	1947	0-6-2	Tank (with pre-war body)	2594	SR	Olive Green	3	HS	**£550-700** ❑
EDL7	1948-53	0-6-2	Tank	2594	SR	Malachite	3	HS/HI	**£250-350** ❑
EDL7	1947-48	0-6-2	Tank (LMS in serif letters)	6917	LMS	Black	3	HS	**£175-250** ❑
EDL7	1949-53	0-6-2	Tank (LMS in block letters)	6917	LMS	Black	3	HI	**£50-100** ❑
EDL7	1947	0-6-2	Tank (pre-war body)	2690	LNER	Black	3	HS	NGPP ❑
EDL7	1947	0-6-2	Tank	9596	LNER	Black	3	HS	NGPP ❑

Cat	Years	Wheels	Description	No.	Railway	Colour		Box	Price	
EDL7	1948-53	0-6-2	Tank	9596	LNER	Green	3	HS/HI	**£125-175**	❏
EDL7	1947-53	0-6-2	Tank	6699	GWR	Green	3	HS/HI	**£200-250**	❏
EDL7	1948/	0-6-2	Tank (Duchess of Atholl Engine No)	6231	GWR	Green	3	HI	NGPP	❏
EDL7	1953	0-6-2	Tank (only one known example)	E9560	BR ER	Green	3	HI	NGPP	❏
EDL7	1953-54	0-6-2	Tank (no coal in bunker)	69567	BR ER	Gloss Black	3	HI	**£125-150**	❏
EDL17/ /L17	1954-58	0-6-2	Tank (no coal in bunker)	69567	BR ER	Matt Black	3	HI	**£50-70**	❏
3217	1961-63	0-6-2	Tank (with coal in bunker)	69567	BR ER	Matt Black	3	HI	**£200-300**	❏
2217	1960-63	0-6-2	Tank (small safety valve)	69550	BR ER	Matt Black	2	HI	**£100-125**	❏
	1963-64	0-6-2	Tank (large safety valve)	69550	BR ER	Matt Black	2	HI	**£125-150**	❏
EDLT20/ /LT20/ /3220	1957-61	4-6-0	'Bristol Castle'	7013	BR WR	Matt Green	3	HI	**£100-150**	❏
3221	1961-61	4-6-0	'Ludlow Castle'	5002	BR WR	Matt Green	3	RF	**£400-450**	❏
3220	1959-59	4-6-0	'Denbigh Castle'	7032	BR WR	Matt Green	2	HI	**£175-200**	❏
2221	1960-64	4-6-0	'Cardiff Castle'	4075	BR WR	Matt Green	2	RF	**£150-175**	❏
EDL18	1954-58	2-6-4	Tank (1st issue in plain blue box)	80054	BR	Matt Black	3	HI	**£175-200**	❏
EDL18	1955-58	2-6-4	Tank (2nd issue in picture box)	80054	BR	Matt Black	3	HI	**£125-150**	❏
3218	1961-63	2-6-4	Tank	80059	BR	Matt Black	3	HI	**£400-500**	❏
2218	1959-64	2-6-4	Tank	80033	BR	Matt Black	2	HI	**£150-200**	❏
3225/ /LT25	1958-61	2-8-0	BR Class 8F	48158	BR	Matt Black	3	HI	**£125-175**	❏
3224	1961-63	2-8-0	BR Class 8F	48094	BR	Matt Black	3	RF	**£350-450**	❏
2225	1959-59	2-8-0	BR Class 8F	48109	BR	Matt Black	2	HI	**£180-230**	❏
2224	1960-64	2-8-0	BR Class 8F	48073	BR	Matt Black	2	RF	**£125-160**	❏
2226	1959-64	4-6-2	'City of London'	46245	BR MR	Maroon	2	HI	**£125-175**	❏
3226	1961-63	4-6-2	'City of Liverpool'	46247	BR MR	Maroon	3	HI	**£450-600**	❏
2206	1959-64	0-6-0	Tank, Class R1 (plastic body, metal chassis)	31337	BR SR	Black	2	HI	**£60-80**	❏

Normal buffers nickel plated but the Red plastic versions sell for 75 percent more

Cat	Years	Wheels	Description	No.	Railway	Colour		Box	Price	
2207	1959-64	0-6-0	Tank, Class R1 (plastic body, metal chassis)	31340	BR SR	Green	2	HI	**£50-70**	❏
2235	1961-64	4-6-2	'Barnstaple'	34005	BR SR	Matt Green	2	RF	**£125-175**	❏
3235	1961-63	4-6-2	'Dorchester'	34042	BR SR	Matt Green	3	RF	**£350-450**	❏

Diesel, Diesel-Electric and Electric Outline Locomotives

Cat	Years	Wheels	Description	No.	Railway	Colour		Box	Price	
L30/ /3230	1958-62	D8000	Diesel-Electric 1000 loco, 'Bo-Bo' (Blue striped box) *		BR	Green	2	HI	**£75-125**	❏
2230	1959-62	D8017	Diesel-Electric 1000 loco, (picture box) *		BR	Green	2	HI	**£75-125**	❏
2230	1959-62	D8017	Diesel-Electric 1000 loco, (Red box) *		BR	Green	2	HI	**£75-125**	❏

L30/ /2230   Versions of the above locos, without buffers but otherwise identical,* were produced for the Canadian market .... **£450-650** ❏

Cat	Years	Wheels	Description	No.	Railway	Colour		Box	Price	
2231	1960-64	0-6-0	Diesel-Electric shunter *	D3302	BR	Green	2	RF	**£60-85**	❏
3231	1961-63	0-6-0	Diesel-Electric shunter *	D3763	BR	Green	3	RF	**£150-195**	❏

Note: Variations are available with split coupling rods on each side. Expect them to be **£20 to £25** more.

Cat	Years	Wheels	Description	No.	Railway	Colour		Box	Price	
2232	1961-64	'Co-Co'	Deltic Class 3300 hp Diesel-Electric	none	BR	Green	2	RF	**£100-120**	❏
3232	1961-63	'Co-Co'	Deltic Class 3300 hp Diesel-Electric	none	BR	Green	3	RF	**£150-180**	❏
2234	1962-64	'Co-Co'	Deltic 'Crepello' 3300 hp Diesel-Electric	D9012	BR	Green	2	RF	**£125-250**	❏
3234	1962-63	'Co-Co'	Deltic 'St.Paddy' 3300 hp Diesel-Electric	D9001	BR	Green	3	RF	**£300-400**	❏
2233	1961-64	'Co-Bo'	1200 hp Diesel-Electric loco	D5702	BR	Green	2	RF	**£120-160**	❏
			As above a version exists which has a working light at the non driving end						NGPP	❏
3233	1961-64	'Co-Bo'	1200 hp Diesel-Electric loco	D5713	BR	Green	3	RF	**£150-175**	❏
2250	1962-64		Suburban Electric loco (Drive Coach / Trailer Car)	S65326	BR SR	Green	2	RF	**£300-350**	❏
3250	1962-63		Suburban Electric loco (Drive Coach / Trailer Car)	S65326	BR SR	Green	3	RF	**£350-400**	❏

Note: Both the above sets were sold with dummy Driving Coach Trailer S77511.

Cat	Years	Wheels	Description	No.	Railway	Colour		Box	Price	
2245	1964		'Bo-Bo' 3300 hp Electric locomotive * with twin overhead pantographs	E3002	BR	Blue	2	RF	**£500-600**	❏

* **Note:** These models have moulded plastic bodies with diecast metal chassis.

See the Auction Results sections for additional technical information and locomotive variations.

Hornby Dublo Coaches 1938 – 1964

Ref.	Year(s)	Model name	Class	Railway	Number	Livery and Box reference	Market Price Range

Passenger Coaches (pre-war Three-Rail)

Ref.	Year(s)	Model name	Class	Railway	Number	Livery and Box reference	Market Price Range	
D1	1938-40	Corridor Coach	1st/3rd	LNER	42759	Teak finish with White roof (D251)	**£100-150**	❏
D2	1938-40	Two Coach Articulated Unit	All 3rd / Brake 3rd	LNER	45401/2	Teak finish with White roof (D252)	**£650-850**	❏
D3	-	Corridor Coach	1st/3rd	LMS	4183	Maroon body, Silver Grey roof (not issued pre-war)	NPP	
			Brake/3rd	LMS	26133	Maroon body, Silver Grey roof (not issued pre-war)	NPP	

Passenger Coaches (post-war Three-Rail)

Ref.	Year(s)	Model name	Class	Railway	Number	Livery and Box reference	Market Price Range	
D1	1948-53	Corridor Coach	1st/3rd	LNER	42759	Teak finish with Brown coach ends (32010)	**£30-40**	❏
D1	1953-55		All 3rd	LNER	45401	Teak finish, Brown coach ends (DR361 & 32012)	**£50-70**	❏
						with Grey roof (similar to D11)	**£75-100**	❏
D1	1948-53		Brake 3rd	LNER	45402	Teak finish, Brown or Teak coach ends (DR361 and 32011)	**£40-60**	❏
D2	1948-49	Two Coach Articulated Unit	All 3rd / Brake 3rd	LNER	45401/2	Teak finish with White roof (D252). Export only	**£750-1,000**	❏
D3	1949-53	Corridor Coach	1st/3rd	LMS	4183	Maroon body, Silver-Grey or Grey roof (DR363 and 32015)	**£40-60**	❏
			Brake/3rd	LMS	26133	Maroon body, Silver-Grey or Grey roof (32016)	**£40-60**	❏
D11	1953-56	Corridor Coach	1st/3rd	BR (E)	E42759E	Red and Cream body, Grey roof, PWG (32013)	**£20-35**	❏
			Brake/3rd	BR (E)	E45402E	Red and Cream body, Grey roof, PWG (32014)	**£20-35**	❏
D12	1953-56	Corridor Coach	1st/3rd	BR (M)	M4183	Red and Cream body, Grey roof, TRW, (32017)	**£20-25**	❏
			Brake/3rd	BR (M)	M26143	Red and Cream body, Grey roof, TRW, (32018)	**£20-25**	❏
32017	1956-58	Corridor Coach	1st/2nd	BR (M)	M4183	Red and Cream body, Grey roof, TRW, (32017)	**£20-25**	❏
			1st/3rd	BR (M)	M4183	As previous model but Black coach ends (32017)	**£25-35**	❏
32018	1956-58	Corridor Coach	Brake/2nd	BR(LMR)	M26143	Red and Cream body, Grey roof, TRW, (32018)	**£20-25**	❏
			Brake/3rd	BR(LMR)	M26143	As previous model but Black coach ends (32018)	**£25-35**	❏
D13	1954-56	Suburban Coach	1st/3rd	BR		Maroon body, Grey roof, PWG, (32090)	**£20-25**	❏
			Brake/3rd	BR		Maroon body, Grey roof, PWG, (32091)	**£20-25**	❏
32090	1956-57	Suburban Coach	1st/2nd	BR		Maroon body, Grey roof, PWG, (32090)	**£20-25**	❏
			1st/3rd	BR		Maroon body, Grey roof, PWG, (32090)	**£20-25**	❏
32091	1956-57	Suburban Coach	Brake/2nd	BR		Maroon body, Grey roof, PWG, (32091)	**£20-25**	❏
			Brake/3rd	BR		Maroon body, Grey roof, PWG, (32091)	**£20-25**	❏
D14	1956-57	Suburban Coach	1st/3rd	BR		Maroon body, Grey roof, TRW, (32092) with windows at one end (as brake van)	**£20-25**	❏
			Brake/3rd	BR		Maroon body, Grey roof, TRW, (32093)	**£20-25**	❏
32092	1956-58	Suburban Coach	1st/2nd	BR		Maroon body, Grey roof, TRW, (32092)	**£20-25**	❏
32093	1956-58	Suburban Coach	Brake/2nd	BR		Maroon body, Grey roof, TRW, (32093)	**£20-25**	❏
D21	1957-58	Corridor Coach	1st/2nd	BR (W)	W15862	Brown/Cream body, Grey roof, TRW, (32094)	**£20-25**	❏
			Brake/2nd	BR (W)	W34481	Brown/Cream body, Grey roof, TRW, (32095)	**£20-25**	❏
32094	1957-58	Corridor Coach	1st/2nd	BR (W)	W15862	Brown/Cream body, Grey roof, TRW, (32094)	**£20-25**	❏
32095	1957-58	Corridor Coach	Brake/2nd	BR (W)	W34481	Brown/Cream body, Grey roof, TRW, (32095)	**£20-25**	❏
D22	1957-58	Corridor Coach	1st/2nd	BR (M)	M4193	Maroon body, Grey roof, TRW, (32023)	**£30-40**	❏
			Brake/2nd	BR (M)	M26143	Maroon body, Grey roof, TRW, (32023)	**£25-35**	❏
32022	1957-58	Corridor Coach	1st/2nd	BR (M)	M4193	Maroon body, Grey roof, TRW, (32022)	**£20-25**	❏
32023	1957-58	Corridor Coach	Brake/2nd	BR (M)	M26143	Maroon body, Grey roof, TRW, (32023)	**£20-25**	❏

Passenger Coaches (post-war Two-Rail)

Ref.	Year(s)	Model name	Class	Railway	Number	Livery and Box reference	Market Price Range	
4005	1959-61	Corridor Coach	1st/3rd	BR (M)	M4183	Red and Cream body, Grey roof, TRW, (36005)	**£35-45**	❏
4006	1959-61	Corridor Coach	Brake/2nd	BR (M)	M26133	Red and Cream body, Grey roof, TRW, (36006)	**£30-40**	❏
4009	1959-61	Corridor Coach	1st/2nd	BR (W)	W15862	Brown and Cream body, Grey roof, TRW, (36009)	**£30-40**	❏
4010	1959-61	Corridor Coach	Brake/2nd	BR (W)	W34481	Brown and Cream body, Grey roof, TRW, (36010)	**£25-35**	❏
4013	1959-62	Corridor Coach	1st/2nd	BR (M)	M4193	Maroon body, Grey roof, TRW, (36013)	**£30-40**	❏
4014	1959-61	Corridor Coach	Brake/2nd	BR (M)	M26143	Maroon body, Grey roof, TRW, (36014)	**£25-35**	❏
4021	1959-64	Suburban Coach	1st/2nd	BR		Maroon body, Grey roof, TRW, (36021)	**£20-25**	❏
4022	1959-64	Suburban Coach	Brake/2nd	BR		Maroon body, Grey roof, TRW, (36022)	**£20-25**	❏
4025	1959-64	Suburban Coach	1st/2nd	BR (SR)	S41060	Green body, Grey roof, TRW, (36025)	**£35-50**	❏
4026	1959-64	Suburban Coach	Brake/2nd	BR (SR)	S43374	Green body, Grey roof, TRW, (36026)	**£30-40**	❏

Ref.	Year(s)	Model name	Class, Export No.	Railway	Number	Livery and Box reference	Market Price Range

Passenger Coaches (with 'Super Detail' features)

All have transparent windows.

Ref.	Year(s)	Model name	Railway	Number	Livery and Box reference	MPR
4035	1961-64	Pullman Car - First Class (4185)	BR	ARIES	Brown and Cream body, Grey roof (36035)	**£40-50** ❏
4036	1961-64	Pullman Car - Second Class (4186)	BR	Car 74	Brown and Cream body, Grey roof (36036)	**£40-50** ❏
4037	1961-64	Pullman Car - Brake/2nd (4187)	BR	Car 79	Brown and Cream body, Grey roof (36037)	**£40-50** ❏
4050	1960-64	Corridor Coach - 1st/2nd (4200)	BR (W)	W15870	Brown and Cream body, plastic roof (36050)	**£20-30** ❏
4051	1960-64	Corridor Coach - Brake/2nd (4201)	BR (W)	W34290	Brown and Cream body, plastic roof (36051)	**£20-30** ❏
4052	1961-64	Corridor Coach - 1st/2nd (4202)	BR (E)	E15770	Maroon body, Grey roof, (36052)	**£20-30** ❏
4053	1961-64	Corridor Coach - Brake/2nd (4203)	BR (E)	E35173	Maroon body, Grey roof, (36053)	**£20-30** ❏
4054	1962-64	Corridor Coach - 1st/2nd (4204)	BR (SR)	S15573	Green body, Grey roof	**£35-45** ❏
4055	1962-64	Corridor Coach - Brake/2nd (4205)	BR (SR)	S35001	Green body, Grey roof	**£35-45** ❏
4060	1961-64	Open Corridor Coach - 1st (4210)	BR (W)	W3085	Brown and Cream body, Grey roof, (36060)	**£25-30** ❏
4061	1961-64	Open Corridor Coach - 2nd (4211)	BR (W)	W3984	Brown and Cream body, Grey roof, (36061)	**£25-30** ❏
4062	1961-64	Open Corridor Coach - 1st (4212)	BR (M)	M3002	Maroon body, Grey plastic roof, (36062)	**£25-35** ❏
4063	1961-64	Open Corridor Coach - 2nd (4213)	BR (M)	M3716	Maroon body, Grey plastic roof, (36063)	**£25-35** ❏
4075	1961-64	Passenger Brake Van (4225)	BR (E)	E81312	Maroon body, Grey roof, (36075)	**£20-30** ❏
4076	1963-64	Six-wheel Passenger Brake	BR (M)	M32958	Maroon body, Grey roof, (34076)	**£100-150** ❏
4081	1962-64	Suburban Coach - 1st/2nd (4231)	BR (SR)	S46291	Green body, Grey roof, (36081)	**£50-70** ❏
4082	1962-64	Suburban Coach - Brake/2nd (4232)	BR (SR)	543381	Green body, Grey roof, (36082)	**£50-70** ❏
		variation:	BR (SR)	S43381	with correct coach number (rare), (36082)	**£110-130** ❏
4083	1962-64	Suburban Coach - 1st/2nd (4233)	BR (M)	M41012	Maroon body, Grey roof, (36083)	**£50-70** ❏
4084	1962-64	Suburban Coach - Brake/2nd (4234)	BR (M)	M43277	Maroon body, Grey roof, (36084)	**£45-60** ❏
4150	1962-64	Electric Driving Trailer Coach (4250)	BR (SR)	S77511	Green, Yellow band on drive end, Black rear panel	**£110-130** ❏
		variation:	BR (SR)	S77511	As previous model but Green inner panel on rear	**£130-150** ❏

Note: The Export issues packed in boxes displaying the special Export Numbers are rare – expect to pay an additional **£20** per issue.

Restaurant Cars

All have transparent windows.

Ref.	Year(s)	Model name	Railway	Number	Livery and Box reference	MPR
D20	1957 only	Restaurant Car	BR (W)	W9562	Brown and Cream body, Grey roof, (32097)	**£25-35** ❏
32096	1957-58	Restaurant Car	BR (W)	W9572	Brown and Cream body, Grey roof, (32096)	**£25-35** ❏
32097	1957-58	Restaurant Car	BR (W)	W9562	Red and Cream body, Grey roof, (32097)	**£25-35** ❏
4047	1959-64	Restaurant Car	BR (W)	W9572	Brown and Cream body, Grey roof, (36047)	**£30-40** ❏
4048	1959-64	Restaurant Car	BR(LMR)	W9562	Red and Cream body, Grey roof, (36048)	**£30-40** ❏
4049	1959-61	Restaurant Car	BR (M)	W9566W	Maroon body, Grey roof, Red window frames	**£30-40** ❏
4049	1961-64	Restaurant Car	BR (M)	W9566W	As previous model but with White window frames	**£30-40** ❏

Restaurant Cars and Sleeping Car ('Super Detail')

All have transparent windows.

Ref.	Year(s)	Model name	Railway	Number	Livery and Box reference	MPR
4070	1963-64	Restaurant Car	BR (W)	W1910	Brown and Cream body, Grey roof, (34070)	**£90-120** ❏
4071	1963-64	Restaurant Car	BR (E)	E1939	Maroon body, Grey roof, (34071)	**£120-180** ❏
4078	1961-64	Sleeping Car (4228)	BR (W)	W2402	Maroon body, Grey roof, (36078)	**£35-60** ❏

Abbreviations used in these listings:

MPR = Market Price Range   NGPP = No grading possible at present   SD = 'Super Detail'

HS = Horseshoe magnet motor   HI = Half inch block magnet motor   RF = Ringfield motor

Railway Companies, Pre-Nationalisation:
GWR = Great Western Railway   LMS = London, Midland and Scottish Railway
LNER = London and North Eastern Railway   SR = Southern Railway

Post-Nationalisation (1948) British Railways:
WR = Western Region   MR = Midland Region   ER = Eastern Region   SR = Southern Region

Ref.	Year(s)	Model name	Livery, details	Market Price Range

Pre-war, Three-Rail

Model identification: All have White lettering and Black chassis unless shown differently.
See 'Technical Notes' for types of wheels and couplings.

'Great Western Railway' - 'G. W.' issues

D1	1938-40	Open Goods Wagon	Grey body	£25-35 ❑
D1	1938-40	Goods Van	Grey body, White roof, 'RETURN TO G. W. R.'	£55-75 ❑
D1	1938-40	Goods Brake Van	Grey body, White roof, 'PARK ROYAL' logo	£45-65 ❑
D1	1938-40	Coal Wagon	Grey body	£25-35 ❑
D1	1938-40	Cattle Truck	Grey body, White roof	£25-35 ❑

'London, Midland & Scottish' - 'L. M. S.' issues

D1	1938-40	Open Goods Wagon	Bauxite Brown body	£25-35 ❑
D1	1938-40	Goods Van	Bauxite Brown body, Silver-Grey roof	£25-35 ❑
D1	1938-40	Goods Brake Van	Bauxite Brown body, Silver-Grey roof	£25-35 ❑
D1	1938-40	Coal Wagon	Bauxite Brown body	£25-35 ❑
D1	1938-40	'MEAT' Van	Bauxite Brown body, Silver Grey roof	£25-35 ❑
D1	1938-40	Cattle Truck	Bauxite Brown body	£45-65 ❑
D2	1938-40	High-Sided Coal Wagon	Bauxite Brown body	£25-35 ❑

'London & North Eastern Railway' - 'N. E.' issues

D1	1938-40	Open Goods Wagon	Grey body	£25-35 ❑
D1	1938-40	Goods Van	Grey body, White roof	£25-35 ❑
D1	1938-40	Goods Brake Van	Brown body, White roof	£25-35 ❑
D1	1938-40	Coal Wagon	Grey body	£25-35 ❑
D1	1938-40	'FISH' Van	Light Brown body, White roof	£25-35 ❑
D1	1938-40	High Capacity Wagon	Brown body, White 'BRICK' and 'RETURN TO FLETTON' logos, Black or Brown chassis	£60-75 ❑
D1	1938-40	Horse Box	Teak body, White roof	£25-35 ❑
D2	1938-40	High-Sided Wagon	Seven-plank Grey body	£40-50 ❑
D2	1938-40	High-Sided Coal Wagon	Seven-plank Grey body	£40-50 ❑

'Southern Railway' - 'S. R.' issues

D1	1938-40	Open Goods Wagon	Chocolate Brown body	£40-50 ❑
D1	1938-40	Goods Van	Chocolate Brown body, White roof	£75-85 ❑
D1	1938-40	Goods Brake Van	Chocolate Brown body, White roof	£125-150 ❑
D1	1938-40	Coal Wagon	Chocolate Brown body	£40-50 ❑

Tank Wagons

D1	1938-40	'ROYAL DAYLIGHT'	Red tank, Gold logo	£80-100 ❑
D1	1938-40	'POWER ETHYL'	Green tank, White and Red logo and 'hand' motif	£80-100 ❑
D1	1938-40	'ESSO'	Buff tank with Red stripe, Dark Blue logo with Red shadow	£80-100 ❑

Post-war Pre-Nationalisation Liveries, Three-Rail

Model identification: All have White lettering and Black chassis unless shown differently.
See 'Technical Notes' for types of wheels and couplings

'Great Western Railway' - 'G W ' issues

D1	1948-53	Open Goods Wagon	Grey body	£30-40 ❑
D1	1948-53	Goods Van	Grey body, White roof, 'RETURN TO G. W. R.'	£75-100 ❑
D1	1948-53	Goods Brake Van	Grey-Green body, White roof, 'PARK ROYAL' logo	£70-90 ❑
D1	1948-53	Coal Wagon	Grey body	£20-30 ❑
D1	1948-53	Cattle Truck	Grey-Green body, White roof with two small windows	£20-30 ❑
D1	1948-53	Cattle Truck	Grey-Green body, White roof with one long window	£40-60 ❑

Post-war Pre-Nationalisation Liveries, Three-Rail, continued

'London, Midland & Scottish' - 'L M S ' issues
D1	1948-53	Open Goods Wagon	Bauxite Brown body	£30-40	❏
D1	1948-53	Goods Van	Bauxite Brown body, Silver-Grey or Grey roof	£15-20	❏
D1	1948-53	Goods Brake Van	Bauxite Brown body, Silver-Grey or Grey roof	£15-20	❏
D1	1948-53	Coal Wagon	Bauxite Brown body	£10-15	❏
D1	1948-53	Cattle Truck	Bauxite Brown body, Cream interior, 2 small windows, Silver-Grey roof	£100-130	❏
D1	1948-53	'MEAT' Van	Bauxite Brown body, Silver-Grey or Grey roof	£10-15	❏
D1	1948-53	High-sided Coal Wagon	Bauxite Brown body	£10-15	❏
D2	1948-53	High-sided Wagon	Bauxite Brown body	£10-15	❏

'London & North Eastern Railway' - 'N E ' issues
D1	1948-53	Open Goods Wagon	Grey-Green or Grey body	£15-20	❏
D1	1948-53	Goods Van	Brown body, White roof	£15-20	❏
D1	1948-53	Goods Brake Van	Brown body, White roof	£15-20	❏
D1	1948-53	Coal Wagon	Grey-Green or Grey body	£15-20	❏
D1	1948-53	'FISH' Van	Brown body, White roof	£15-20	❏
D1	1948-53	High Capacity Wagon	Brown body with White 'BRICK' and 'RETURN TO FLETTON' logos	£15-20	❏
D1	1948-53	Horse Box	Teak body, White roof	£15-20	❏
D2	1948-53	High-sided Coal Wagon	Seven-plank Grey-Green body	£80-120	❏
			As previous model but with seven-plank Grey body	£40-60	❏

'Southern Railway' - 'S R ' issues
D1	1948-53	Five Plank Open Goods Wagon	Chocolate Brown body	£80-100	❏
D1	1948-53	Goods Van	Chocolate Brown body, White roof	£100-150	❏
D1	1948-53	Goods Brake Van	Chocolate Brown body, one window on end	£100-150	❏
D1	1948-53	Goods Brake Van	Chocolate Brown body, window each side of end door	£80-100	❏
D1	1948-53	Coal Wagon	Chocolate Brown body	£80-100	❏
D1	1948-53	'MEAT' Van	Buff body, Silver-Grey roof	£100-150	❏
D1	1948-53	'MEAT' Van	Buff body, White roof	£60-80	❏

Tank Wagons
D1	1948-53	'ROYAL DAYLIGHT'	Red tank, Gold logo, (no 'ESSO' or 'PARAFFIN' logos on tank sides)	£80-100	❏
D1	1948-53	'POWER PETROL'	Green tank, Silver logo, Red 'ETHYL' logos, White 'hand' design	£100-150	❏
D1	1948-53	'ESSO'	Buff tank with Red stripe, Dark Blue logo with Red shadow	£140-180	❏

Post-Nationalisation 'British Rail' issues, Three-Rail

Model identification: All have White lettering and Black chassis unless shown differently See 'Technical Notes' for types of wheels and couplings Models have a diecast chassis and a tinplate body .

D1/32020	1954-58	Cattle Truck	Brown body, Grey roof, metal wheels	£10-15	❏
32021	1958	Cattle Wagon	Brown body, Grey roof, spoked plastic wheels, plastic body	£10-15	❏
D1/32025/6	1954-58	Coal Wagon	Grey body, metal or spoked plastic wheels	£10-15	❏
D1/32035	1954-58	Fish Van	Brown body, Grey roof	£10-15	❏
D1/32040	1954-58	Goods Van	Brown body, Grey roof	£10-15	❏
D1/32044/5	1954-58	Goods Brake Van	All Grey body, Grey roof	£10-15	❏
32046	1954-58	Goods Brake Van	Brown body, Grey roof	£10-15	❏
D1/32047	1954-58	Goods Brake Van	All Grey body, 'PARK ROYAL' logo	£10-15	❏
32047	1954-58	Goods Brake Van	All Grey body, 'SOUTHALL' logo	£10-15	❏
D1/32049	1954-58	Caboose	Black body, 'CANADIAN PACIFIC RAILWAY' logo	£90-140	❏
D1/32050	1954-58	High Capacity Wagon	Brown body, 'BRICK - EMPTY TO FLETTON'	£10-15	❏
D1/32051	1954-58	30 ton Wagon	'BOGIE BOLSTER', Grey	£10-15	❏
D1/32058/ /32041	1954-58	Ventilated Van	Brown body, White or Grey roof	£10-15	❏
D1/32060	1954-58	Horse Box	Red body, Grey roof	£10-15	❏
D1/32065	1954-58	Meat Van	White body, Grey roof	£10-15	❏

Vans and Wagons

D1/32067	1958	Bulk Grain Wagon	Grey body	£10-15 ❏
D1/32068	1958	Salt Wagon	Yellow body, Grey roof, Red 'SAXA SALT' logo, plastic body	£10-15 ❏
D1/32069	1958	'U.G. B.' Sand Wagon	Yellow body, Black 'United Glass Bottle Co.' logo, plastic body	£10-15 ❏
32070	1953-55	Tank Wagon	Red tank, Red/White/Blue 'ESSO', Gold 'ROYAL DAYLIGHT', Black 'PARAFFIN' logos	£20-25 ❏
D1/32076	1956-58	'TUBE' Wagon	Brown body	£10-15 ❏
D1/32080	1954-56	Tank Wagon	Green tank with Gold/Yellow 'POWER PETROL' logo	£20-25 ❏
D1/32081	1953-58	Tank Wagon	Silver-Grey tank, Red/White/Blue 'ESSO' logo	£15-20 ❏
D1/32082	1955-58	Tank Wagon	Yellow tank, Red 'SHELL LUBRICATING OIL' logo	£20-25 ❏
D1/32083	1955-57	Tank Wagon	Red tank, White 'VACUUM OIL COMPANY' logo plus 'MOBILGAS' and 'MOBILOIL' motifs	£25-35 ❏
D1/32084	1956-57	'MOBIL' Tank Wagon	Red tank, White 'MOBIL OIL COMPANY LTD' logo plus 'MOBILOIL' and 'MOBILGAS' motifs	£25-35 ❏
	1957-58		Red tank, Dark Blue 'MOBIL' logo on White background	£25-35 ❏
D1/32086	1953-59	Low sided Wagon	'LIVERPOOL CABLES'	£10-15 ❏
D1/32098	1957-59	TPO Mail Van	Maroon body, Grey roof, in box with catcher	£20-30 ❏
D2/32030	1954-58	High-sided Coal Wagon	Grey body	£10-15 ❏
D2/32052	1954-58	Double Bolster Wagon	Grey body	£10-15 ❏
D2/32055	1954-58	High-sided Coal Wagon	Grey body	£10-15 ❏
D2/32056	1954-58	Mineral Wagon	Grey body	£10-15 ❏
	1953	New version	With labels at the wrong end	£25-40 ❏

THREE RAIL - TWO RAIL TRANSITION 1958, Box numbering identification.
The box numbers changed from their 3-rail reference numbers (e.g., 32048 WR) to their new 2-rail numbers, (32048–WR became 4312–WR, etc.). The early models continued to be issued in blue boxes with white stripes and also displayed an 'SD6' number to denote that they were 'Super Detail' models. The 'SD6' reference only appeared on the blue/white box. Eventually the 'SD6' was dropped and the red box (with white lines) was introduced.

'British Rail' issues, Two-Rail

4300	1961-64	Blue Spot Fish Van	White or Cream body, Grey roof, Blue spot, 'INSUL FISH' logo (SD)	£25-30 ❏
4301	1962-64	Banana Van	Brown body, Grey roof with Yellow identification spot (SD)	£20-25 ❏
4305	1960-64	Passenger Fruit Van	Maroon body, Black or Grey roof, (SD)	£35-45 ❏
4310	1958-61	Goods Brake Van	Grey body and roof, (M730012), (SD)	£10-15 ❏
	1962-64		Brown body, Grey roof, (M730973), (SD)	£35-40 ❏
4311	1959-64	Goods Brake Van	Brown body, 'B.R.', (SD)	£10-15 ❏
4312	1959-64	Goods Brake Van	Grey body, 'W.R.', (SD)	£10-15 ❏
4313	1962-64	Gunpowder Van	Brown body, Grey roof, (SD)	£15-20 ❏
4315	1960-64	'B.R.' Horse Box	Maroon body, Grey roof, Light Brown or Buff plastic horse, (SD)	£75-100 ❏
4316	1960-64	'S.R.' Horse Box	Green body, Grey roof, Light Brown or Buff plastic horse, (SD)	£100-125 ❏
4318	1961-62	Packing Van for Breakdown Train	Red body, Grey roof, (SD), with closed brake gear	£25-35 ❏
	1962-64		With open brake gear	£40-50 ❏
4320	1959-64	Refrigerator Van	White or Cream body, Grey roof, (SD)	£10-15 ❏
4323	1961-64	'S.R.' Utility Van	Green body, Grey roof, (SD)	£35-45 ❏
4325	1959-64	12 ton Ventilated Van	Brown body, White roof, (SD)	£7-9 ❏
4401	1959-64	T. P. O. Mail Van	Maroon body, Grey roof, in box with catcher	£20-30 ❏
4605	1959-64	40 ton Bogie Well Wagon	Grey body with White 'WELTROL' logo, (SD)	£10-15 ❏
4610	1959-64	'BOGIE BOLSTER' Wagon	Grey body, (SD)	£10-15 ❏
4615	1959-64	Double Bolster Wagon	with Timber Load, Grey body, Black base	£10-15 ❏
4620	1959-61	Breakdown Crane Wagon	Red matt finish, White on Black 'No 133'	£40-50 ❏
	1961-64		Red gloss finish, White on Black 'No 133', Yellow picture box	£200-300 ❏
4625	1959-64	20 ton Wagon	'BULK GRAIN', Grey body, (SD)	£15-20 ❏
4626	1960-64	Bulk Cement Wagon	'PRESFLO', Bauxite Brown body, (SD)	£10-15 ❏
4627	1960-64	'I.C.I.' 20 ton Salt Wagon	'BULK SALT', all-Blue body, (SD)	£10-15 ❏
4630	1958-64	8 ton Cattle Wagon	Brown body, Grey roof, (SD)	£10-15 ❏
4635	1958-64	13 ton Coal Wagon	Grey body, with coal load, (SD)	£15-20 ❏
4640	1959-64	12 ton Steel Type Goods Wagon	Brown body, (SD)	£10-15 ❏
4644	1963-64	21 ton Hopper Wagon	Grey body, (SD)	£75-100 ❏
4645	1961-64	Low-sided Wagon	Brown body, (SD)	£10-15 ❏

4646	1961-64	Low-sided Wagon	Grey body, two Yellow plastic cable drums, 'ALUMINUM WIRE AND CABLE Co'	£35-45	❏
4646	1959-62	Low-sided Wagon	Grey, two Black/Beige wooden cable drums, 'LIVERPOOL CABLES'	£9-12	❏
4647	1959-64	Low-sided Wagon	Brown body, Red/Grey container, 'BRITISH RAILWAYS', 'FURNITURE'	£9-12	❏
4648	1959-64	Low-sided Wagon	Brown body with White/Grey container, 'BRITISH RAILWAYS', 'INSUL-MEAT'	£9-12	❏
4649	1961-64	Low-sided Wagon	Brown body with Hornby Dublo tractor (Blue)	£40-55	❏
4652	1959-64	Machine Wagon	'LOWMAC', Brown body, (SD)	£10-15	❏
4654	1964	'RAIL CLEANING WAGON'	White logo on Black wagon plus six cleaning plugs, (SD), (900 only)	£300-500	❏
4655	1959	Mineral Wagon	Grey metal body with plastic disc type wheels, (SD)	£60-75	❏
	1959-62		Same model but with Grey plastic body, plastic wheels, closed brake gear	£10-15	❏
	1962-64		With open brake gear	£18-23	❏
4656	1962-64	16 ton Mineral Wagon	Brown plastic body, plastic wheels	£30-45	❏
4657	1962-64	United Dairies Milk Tank	Six-wheeled 'Super Detail' vehicle:		
			Off-White tank, Yellow 'U.D.' logo, High and Low supports	£25-55	❏
			Off-White tank, Yellow 'U.D.' logo, plus High supports	£25-35	❏
			Off-White tank, Yellow 'U.D.' logo, plus Low supports	£25-35	❏
			White tank, Yellow 'U.D.' logo, plus High and Low supports	£25-35	❏
			Cream tank, Yellow 'U.D.' logo, plus High supports	£35-45	❏
			Cream tank with High and Low supports	£35-45	❏
4658	1962-64	'PRESTWIN' Silo Wagon	Brown body, (SD)	£10-15	❏
4660	1962-64	'U.G.B.' Sand Wagon	Yellow body, Black 'United Glass Limited' logo, (SD)	£35-45	❏
	1959-62	Private Owners variation	Yellow body, Black 'United Glass Manufacturing Company Ltd' logo	£12-15	❏
	1961-62		As Private Owners variation but with open brake gear	£15-25	❏
4665	1959-62	'SAXA SALT' Wagon	Yellow body, Grey roof, Red logo, (SD), with closed brake gear	£10-15	❏
	1962-64		With open brake gear	£20-25	❏
4670	1959-64	13 ton Standard Wagon	Grey body, (SD)	£10-15	❏
4675	1959-64	Tank Wagon	White Chlorine tank, Yellow top, Black I.C.I. motif and star, (SD)	£10-15	❏
4676	1959-62	Tank Wagon	Silver-Grey tank with two Red/White/Blue 'ESSO' motifs plus Black star, closed brake gear, (SD)	£10-15	❏
	1962-64		With open brake gear	£25-35	❏
4677	1959-62	Tank Wagon	Red tank with Dark Blue 'MOBIL' logo on White background, closed brake gear, (SD)	£15-20	❏
	1962-64		With open brake gear	£30-35	❏
4678	1959-62	Tank Wagon	Yellow tank with Red 'SHELL LUBRICATING OIL' logo, closed brake gear, (SD)	£15-20	❏
	1962-64		With open brake gear	£20-30	❏
4679	1959-64	Tank Wagon	Silver-Grey tank with Black 'TRAFFIC SERVICES Ltd' logo, two Black stars, (SD)	£20-30	❏
4680	1959-62	Tank Wagon	Black tank with Red 'ESSO' motif plus White 'ESSO PETROLEUM COMPANY LTD' logo and 2 Black stars, closed brake gear, (SD)	£20-30	❏
	1962-64		With open brake gear	£35-50	❏
4685	1959-64	Tank Wagon	Dark Blue 'I.C.I.' Caustic Liquor Bogie Wagon, (SD)	£65-85	❏
	variation:		As previous model but with Diamond bogies	£200-300	❏
4690	1959-60	Tube Wagon	Brown body with spoked wheels (SD6), but a red box was not issued with 4690 on it	£10-15	❏

Notes

'Super Detail' – Models with the abbreviation 'SD' have greatly enhanced 'SUPER DETAIL' features.

Black Stars – Two black stars on a wagon indicates that the vehicle can travel by the fastest freight train.

Silver Tank – A Tank Wagon painted silver indicates that it is carrying an inflammable liquid.

Screwed couplings indicate model is an Export issue and worth more (normal couplings rivetted). Exceptions to this rule are 4625 20-ton 'BULK GRAIN' and 4627 'I.C.I.' Salt Wagon.

Brake Gear – Some wagons will be found with open brake gear, but this does not greatly affect their value and their availability is equal to those with closed brake gear.

Hornby Dublo Train Sets

Ref.	Year(s)	Set name	Contents	Market Price Range

Pre-war issues

Note: The Market Price Range for sets marked '*' reflects the great variation in market prices for the individual locomotives (see the Locomotives listing).

DP1.......1938-40.....Clockwork Passenger Train Set, 'LNER'.....Contains DL1 'Sir Nigel Gresley' loco and tender plus two Articulated Coaches, 8 curved and 2 straight rails............**£1,000-1,250** ❑

DG7......1938-40.....Clockwork Tank Goods Train Sets, 'GWR', 'LMS', 'LNER', 'SR'....................Contains DL7 Tank loco plus Open Wagon, Goods Van and Goods Brake Van.........................**£300-900*** ❑

EDP1 ....1938-40.....Electric Passenger Train Set, 'LNER' ....Contains EDL1 'Sir Nigel Gresley' loco and tender plus two Articulated Coaches, 8 curved and 2 straight rails ....**£900-1,250** ❑

EDG7 ...1938-40.....Electric Tank Goods Train Sets, 'GWR', 'LMS' ....Contains EDL7 loco plus Open Wagon, Goods Wagon and Goods Brake Wagon.........................**£300-900*** ❑

DG7......1938-40.....Electric Tank Goods Train Set, 'SR' ....D104, EDL7 Electric 'SR' Locomotive in first issue box without a printed label on interior cardboard divider. Coal Wagon with load, plus two other trucks. Instructions dated 2/938/25 ....**£700-900** ❑

EDG7 ...1939-40.....Electric Tank Goods Train Set, 'NE' ....Contains EDL7 'NE' loco in second issue box with interior printed label plus three Rolling Stock ....**£700-900** ❑

EDGA7 ....Electric Tank Goods Train Set, 'GWR' ....Comprising Tank Locomotive 6699, Open Wagon, Goods Van, Brake Van and No. 1A Controller for use with an accumulator....**£500-750** ❑

Post-war issues (Pre-Nationalisation Liveries)

EDP1 ....1948..........Electric Passenger Train Set, 'LNER' ....First issue 1948. Locomotive with horseshoe magnet, split pin and washer to pony truck. Tender with plated bogies, First/Third and Brake/Third Corridor Coaches, oil, spanner, controller, four green wire coils, instructions dated 5.48, cover strap and keeps............**£600-800** ❑

EDP1 ....1948-53.....Electric Passenger Train Set, 'LNER' ....Contains EDL1 'Sir Nigel Gresley' loco and tender plus D1 1st/3rd and Brake/3rd Coaches.................................**£150-200** ❑

EDP2 ....1948-53.....Passenger Set, 'LMS' ....Contains EDL2 'Duchess of Atholl' loco and tender plus D3 'LMS' Coaches '3rd' and 'Brake 3rd' ....**£120-160** ❑

EDP2 ....1948-53.....Passenger Set, 'CANADIAN PACIFIC' ......Contains EDL2 loco (1215) and tender plus D3 'LMS' Coaches '3rd' and 'Brake 3rd'...**£650-850** ❑

EDG3 ...1948-53.....Freight Train Set, 'CANADIAN PACIFIC RAILWAY' ....Contains EDL2 loco and tender plus 32049 'CP' Caboose and D1 Bogie Bolster Wagon ....**£650-850** ❑

EDG7 ...1948-53.....Tank Goods Train Sets, 'LMS', 'LNER' or 'SOUTHERN' ....Contains EDL7 0-6-2 loco plus D1 Goods Van, D1 Open Wagon and D1 Goods Brake Wagon..........................**£300-900*** ❑

EDG7 ...1948-53.....Tank Goods Train Sets 'GWR'....................Locomotive EDL7 with gold label, small windows and cabside number. Instructions dated 5.48, guarantee 11.48. Mid-blue box with two children on label..**£300-500** ❑

EDL7 ....1947..........Tank Goods Train Set, 'LNER' ....First post-war issue. Black livery, horseshoe magnet, elongated pick-ups, gold label, large windows, all stock in early colours, EPW, instructions dated 9.47. Mid-blue box with 'ROYAL SCOT' label and eight keeps. Very few issued in the autumn of 1947 as most production was exported..**£700-900** ❑

EDL7 ....1948..........Tank Goods Train Set, 'LNER' ....Second post-war issue. Same as previous model but box has picture label of two small boys, instructions dated 5.48, guarantee dated 2.48 ....**£500-600** ❑

EDL7 ....1948..........Tank Goods Train Set, 'SR' ....First post-war issue. Horseshoe magnet, elongated pick-ups, gold label, large windows, disc wheels, all stock EPW, instructions dated 9.47. Mid-blue box with 'ROYAL SCOT' label................**£1,000-1,500** ❑

EDL7 ....1948..........Passenger Train Set, 'LMS' 'Duchess of Atholl' ....First post-war issue. Horseshoe magnet, elongated pick-ups, fine buffer heads, thin cabside numbers, tender base tabbed not rivetted. Coaches with pre-war matt or semi-matt sides, silver roof, EPW. Instructions dated 9.47, guarantee 2.48. Mid-blue box, 8 keeps..**£300-400** ❑

Post-Nationalisation 'British Railways' issues (Three-Rail)

EDP10 ..1954-58.....Passenger Train Set 'BR'............................EDL17 0-6-2 Tank loco (69567) and
D14 Suburban Coaches '1st/3rd' and 'Brake/3rd'........................**£100-125** ❏

EDP11 ..1954-58.....Passenger Train Set 'BR'............................EDL11 'Silver King' loco and tender plus
D11 Coaches '1st/2nd' and 'Brake/2nd'......................................**£100-125** ❏

EDP12   1954-58   Passenger Train Set 'BR'............................EDL12 'Duchess of Montrose' (gloss finish) with
D11 Coaches '1st/2nd' and 'Brake/2nd'....................................**£120-140** ❏
Same set but with matt finish locomotive ....**£90-105** ❏

EDP13 ..1954-58.....Tank Passenger Set 'BR'............................EDL18 2-6-4 Tank loco (no. 80054) plus
D13 Suburban Coaches '1st/3rd' and 'Brake/3rd'........................**£100-125** ❏

EDP14 ..1954-58.....Passenger Train Set 'BR'............................EDL18 2-6-4 Tank loco (no. 80054) plus
D14 Suburban Coaches '1st/2nd' and two 'Brake/3rd'................**£120-140** ❏

EDP15 ..1954-58.....Passenger Train Set 'BR'............................Contains EDP11 'Silver King' loco and tender plus
D12 Coaches '1st/3rd' and 'Brake/3rd'....................................**£125-150** ❏
EDP15 ..1954-58.....Passenger Train Set 'BR'............................As previous set but locomotive has matt finish............................**£200-250** ❏

EDG16 .1954-58.....Tank Goods Set 'BR'.................................EDL17 0-6-2 Tank loco (no. 69567) plus
D1 issues: 2 Open Wagons and a Goods Brake Van ....**£100-125** ❏

EDG17 .1954-58.....Tank Goods Set 'BR'.................................EDL17 0-6-2 Tank loco (no. 69567) plus D1 issues: Meat Van,
Open Wagon, 'MOBIL' Tank Wagon, Goods Brake Van ....**£100-125** ❏

EDG18 .1954-58.....Tank Goods Set 'BR'.................................EDL18 2-6-4 Tank loco (no. 80054) plus D1 issues: High
Capacity Wagon, Bogie Bolster Wagon, Goods Brake Van...........**£100-125** ❏

EDG19 .1954-58.....Tank Goods Set 'BR'.................................EDL18 2-6-4 Tank loco (no. 80054) plus D1 issues:
Ventilated Van, 'MOBIL' Tank Wagon, Double Bolster Wagon,
Tube Wagon, Goods Brake Van ....**£130-150** ❏

EDP20 ..1954-58.....'BRISTOLIAN' Passenger Train Set...........Contains LT 20 'Bristol Castle' loco and tender plus
D21 Coaches '1st/2nd' and 'Brake/2nd'......................................**£160-180** ❏

EDP22 ..1954-58.....Passenger Train Set 'BR'............................Contains EDL12 'Duchess of Montrose' loco and tender plus
D22 Coaches '1st/2nd' and 'Brake/2nd'......................................**£100-125** ❏

G 16......1959..........Tank Goods Set 'BR'.................................0-6-2 locomotive plus 3 plastic wagons, 7 keeps ....**£125-175** ❏

G 19......1959..........Tank Goods Set 'BR'.................................2-6-4 locomotive No. 80054, tinplate 'MOBIL' Tank Wagon,
die-cast Double Bolster Wagon and Super Detail plastic stock
W.R. Brake Van, 8-ton Cattle Wagon and steel-type Goods
Wagon, metal couplings throughout, instructions dated 2.59.......**£350-450** ❏

G 25......1954-58.....Freight Train Set 'BR' ....Contains: 3225/LT25 Class 8F loco (2-8-0, no. 48158) plus
D1 Refrigerated Van, 'WELTROL' Bogie Wagon, D1 'SHELL'
Tank Wagon, D1 Open Wagon and Goods Brake Van..................**£100-125** ❏

P 15 ......1959..........'FLYING SCOTSMAN' Set ....'Mallard' No. 60022 Loco and tender, D12 Corridor Coaches
1st/3rd and Brake/3rd, instructions dated 2.59 ....**£350-450** ❏

P 20 ......1959..........'The BRISTOLIAN' Passenger Set.............Headboard with label, D21 Coaches with nameboard,
stickers, eight keeps, spanner...**£350-450** ❏

P 22 ......1958..........'ROYAL SCOT' Passenger Set....................EDL12 Loco 'Duchess of Montrose' with named headboard,
D22 Coaches with plastic wheels, 1st/2nd and Brake/2nd, each
with applied nameboard stickers, instructions dated 2.58 ....**£250-350** ❏

Train Sets

'British Railways' issues (Two-Rail)

2001......1959-64.....Tank Goods Set..'Ready to Run'. Black or Blue 0-4-0 Tank loco plus two
open wagons and Goods Brake Van 'BR'.....................................**£75-100** ❏

2004......1959-64.....Diesel Shunter Goods Set...........................'Ready to Run'. Contains Yellow 0-4-0 loco plus two
open wagons and Goods Brake Van 'BR'.....................................**£50-75** ❏

2006......1959-64.....Southern Tank Goods Set ....2207 Green loco (0-6-0, no. 31340), 4660 'UGB' Sand Wagon,
4646 Steel Goods Wagon, 4312 Goods Brake Van 'WR' ....**£100-125** ❏

2007......1959-64.....Southern Tank Passenger Set......................2207 Green loco (0-6-0, no. 31340) plus
4025/6 Suburban Coaches '1st/2nd' and 'Brake/3rd'...................**£100-125** ❏

2008......1959-64.....Tank Goods Set..2206 Black loco (0-6-0, no. 31337), 4660 'UGB' Sand Wagon,
4640 Steel Goods Wagon, 4312 Goods Brake Van.......................**£100-125** ❏

2009......1959-64.....Tank Passenger Set 'SR'..............................2206 Black loco (0-6-0, no. 31337) plus
4025/6 Suburban Coaches '1st/2nd' and 'Brake/2nd' 'SR'..........**£100-125** ❏

2015......1959-64.....'The TALISMAN' Passenger Train Set........'ER', 2211 'Golden Fleece' loco and tender plus
4052/3 Coaches '1st/2nd BR' and 'Brake/2nd BR'.....................**£200-300** ❏

2016......1959-64.....Tank Goods Set..2217 loco (0-6-2, no. 69550) plus 4665 'SAXA SALT' Wagon,
4677 'MOBIL' Tank Wagon, 4646 Cable Wagon (2 drums),
and 4310 Goods Brake Van 'LMR'...**£100-125** ❏

2019......1959-64.....Tank Goods Set..2218 loco (2-6-4, 80033) 4648/9 Low-sided Wagons (Meat
Container and Tractor), Double Bolster Wagon (Timber load),
and Goods Brake Van 'LMR' or 'ER' ....**£100-125** ❏

2020......1959-64.....'TORBAY EXPRESS'
Passenger Train Set 'WR' ....2220 'Denbigh Castle' loco and tender, with
4050/1 Coaches '1st/2nd' and 'Brake/2nd'................................**£200-250** ❏

2021......1959-64.....'RED DRAGON' Passenger Train Set ....2221 'Cardiff Castle' loco and tender plus
D1 or 4050/1 Coaches '1st/2nd' and 'Brake/2nd' ....**£200-250** ❏

2022......1959-64.....'THE CALEDONIAN'
Passenger Train Set ....2226 'City of London' loco and tender plus
D22 Coaches '1st/2nd' and 'Brake/2nd' ....**£200-300** ❏
As previous set but with updated
4052/3 Coaches '1st/2nd' and 'Brake/2nd' ....**£200-300** ❏

2024......1959-64.....Express Goods Set 'LMR'...........................Contains 2224 loco (2-8-0, no. 48073) plus 4320 Refrigerator
Van, 4605 Bogie Well Wagon, 4678 'SHELL' Tank Wagon,
4670 Standard Wagon, 4310 Goods Brake Van 'LMR' ....**£100-125** ❏

2025......1959-64.....Express Goods Set 'LMR'...........................2225 loco (2-8-0, no. 48109) plus rolling stock as set 2024........**£200-250** ❏

2030......1959-64.....Diesel-Electric Goods Set...........................Contains 2230 'Bo-Bo' loco (no8017) plus
4320 Refrigerator Van 'WR', 4625 Grain Wagon,
4325 Ventilated Wagon, 4310 Goods Brake Van 'LMR'............**£100-125** ❏

2033......1959-64.....Diesel-Electric Goods Set...........................2233 'Co-Bo' loco (D5702) plus rolling stock as set 2030..........**£200-250** ❏

2034......1959-64.....'THE ROYAL SCOT'
Passenger Train Set ....2234 Deltic loco 'Crepello' plus 4052/3 Maroon Coaches
'1st/2nd' and 'Brake/2nd' ....**£200-250** ❏

2035......1959-64.....'BOURNEMOUTH BELLE'
'SR' Pullman Set ....'Barnstaple' No. 34005 with head and nameboard in original
Hornby sachet. Pullman cars 4035 'ARIES', 4036 Second and
4037 Brake/Second. Instructions dated 3.61 in yellow and blue
set box labelled 'Luxury Set of the Year' ....**£200-250** ❏

2035......1959-64.....'BOURNEMOUTH BELLE' Set ....As previous set but in blue and white set box with hard
polystyrene interior, instructions dated 3.61 ....**£1,000-1,250** ❏

2045......1959-64.....3300 hp Electric Loco Set ....Illustrated in 1964 catalogue but not issued ....NPP

2049......1959-64.....Breakdown Train Set ....Contains 2217 loco (0-6-2, no. 69550) plus 69550 Crane,
4318 Packing Van and Brake/2nd Suburban Coach ....**£200-300** ❏

2050......1959-64.....Suburban Electric Train Set........................Contains 2250 Drive Coach and Trailer Car 4150. Shown in
Oct. 1962 catalogue as Three Car Unit but only marketed as
a Two Car Unit ....**£200-250** ❏

Train Set enclosures: Operating instructions, track layout plans, 'Tested' label, guarantee,
application form to join the 'Hornby Railway Club'.

Hornby Dublo Accessories

Ref.	Year(s)	Accessory	Details	Market Price Range

Pre-war accessories (1938 - 1940)

Ref.	Year(s)	Accessory	Details	Market Price Range
D1	1938-40	Main Line Station Building	Cream with Red or Green roof, wooden construction	**£200-250** ❑
D1	1938-40	Goods Depot	Cream with Red or Green roof, wooden construction	**£200-250** ❑
D1	1938-40	Engine Shed	Cream with Red or Green roof, wooden construction	**£200-250** ❑
D1	1938-40	Signal Cabin	Cream with Red or Green roof, wooden construction	**£50-75** ❑
D1	1938-	Through Station	With Green roof	**£150-175** ❑
D1	1938-	Island Platform	With Red roof, D403, box MW 1780, 3,250, 8.38	**£150-175** ❑
D1	1938-	Island Platform	With Green roof, D403, box MW 1780, 3,250, 8.38	**£200-250** ❑
D1	1938-40	Tunnel (short)	Cardboard construction	**£40-50** ❑
D1	1938-40	Tunnel (long)	Cardboard construction	**£40-50** ❑
D1	1938-40	Footbridge		**£30-40** ❑
D1	1938-40	Buffers (single)	or D2 Buffers (double)	**£15-25** ❑
D1	1938-40	Buffer Stops	Six in a box	**£35-50** ❑
D1	1938-40	Signal (single)	or D2 Signal (double) or D3 Signal (Junction)	**£7-12** ❑
D1	1938-40	Railway Staff	6 metal figures: Guard, Porter with luggage, Ticket Collector, Shunter, Engine Driver, Station Master	**£75-100** ❑
D2	1938-40	Station Building	Cream with Green roof, wooden construction	**£300-400** ❑
D2	1938-40	Arched roof	Wooden construction, perspex roof	**£200-250** ❑
D2	1938-40	Centre platform	Wooden construction	**£30-40** ❑
D2	1938-40	Side platform	Wooden construction	**£30-40** ❑
D2	1938-40	Centre platform ramps	Wooden construction	**£20-30** ❑
D2	1938-40	Side platform ramps	Wooden construction	**£20-30** ❑
D2	1938-40	Railway Passengers	6 metal figures: 3 males, 3 females	**£75-100** ❑
---	1938-40	Miscellaneous items	include transformers, electrically operated points, switches, etc	**£6-12** ❑
---	1938-40	'Clockwork' Track Points		**£30-40** ❑
---	1938-40	'Clockwork' Track		**£1-2** ❑
---	1938-40	Electric Track		**£1-2** ❑

Post-war accessories (1948 - 1958) Three-Rail

Ref.	Year(s)	Accessory	Details	Market Price Range
D1	1948-58	Through Station	(Diecast Cream with Orange roof, Green doors and windows)	**£50-70** ❑
D1	1948-58	Island Platform	(Diecast Cream with Orange roof, Green doors and windows)	**£30-40** ❑
D1	1948-58	Platform extension	with wall for Through Station	**£35-45** ❑
D1	1948-58	Platform extension	with wall for Island Platform	**£35-45** ❑
D1	1948-58	Turntable (32180)	Metal, Grey-Green with Orange sideframes	**£40-60** ❑
D1	1948-58	Footbridge	All Cream three-piece construction	**£20-30** ❑
D1	1948-58	Level Crossing (3460 3 R)	Metal, White gates with Red warning circles, Green verges	**£10-15** ❑
		Plastic version:	Cream base and gates, White posts, Red warning circles	**£25-35** ❑
D1	1948-58	Girder Bridge	Diecast metal, Orange	**£40-50** ❑
D1	1948-58	TPO Mail Van Set	with Mail Van, lineside apparatus and two mailbags	**£20-30** ❑
D1	1948-58	Loading Gauge		**£10-15** ❑
D1	1948-58	Water Crane	Brown	**£5-10** ❑
D1	1948-58	(051) Station Staff	6 metal figures: Guard, Porter, Ticket Collector, Shunter, Engine Driver, Station Master	**£40-50** ❑
D2	1948-58	(053) Passengers	6 metal figures: 3 males, 3 females	**£40-50** ❑
3450	1948-58	Buffers Stop	Box of 2	**£10-15** ❑

Accessories

Signals and Switches

D1	1948-58	Switch	Red, for electrically operated points and signals	**£7-10**	❏
D1/5050	1948-58	Signal	Hand operated, single arm, 'Home'	**£10-15**	❏
D1/5051	1948-58	Signal	Hand operated, single arm, 'Distant'	**£7-10**	❏
D2	1948-58	Switch	Black, for isolating rails	**£7-10**	❏
D2/5055	1948-58	Signal	Hand operated, double arm, 'Home - Distant'	**£7-10**	❏
D3/5060	1948-58	Junction Signal	Hand operated, two arms, 'Home'	**£12-18**	❏
D3/5061	1948-58	Junction Signal	Hand operated, two arms, 'Distant'	**£12-18**	❏
ED1/5065	1948-58	Signal	Electrically operated, single arm, 'Home'	**£7-12**	❏
ED1/5066	1948-58	Signal	Electrically operated, single arm, 'Distant'	**£7-12**	❏
ED2/5070	1948-58	Signal	Electrically operated, double arm, 'Home - Distant'	**£12-18**	❏
ED3/5075	1948-58	Junction Signal	Electrically operated, two arms, 'Home'	**£12-18**	❏
ED3/5076	1948-58	Junction Signal	Electrically operated, two arms, 'Distant'	**£12-18**	❏
G3	1948-58	Switch	Green, for coloured light signals (rare)	**£20-30**	❏
32115	1948-58	Colour Light Signal ES6	'Home'	**£7-12**	❏
32116	1948-58	Colour Light Signal ES6	'Distant'	**£7-12**	❏
32117	1948-58	Colour Light Signal ES6	'Junction - Home'	**£10-15**	❏

Accessories (1959 - 1964) Two-Rail

050	1959-64	Railway Staff	12 moulded plastic figures	**£100-125**	❏
052	1959-64	Railway Passengers	12 moulded plastic figures	**£30-40**	❏
790	1959-64	Granite Chippings		**£2-3**	❏
791	1959-64	Coal (imitation)	per bag	**£2-3**	❏
1575	1959-64	Lighting Kit		**£10-15**	❏
2400	1959-64	TPO Mail Van Set	Mail Van plus lineside apparatus, two mailbags	**£20-30**	❏
2450	1959-64	Buffers Stop		**£10-15**	❏
2451	1959-64	Illuminated Buffers		**£15-20**	❏
4620	1959-64	Breakdown Crane	Gloss or Matt, with 2 support wagons each with two screw jacks plus match truck (see Wagons listing)	**£75-90**	❏
5005	1959-64	Engine Shed Kit - Two Road	Cream and Green with Grey roof, plastic	**£60-70**	❏
5006	1959-64	Engine Shed Extension Kit	plastic	**£20-30**	❏
5010	1959-64	Footbridge	plastic	**£10-20**	❏
5015	1959-64	Girder Bridge	Red plastic (rare - only 3,000 made)	**£300-400**	❏
5020	1959-64	Goods Depot Kit	Cream and Green, Grey roof, Red/Yellow static working jib, plastic	**£30-50**	❏
5025	1959-64	Gradient and Mile Posts	Box of 12	**£40-50**	❏
5030	1959-64	Island Platform Kit	Cream and Green, Grey roof, plastic	**£30-40**	❏
5035	1959-64	Loading Gauge		**£15-20**	❏
5037	1959-64	Lineside Notices	Box of six	**£25-35**	❏
5040	1959-64	Platelayers' Hut	Box of 6, plastic	**£25-35**	❏
5080	1959-64	Signal Cabin	Cream and Green, Orange roof, plastic	**£10-20**	❏
		Rare variation:	As previous model but with Green roof	**£150-200**	❏
5083	1959-64	Station Composite Kit	'Terminal and Through', plastic	**£200-300**	❏
5084	1959-64	Station Canopy Extension Kit	(Tri-ang - Hornby) Box with large top opening, Red/Yellow printing	**£400-500**	❏
R5084	1959-64	Station Canopy Extension Kit	(late Tri-ang - Hornby) Plain White box, Black/White end labels	**£200-300**	❏

N.B. 5084 and R5084 also housed in 3rd type of Red box (Tri-ang - Hornby).

5085	1959-64	Suburban Station Kit	Cream and Green with Grey roof, plastic	**£30-40**	❏
5086	1959-64	Platform extension	plastic	**£5-10**	❏
5087	1959-64	Platform Fence extension	plastic	**£10-20**	❏
5089	1959-64	Platform Side extension	plastic	**£20-30**	❏
5090	1959-64	Telegraph Poles	Box of 12	**£50-75**	❏
5091/2	1959-64	Tunnel	Single or Double, price for either	**£50-100**	❏
5094	1959-64	Tunnel Ends	Box of 6	**£100-150**	❏
5095	1959-64	Water Crane	Buff	**£35-45**	❏

Hornby Dublo Catalogues

Ref.	Year(s)	Publication	Cover features and details	Market Price Range
7/938/185 UK	1938-39	Catalogue	First catalogue dedicated solely to Hornby Dublo White cover with colour picture of pre-war layout and boy with flag and whistle plus man and seated boy. Lists all pre-war issues with prices and pictures	**£75-100** ❑
1/939/27	1939	Leaflet (one page)	Gives details of the new EDP2 'LMS' Electric Passenger Set plus list of rolling stock and prices	**£15-20** ❑
12/1039 /70 UK	1939	Leaflet (8 pages)	A large leaflet with Orange cover listing the entire pre-war range	**£75-100** ❑
7/1053/250	1953-54	Leaflet	Colour cover Lists new 'BR' liveries	**£30-40** ❑
7/754/200	1954-55	Leaflet	Colour cover, products price list	**£30-40** ❑
7/755/550	1955-56	Leaflet	Colour cover depicting attractive layout. Includes superb colour pictures of entire range	**£30-40** ❑
7/556/500	1956-57	Leaflet	With colour picture of 'Duchess of Montrose'	**£30-40** ❑
7/857/500	1957	Three-fold Leaflet	With excellent centre page layout spread (man with FIVE fingers pointing to layout)	**£20-30** ❑
7/858/500	1958	Three-fold Leaflet	Cover depicts 'Duchess of Montrose' 'ROYAL SCOT'	**£15-25** ❑
HD/CF/1	1959	Three-fold Leaflet	Cover depicts 2236 'City of London' 'THE CALEDONIAN'	**£15-25** ❑
18/259/ 300	1959	'Hornby Book of Trains'	Cover shows green loco (4472) and price '1/6d'. 64 pages	**£10-15** ❑
92016	1960	24 page Catalogue	The cover depicts a Blue 'English Electric' loco	**£10-15** ❑
72236/02	1961	24 page Catalogue	Cover depicts D9002 Diesel Electric loco with excellent pictures of all items manufactured	**£10-15** ❑
77250/02	1961	3 fold Leaflet	'City of Liverpool' (No. 46247) on the cover	**£7-12** ❑
18/561/ 500	1961	24 page Catalogue	Cover picture shows 'Barnstaple' loco	**£10-15** ❑
13/162/ 500	1962	28 page Catalogue	Cover picture shows 'Deltic' locomotive	**£10-15** ❑
72245/02	1962	4 page Leaflet	Excellent cover picture shows the front ends of 'Barnstaple' and 'Crepello' locos	**£10-15** ❑
7/363/400 ?				
722257/ 02	1963	20 page Booklet	Pocket sized booklet depicting 'Kingfisher' loco, introduces the E3001 Loco with Pantographs	**£10-15** ❑
13/464/ 100	1964	4-fold Leaflet	With view of two green locos	**£10-15** ❑
R 280 S	1965	Tri-ang and Hornby Dublo Amalgamation Issue	Night scene on cover	**£10-15** ❑

In addition to the foregoing basic listing of leaflets and catalogues dedicated to Hornby Dublo, many other publications listed the products:

Meccano Magazines - pre-war and post-war
Meccano General Products catalogues
Large stores own catalogues - 'Hamleys', 'Gamages', 'Bentalls', etc
Hornby 'Book of Trains' - pre-war and post-war
'Hornby Trains' leaflets and illustrated price lists - pre-war and post-war from 1948.

Hornby Dublo model pricing guidelines

Post-war Locomotives.
All were issued both as individual models and in sets. Post-war re-issued models are priced at 20% less than pre-war examples.

Horse-shoe (HS) and Half Inch (HI) Motors.
Prices shown assume a Horseshoe Motor has been fitted. For Half Inch Motor deduct 15%.

Binns Road Repair Locomotives.
Variations exist such as nickel silver wheels replacing alloy wheels, and plastic wheels replacing small pony and bogie wheels. These variations could affect prices by up to 20%.

Early Boxes.
Models EDL1 and EDL2 packed in light powder-blue boxes are priced at 33% more than those in dark blue boxes.

'Gloss' finished Locomotives.
The only locomotives to be issued in a glossy paint livery were: EDL11 'Silver King', EDL12 'Duchess of Montrose', N2 69567 Tank Locomotive.

Qualifying Standards. The prices shown in this Catalogue have been based on the following qualifying standards:
Locomotives to be in exceptional condition showing no signs of wear or fingerprints, to be in working order, and to be in its original box. Boxes to be in pristine, unmarked condition, complete with any original packing or labelling. See the following section on 'Packaging'.

Prices for non-Mint or unboxed models. Models in near mint condition but unboxed are usually priced at approximately 60% to 70% of the mint and boxed price shown.

Packaging and box types

Locomotives, pre-war packaging

A boxed model should include the original corrugated cardboard wrapper which displays a white 'Meccano' sticky label with red printing, plus a small sticker indicating the locomotive's livery. A further sticker indicates whether the model is 'Clockwork' or 'Electric'.

The ends of the locomotive should be protected by cardboard core end rings.

Each locomotive was packed with a brown 'TESTED' label together with operating instructions, a track layout guide, plus an application form to join the 'Hornby Railway Company'. A guarantee was also enclosed with the number shown matching the number stamped on the bottom of the box.

Locomotives, post-war packaging

Packing materials should include a cover protector strip which covers the entire length of the boxed model, tucking into the box ends. The ends of the locomotive should be protected by engine housing cores plus top and bottom cardboard strip protectors.

Enclosed with the model should be operating instructions, a track layout leaflet/booklet and a guarantee with the number matching the number stamped on the bottom of the box.

Early post-war models were packed with a brown 'TESTED' label, later issues received just a white rubber stamped label and the last locomotives had a yellow/black label.

A combined 'TESTED AND GUARANTEED' certificate (ref. 16/500) was also used in the early post-war 'long box' sets (the certificate had blue printing on pale blue paper). All sets contained a 'TESTED' label.

Passenger Coaches, Vans and Wagons packaging

All models issued from 1938 until 1955 were housed in strong cardboard boxes. On the side of most boxes was printed a date manufacturing code together with a quantity code plus a prominent Box Number. D3 Corridor Coach, L.M.S. Brake/3rd for example: Box

Number 'DR 363', Date '6 49' (June 1949) Manufacturing Code '3.5 N' (3,500). A printing reference was also shown - 'BWW9232'. Stamped on the box, usually on its back, was the date the model was actually issued - often some months later than the manufacturing date shown. It is not always possible to find the release date stamp. In addition the colours of the boxes and the colour of the box lettering were changed at regular intervals.

The main changes were as follows:

1938 - 1940	Pale blue boxes with dark blue printed letters
1948 - 1949	Pale blue boxes with dark blue printed letters. The first post-war models were issued in plain brown cardboard with blue printing.
1950 only	Grey-blue boxes with dark blue printed letters
1951 only	Grey-blue boxes with white printed letters
1952 - 1955	Dark blue boxes with white printed letters
1955 - 1958	Dark blue boxes with white parallel lines and without the date and manufacturing information. The box numbers continued to be shown and were prominently featured in catalogues. Pictures added to boxes in 1958 when 'Super Detail' models introduced.
1958 - 1964	Red boxes with white parallel lines and without date and manufacturing information.

N.B. Assembly dates and Packers' initials shown on the end flaps of some boxes, for example 'HG 358'.

Model and Box Numbers

When the Hornby Dublo range was launched in 1938 each model reference received a 'D' prefix. This referred to 'Dublo' in order to differentiate the models from existing Hornby trains. In addition each box (as described above) was given a separate reference number. This system continued until 1956 when the box number effectively became the catalogue number. As a consequence the models listed include both the original simple 'D' reference numbers and their box numbers.

Hornby Dublo information sources

The Swapmeet Toys and Models Ltd., the Dick Fawcett and Terry Durrant 'Hornby Dublo' collections,
Hornby Dublo catalogues 1938 - 1964,
models sold at Christie's' London Auction sales,
models sold at Vectis, Guildford, Auction sales,
models sold at the regular Lacy Scott Auction sales in Bury St.Edmunds,
models sold at Phillips West Two, London, Auction sales, and Wallis & Wallis, Lewes, Sussex, sales.
models sold at Barry Potters Toy & Train Auctions, The Benn Hall, Rugby, Warks.

Acknowledgements
Chris Dyer of Somerset for additional information.

Books and further information.
The following are recommended:
'The Hornby Dublo Post-war 3-Rail Collectors Guide' - Tony Oakes, Mayfleld Publishing, 68, Main Road, Wynbunbury, Nantwich, Cheshire, CW5 7LS.
'Hornby Dublo Trains', Hornby Companion Series, Vol.3 - Michael J. Foster, Guild Publishing, London (by arrangement with New Cavendish Books).
The many monographs and notes published by the Dublo Circle of the Hornby Railway Collectors Association in the H.R .A. Journal.

Hornby Railway Collectors Association (H.R.C.A.)
Membership Secretary: Bob Field, 2 Ravensmore Road, Sherwood, Nottingham, NG5 2AH.

Technical notes

Early post-war identification features

Locomotives: Horse-shoe magnet, fine buffer heads, elongated pick-ups, disc wheels, lightweight bogies and pony trucks, split-pin pony fixing, thin cabside numbers.

Tenders: Plated bogies, thin lettering, base tabbed not rivetted.

Coaches: Pre-war matt or semi-matt sides, silver roofs.

Accessories: Early date, e.g., 9.47, 5.48, 8.49.

Guarantee: Early date, e.g., 2.48.

Boxes: Mid blue boxes with 1947, 1948, 1949, 2.50 or 1950.
Powder blue boxes with 6.49 or 1949.

Model construction materials

Locomotives: Die-cast zinc alloy bodies, wheels and chassis until 1958 when polystyrene features were introduced.

Coaches: The early coaches had die-cast bogies and wheels with lithographed tinplate bodies.
From 1959 polystyrene ends, roofs and underframes were introduced.

Vans and Wagons: Die-cast underframes and wheels until 1958 when polystyrene introduced.

Locomotive wheel arrangements

Steam Locomotives are classed by the number of wheels in the order: Leading - Driving - Trailing. Some wheel arrangements have a general type name, for example 4-6-2 'Pacific', or 4-4-2 'Atlantic'. Two leading or trailing wheels are a 'pony truck'. Four leading or trailing wheels are a 'bogie truck'. Diesel and Electric engines have their own classifications:

'BO - BO' A locomotive fitted with two pairs of wheels at both front and rear

'CO - CO' A locomotive fitted with three pairs of wheels at both front and rear (Deltic)

'CO - BO' A locomotive with three pairs of wheels at the front and two pairs at the rear

'Totem' motifs

These refer to the motifs on 'British Railways' locomotive tenders.

1st type: Lion on a wheel,   2nd type: Lion on a Crown.

References to totems facing forwards or backwards indicate the direction the head of the lion is facing.

The tails of the lions in the 1st type of motif have four variations. Each variation is linked to a matching cab number design:

1: Lion with thin short tail - small thin matching cab number
2: Lion with thick short tail - small thick matching cab number
3: Lion with thick long tail - large thick matching cab number
4: Lion with thin long tail - large thin matching cab number

Hornby Dublo model scale

Double -'0' ('00') scale is 4 mm. to the foot (1:76) and is thus slightly larger than the 3.5 mm. 'HO' scale, but still using the same 16.5 mm. rail gauge.

Wheel and Coupling types (Passenger Coaches, Vans and Wagons)

Types of wheels
1938 - 40   Wheels have an inner and outer axle rim and often show signs of metal failure. Axles held by single housing.
1948 - 53   Same as pre-war wheels in shape but not prone to metal deterioration. Axles retained by clips to mountings.
1953 - 58   Wheels have no pronounced inner or outer axle rim. Axles retained by mounting clips.
1958 - 64   Nylon 'disc' wheels with no spokes. Axles retained by mounting clips (used on coaches).
1958 - 64   Nylon wheel with eight spokes. Axles retained by mounting clips (used on vans and wagons).

Types of couplings
1938 - 40   A flat spring-steel coupling with an oval end plus a small chassis hook.
1948 - 54   A metal coupling with 'RD.No.848012' on shank and without patent ref. 'PAT NO 605283' .
1954 - 58   Same as previous coupling but with both Registered and Patent Numbers on shank.
1956 - 60   Same as previous coupling but with longer vertical 'hook-up' link.
1963 - 64   Same as previous coupling but finer and made of Nylon.

Reference 'OO' gauge Auction Results

See also 'OO' and 'HO' gauge Auction Results on pages 175 – 190.

Christie's

CHRISTIE'S SOUTH KENSINGTON
85 OLD BROMPTON ROAD, LONDON, SW7 3LD

THE BIANCO HORNBY-DUBLO REFERENCE COLLECTION

FRIDAY 25TH OCTOBER 1996

SPECIAL GLOSSARY ABBREVIATIONS

EPW   Early post-war wheel with squared back to wheel
EMC   Early metal coupling, here used to refer to all couplings with small heads, including LMC as defined in the book
FMC   Final metal coupling with large head
EPC   Large plastic coupling
NPC   Final thin Delrin coupling

HORNBY-DUBLO
PRE-WAR LOCOMOTIVES, STOCK AND ACCESSORIES

All locomotives have original flat pre-war pick-up shoes unless otherwise stated. All locomotives have been successfully test run before being packed for sale; electric locomotives run well and pull reasonable loads. Future running capability cannot be guaranteed. Locomotive boxes are with guarantee, instructions and all original; where stated, locomotive wrappers are replicas accurately reproduced from originals. All boxed sets have oil, spanner and key, as appropriate.

In general, wagon boxes have individual stickers denoting the railway company; exceptions are items such as the Fish Van and Horse Box which only existed in NE. All items are in original boxes unless otherwise stated; they are in good complete condition, but generally staples for rolling stock boxes have rusted and there are some stain marks.

THE NUMBERS PRECEEDING EACH AUCTION RESULT ARE 'LOT NUMBERS' WHICH LINK UP WITH PICTURES OF THE LOTS AS SHOWN IN THE COLOUR SECTION.

1 **EDL1 electric 'Sir Nigel Gresley' Locomotive and Tender**, code MW - 1780 3M 9.38, with spanner and oil bottle **£480**

2 **D2 Two Coach Articulated Unit**, D252, in original box, code BW678 2.5M 8.38............**£750**

5 **EDL1 electric Passenger Set**, D103, 1st issue, in original box without printed label on interior divider 'Hornby-Dublo the perfect table railway', original instruction leaflet 2/938/25 ....**£700**

10 **DL1 clockwork 'Sir Nigel Gresley' Locomotive and Tender**, D171, in original box, code MW-1780 4,250 9.38, contemporary Minic key............**£800**

12 **EDP1 electric Passenger Set**, D103, articulated coaches with pre-war centre bogie and post-war factory repaired bogies at both ends and pre-war couplings, in second issue box with printed label on internal divider and original instruction leaflet 2/938/25............**£800**

14 **DL1 clockwork Tank Locomotive**, D152 NE, in original box, code MW-1780 7,500 9.38 with contemporary Minic key............**£650**

18 **EDL7 electric LMS Tank Locomotive**, D154 electric LMS box code MW-1780 5M 9.38, part original instructions............**£550**

22 **EDL7 electric GWR Tank Locomotive**, D154 electric GWR box code MW-1780 5M 9.38, instructions dated 9.38............**£850**

25 **DL7 clockwork SR Tank Locomotive**, D152 clockwork SR box code MW1780 7,500 9.38 with contemporary Minic key............**£700**

28 **EDG7 electric NE Tank Goods Set**, electric NE second issue box with interior printed label on cardboard divider **£850**

29 **EDG7 electric SR Tank Goods Set**, D104 electric SR first issue box without printed label on interior cardboard divider, coal wagon with coal load, with instructions 2/938/25............**£800**

30 **EDG7 electric SR Tank Goods Set**, D104 electric SR first issue box without printed label n interior cardboard divider, coal wagon with coal load, with instructions dated 9.38............**£850**

31 **DG7 clockwork LMS Tank Goods Set**, D102 clockwork LMS with instruction leaflet............**£900**

PRE-WAR WOODEN BUILDINGS

60 **Short and Long Tunnels** ....U/S

62 **D1 Goods Depot** with green roof, D402 box code MW 7761 650 8.39 ....**£280**

63 **D1 Engine Shed**, D415 box code BW 8530 1M 10.39 (box repaired)............**£280**

64 **D1 Signal Cabins**: one with red roof, one with green roof (unboxed)............**£85**

69 **D1 Mainline Station** with green roof, D407 box code MW4003 1,500 1.39 (box repaired)............**£280**

70 **City Station Set**: Station Building, Canopy with Side Platforms and six green removable panels, Double and Single Buffer Units (buffers post-war), two Side Platforms with Station Walls, two Island Platform Units, two Wide End Ramps and four Narrow End Ramps; with additional replica pieces - two Full Size and two Short Side Platform Extensions with Walls, one Full Length and one Short Island Platform Extension; (unboxed) **£1,100**

POST-WAR LOCOMOTIVES, STOCK AND ACCESSORIES IN PLAIN BLUE BOXES

LNER

72 **First issue EDL1 'Sir Nigel Gresley' Locomotive and Tender**, in 1949 box, horseshoe magnet, lightweight bogies and pony truck, split-pin pony fixing, elongated pick-ups, tender with thin lettering, plated bogies, all EPW, two keeps, pale blue boxes without suppressor label, both dated 1.49, 1949............**£300**

73 **D1 LNER Corridor Coaches**: 1st/3rd and Brake 3rd, both dark brown corridor ends, EPW, pale blue boxes dated 1.49, All 3rd, brown corridor ends, pale blue box dated 7.48 ....**£240**

81 **EDL7 LNER Tank Locomotive**, small numbers on buffer beam, silver label, small windows, instructions dated 11.50, powder blue cover strip, two keeps, mid-blue box..**£120**

98 **First post-war issue LNER EDL7 Tank Goods Train Set**, black livery, horseshoe magnet, elongated pick-ups, gold label, large windows, lightweight pony truck, disc wheels, all stock in early colours, EPW, cover strip, eight keeps, controller instructions, oil, wire, tag, instructions dated 9.47, mid-blue box with 'Royal Scot' label, 1947 ....**£900**

Sets in the 'Royal Scot' box were the first items available in the Hornby-Dublo range after the Second World War; very few were released in the Autumn of 1947 for the Christmas market as most production was intended for export.

LMS

103 **LMS 'Duchess of Atholl' Train**: Locomotive with horseshoe magnet, elongated pick-ups, lightweight bogies and pony truck, fine buffer heads, thin cabside numbers, powder blue cover strip, two keeps, spanner, instructions dated 11.50, Tender with steel riveted base, Coaches - two 1st/3rds and 3rd/Brake with matt pre-war sides, all EPW, all powder blue boxes dated 6.49, 1949 ....**£320**

131 **EDG7 LMS Tank Goods Set**, Locomotive with silver label, small windows, disc wheels, oil, tag, instructions dated 2.51, guarantee stamped 5.52, Rail Layouts dated 12.49, controller instructions, cover strip, eight keeps, mid-blue box, 1952...........**£260**

132 **EDG7 LMS Tank Goods Train Set**, Locomotive with silver label, small windows, oil, tag, tabs, instructions dated 7.52, guarantee dated 8.52, Rail Layouts dated 10.52, cover strip, eight keeps, mid-blue box, 1952 ....**£260**

134 **Rare early post-war EDL7 GWR Tank Locomotive**, horseshoe magnet, pre-war body without cutaway buffer beam, post-war lettering and large cabside numbers, gold label, large windows, disc wheels, lightweight pony frame, powder blue cover strip, two keeps, pale blue box dated 6.48..**£750**

137 **EDG7 GWR Tank Goods Train Set**: Locomotive with horseshoe magnet, elongated pick-ups, gold label, small windows, small cabside number, light pony truck, oil, wire, instructions dated 5.48, guarantee stamped 11.48, tag, controller instructions, first type mid-blue box without suppressor label, two children on label **£500**

138 **EDG7 GWR Tank Goods Set**, Locomotive with silver label, small windows, disc wheels, EPW, oil, tag, controller instructions, instructions dated 7.51, guarantee dated 11.50, Rail Layouts dated 10.50, cover strip, eight keeps, second type mid-blue box **£380**

143 **First post-war issue SR EDL7 Tank Gods Train Set**, horseshoe magnet, elongated pick-ups, gold label, large windows, lightweight pony truck, disc wheels, all stock EPW, cover strip, eight keeps, controller instructions, oil, wire, tag, instructions dated 9.47, guarantee, mid-blue box with 'Royal Scot' label, 1947...........**£1,600**

147 **EDL7 SR Tank Locomotive**, thin sans-serif lettering, silver label, small lettering, disc wheels, instructions dated 4.51, guarantee stamped 5.51, powder blue cover strip, two keeps, mid-blue box with sticker **£350**

BRITISH RAILWAYS, PLAIN BLUE BOXES

173 **BR 'Duchess of Montrose' Passenger Train**: glossy Locomotive, oil, spanner, instructions dated 1.56, guarantee dated 12.55, cover strip, four keeps, mid-blue box with red supressor label, Tender, royal blue box dated 12.52, bright plum Coaches, second type bogies - 1st/3rd, two Brake/3rds, royal blue boxes dated 12.52...**£300**

175 **EDL18 BR Tank Passenger Train**: Locomotive, instructions dated 1.56, guarantee dated 12.55, cover strip, four keeps, plain blue box, D11 Brake/3rd and 1st/3rd, royal blue boxes dated 6.53, D11 1st/3rd, mid-blue box dated 11.53...**£200**

EDL17 BR Tank Locomotive, glossy, instructions, dated 9.54, guarantee dated 10.54, tag, cover strip, two keeps, mid-blue box **£140**

ACCESSORIES IN PLAIN BLUE BOXES

191 **D1 Station Set**, plain mid-blue boxes with picture labels: Through Station, early white platform edge, Island Platform, early white platform edge, Signal Cabin, Footbridge, lugs and small sockets at top of footbridge, plain card packaging piece, three Station Name Packets, Buffer Stops; with Platform Extension with Wall and Platform Extension, in blue striped boxes..................................**£300**

BRITISH RAILWAYS MID-BLUE BOXED SETS WITH LIGHT BLUE INTERIORS

210 **EDL18 Tank Passenger Train**: Locomotive, blue cover strip, four keeps and D13 Coaches - two 1st/3rd and Brake/3rd **£200**
213 **EDL11 BR 'Silver King' Locomotive and Tender**, four keeps, spanner...**£260**

215 **EDL12 'Duchess of Montrose' Train**: Locomotive, blue cover strip, four keeps, Tender, D12 Coaches - 1st/2nd, 1st/3rd, Brake/3rd, D20 Restaurant Car **£350**

216 **EDLT20 'Bristol Castle' Passenger Train**: Locomotive and Tender, picture box, headboard, oil, D21 Coaches - 1st/2nd, Brake/2nd, D20 Brake/2nd...**£260**

219 **EDL17 Suburban Tank Passenger Train**: Locomotive, yellow tag, yellow cover strip, D14 Coaches with windows - two 1st/3rd, Brake/3rd **£190**
222 **3232 Co-Co Diesel-Electric Passenger Train**: Locomotive, D22 BR(M) Coaches - two 1st/2nd, Brake/2nd **£300**

BRITISH RAILWAYS EDP AND EDG SETS WITH YELLOW BOX INTERIORS

228 **EDP15 BR(E) 'Silver King' Passenger Train Set**, plastic coach wheels, yellow label on box end **£240**
230A **EDP20 'Bristolian' Passenger Train Set**, headboard, D21 Coaches, plastic wheels and nameboard stickers, four keeps......**£240**

240 **LT25 LMR 8F 2-8-0 Freight Locomotive and Tender** **£200**

242 **Freight Stock**, second issue blue striped boxes, ten different wagons..**£160**
256 **L30 1,000 bhp Bo-Bo Diesel-Electric Locomotive**...........**£170**

257 **SD6 reference Freight Stock**, third type blue striped boxes with pictures, FMC, solid underframes, with keeps, seven various.....**£100**

Christie's (continued)

258 **EDL18 Tank Locomotive**, FMC, late issue with yellow box interior, yellow cover strip, four yellow keeps **£120**

P AND G SERIES LAST TYPE THREE-RAIL SETS

Blue boxes with yellow interiors, instructions, guarantee, Rail Layouts, oil, unless otherwise stated.

265 **P15 'The Flying Scotsman' Passenger Train Set**, headboard with nameplate, D12 Coaches with plastic wheels, 'Flying Scotsman' headboard stickers, spanner, five keeps **£550**

267 **P22 'The Royal Scot' Passenger Train Set**, Locomotive, nickel-silver unbushed wheels, plastic bogie and pony wheels, headboard with name, spanner, four keeps......................**£480**

269 **Rare G25 LMR 2-8-0 8F Freight Train Set**, ten keeps **£420**

269 A **Rare G19 2-6-4 Tank Goods Train Set**, six keeps **£550**

270 **Very rare 3217 BR 0-6-2 Tank Locomotive** in plain blue box, early type forward and rear facing lion totems, coal in bunker, L17 under body, nickel silver wheels, plastic pony truck, 3217 end label, yellow interior, cover strip, two keeps.....................**£650**

271 **L11 BR 'Mallard' Locomotive and Tender**, Locomotive, headboard with name, one yellow and one repair keep, plain blue box, Tender, blue striped box **£320**

272 **3211 BR(E) 'Mallard' Locomotive and Tender** in rare 3211 plain blue box for Locomotive and Tender **£650**

273 **EDLT20 BR(W) 'Bristol Castle' Locomotive and Tender** **£190**

275 **3235 BR(S) 'Dorchester' Locomotive and Tender**...........**£500**

276 **3224 LMR 8F Goods Locomotive and Tender**, Ringfield motor **£400**

277 **3217 BR 0-6-2 Tank Locomotive**, coal in bunker, last type lion and crown totems, nickel-silver wheels, plastic pony truck, instructions dated 2.59, Italian guarantee, Italian export issue label on box end **£500**

278 **3233 Co-Bo Diesel-Electric Locomotive**, cardboard restraining straps, box with Italian sticker **£280**

279 **3226 LMR 'City of Liverpool' Locomotive and Tender**, instructions dated 2.59 ....**£700**

280 **3231 0-6-0 Diesel-Electric Shunting Locomotive** twin coupling rods **£240**

281 **3221 'Ludlow Castle' Locomotive and Tender**.................**£550**

282 **3211 BR(E) 'Mallard' Locomotive and Tender**, instructions dated 2.59 ....**£420**

ACCESSORIES IN BLUE STRIPED BOXES

295 **D1 Island Platform and two Platform Extensions**, with Station Names packet **£170**

296 **D1 Through Station and Platform Extension** with Wall, with Station Names Packet...**£140**

300 **Rare 3460 plastic Level Crossing and Platform Extension** **£120**

TWO-RAIL RED STRIPED BOXES AND SETS SETS IN YELLOW AND BLUE BOXES

330 **2006 0-6-0 Tank Goods Train Set**....................**£130**

334 2022 **Passenger Train Set**, metal-bodied D22 Coaches, one with nameboard stickers...**£350**

335 **2206 Tank Passenger Train**: black 0-6-0 Locomotive, BR(M) Suburban Coaches - 4021 1st/2nd, two 4022 Brake/2nds...........**£350**

336 **2077 SR Tank Passenger Train**: green 0-6-0 Locomotive, Suburban Coaches - 4025 1st/2nd, 4026 Brake/2nd **£140**

339 **BR(W) metal-bodied Coaches**: 4009 1st/2nd, two 4010 Brake/2nd, 4047 Restaurant Car **£280**

340 **2211 BR(E) 'Golden Fleece' Passenger Train**: Locomotive and Tender, Coaches in rare boxes - 4005 1st/2nd, 4006 Brake/2nd, 4048 Restaurant Car..**£240**

344 **2232 C-Co Diesel-Electric Locomotive** **£140**

347 **2226 LMR 'City of London' Locomotive and Tender**......**£240**

356 **2221 BR(W) 'Cardiff Castle' Locomotive and Tender**, Ringfield motor **£180**

367 **Locomotive and Horsebox**: 2218 2-6-4 Tank and 4315 BR Horsebox (tape tear to top of box) **£240**

373 **Shunting Locomotive and Horsebox**: 2231 0-6-0 Diesel Electric Shunting Locomotive, 4316 SR Horsebox, FMC **£180**

381 **2014 'The Talisman' Passenger Train Set**, Coaches with nameboard stickers applied **£280**

386 **2225 LMR 8F Freight Locomotive and Tender**, plain red box **£220**

390 **2233 Co-Bo Diesel-Electric Locomotive** **£170**

392 **2217 Mixed Tank Freight Train**: Tank Locomotive, Italian export issue, nine various wagons. This lot forms the second part of the reference 'set' **£350**

395 **2224 LMR 2-8-0 8F Freight Locomotive and Tender**, one tender totem inverted...**£180**

399 **Rare 4685 diamond bogie Caustic Liquor Wagon** **£280**

407 **2024 2-8-0 Express Goods Train Set**, early Ringfield motor **£190**

468 **2235 SR 'Barnstable' Locomotive and Tender**.................**£400**

ACCESSORIES - RED STRIPED BOXES

495 **Rare red plastic 5015 Girder Bridge** (some Tippex to one box lid end)..**£400**

499 **Rare 5080 green-roof Signal Cabin**, plain red box **£170**

LATE YELLOW AND RED AND YELLOW AND BLUE PICTURE BOXES

553 **BR(S) EMU: 3250 Electric Motor Coach** Brake/2nd (small mark to centre cab window), 4081 2nd Suburban Coach, 4150 Electric Driving Trailer Coach Motor Coach **£400**

555 **3234 'St. Paddy' Deltic Diesel Electric Locomotive**, with two cardboard restraining straps **£400**
556 **2234 'Crepello' Deltic Diesel Electric Locomotive**, with two cardboard restraining straps **£200**
557 **2245 E3002 3,300 HP Bo-Bo Electric Locomotive** **£650**

561 **4620 Breakdown Crane**, gloss finish, metal hook, EPC, yellow picture box...**£320**

567 **2033 Co-Bo Diesel Electric Goods Train Set**, rare final issue blue and white picture box, with 1962 Catalogue........................**£450**
568 **2034 'The Royal Scot' Passenger Train Set**, Locomotive with plastic side frames, headboard, rare final issue blue and white picture box, with 1962 Catalogue..**£500**
570 **Rare 2035 SR 'Bournemouth Belle' Pullman Train Set**, with 1962 Catalogue. This set is so rare that some have even doubted its existence **£1,700**

The BIANCO REFERENCE COLLECTION
THURSDAY 24TH OCTOBER 1996

801 **Exley GWR bogie K5 Brake/1st Coach**, fitted with sprung bogies...**£207**

802 **Bing electric GWR 4-4-0 Locomotive and Tender** No. 2163, circa 1927 (some retouching to splashers and tender coal rail)...**£322**

BING TABLE TOP RAILWAY

803 **Bing Table Top Railway**, Cat. Ref. 61/7300/2 L&NER electric Tank Passenger Set, in original box with photocopied instructions and products catalogue **£368**

TRIX TWIN, TRIX EXPRESS AND BRITISH TRIX

811 **Trix 5/375 Southern Railway three-car EMU**, circa 1937 (not serviced, motor bogie wheels with slight fatigue and expansion)
....**£276**

812 **Trix F105B black EM 1 Bo-Bo Electric Locomotive**, later type with single roof ventilator moulding and F105G green EMI Bo-Bo Electric Locomotive 'Triton'..**£276**

814 **British Trix Freight Stock**, yellow and black boxes: twenty-three boxed, including 'Birds Eye' Container Wagon, Private Owner Wagons and Bulk Grain Vans, various liveries, five others (unboxed)
....**£161**
815 **British Trix Locomotives**: Western class Diesel Locomotives - 1165 green 'Western Explorer', 1167 maroon 'Western Enterprise', with 1190 blue A4 Locomotive and Tender with valances (renumbered and renamed 'Wild Swan') **£253**

816 **British Trix Construction Kits**: Footplateman - 2117 green class V Locomotive and Tender with motor, 2167 maroon Western class Diesel Locomotive with motor, Wagonmaster - 2010 Breakdown Crane Unit, all unassembled...**£207**

817 **British Trix: 1120 green Warship Class 'Vanguard' Diesel Locomotive**, in original box, 1115 green Class V Locomotive and Tender **£184**

818 **British Trix LNER Locomotives**: 1180 single-tender 'Flying Scot' Locomotive and Tender, 1188 A4 'Silver Link' Locomotive and Tender, in 1931 box, 1186 A H Locomotive and Tender (unboxed)
....**£299**

THE MARKLIN TRANSPORT SALE

PRICES SHOWN REPRESENT CHRISTIE'S
PRE-SALE ESTIMATES

'OO' AND 'HO' COACHES

Coaches, 1930 cream and green 349E LNER 'Pullman' Corridor Coach, blue 342J CIWL Dining Car and green 344 Baggage Car (F, some scratches, LNER lithography sticky, rust patch to roof, lacks one buffer and one celluloid window strip)..............................**£150-200**

A maroon **LMS 342E Passenger Coach**, in original box and maroon **343 Passenger Coach** (P-F, 343 lacks three buffers, 342 has rust patches on one side, box P, taped) **£800-1,000**

A maroon **342E LMS Corridor Coach**, 17.5cm, circa 1937-1938 (F-G, slight chipping to roof)...**£800-900**

A maroon **342E eight-wheel LMS Corridor Coach**, 17.5cm, circa 1937-1938 (F-G, small rust patches to roof) **£800-900**

A maroon **342E eight-wheel LMS Corridor Coach**, 17.5cm., circa 1937-1938 (F-G, scratch to one side) **£800-900**

A maroon **342 eight-wheel LMS Corridor Coach**, in a Marklin coach box (G-E, small dent on roof, box F-G, lid not matching, end label incomplete)...**£1,000-1,200**

A green and cream **349E eight-wheel LNER Pullman Corridor Coach**, 17.5cm, circa 1937-1938 (F-G) **£750-850**

MARKLIN PRE-WAR 'OO' GAUGE

Maroon **HR700 LMS 4-6-2 Locomotive and Tender**, tender with red bogies, 1937-38 (P-F, fatigue, cab section detached and incomplete, hand rails bent)..**£1,000-1,500**

A maroon **R700/R800 LMS four-wheel Tender**, (G-E, very slight wear to lower body, one small graze) **£400-600**

A black **R700 0-4-0 Locomotive and Tender with Cowcatcher** for the American market (locomotive F, minor chipping, small dent to top of smoke box, tender G-E)..**£2,000-3,000**

Maroon **E800 20 Volt electric LMS 4-4-0 Locomotive**, 1938 (P-F, discoloured, lacks front bogie, no tender).....................**£2,000-3,000**

Christie's (continued)

R700 LMS Locomotive and Coach: maroon R700 20-Volt three-rail electric LMS Locomotive (P-F, one smoke deflector fractured, fatigue to diecast components, small dent to cab roof, cab side lettering erased, lacks pick-up, no tender) and 342 LMS Passenger Coach (F, roof overpainted) £1,500-2,000

Black SLR800 20 Volt Streamlined 0-4-0 Locomotive and Tender, 1936-37 (P, chipping, cab side lettering erased, tender with some solder repaired) £300-500

Green R700/LNE 20 Volt electric LNER 0-4-0 Locomotive and Tender, 1937 (P-F, some paint flaking, smoke deflectors fatigued and repair to one facture, tender wheels and coupling rusty) £350-550

R700 LMS Train in a Set box: maroon R700 20 Volt three-rail electric LMS 0-4-0 Locomotive and Tender, two LMS 342 Passenger Coaches, straight and curved track, with original incorrect Set box, lid interior with applied track layout label, dated 9.36 (F-G, minor chipping to lower areas of locomotive, box F, corners split, two internal square spacers missing) £4,000-6,000

Maroon E800 20 Volt Electric LMS 4-4-0 Locomotive and Tender, 1938, (F, replacement chassis and pre-war motor, brush holes filled, front cylinder boxes modified, cab side renumbered 1191) £2,000-3,000

Maroon LMS Tender, for R700 LMS Locomotive, 1937 (F, slight rust patches) £100-200

An LNER R800 Locomotive and Tender, in green livery, 1938 (G, some retouching to locomotive)....................................£2,500-3,000

HR800 DR 01 4-6-2 Locomotive and bogie Tender, black livery, closed-in brush caps '809' cast on tender, in original box (E, box E) £400-600

LMS 352E bogie Dining Car, circa 1938 (G-E) £1,000-1,200
LMS 342E/343E bogie Corridor Coach, lettered 343E, circa 1937-1938 (E, some marking to roof)....................................£800-1,000

An LMS HR700 bogie Tender, in lake livery with gold lettering, type 2.1 plated double claw coupling (G)....................................£600-800

LMS 342E bogie Corridor Coach, circa 1937-1938 (E, slight scratching abrasion to roof) £800-1,000

Pre-war Marklin stock: 342J blue CIWL Dining Car, type 2.2 coupling, 1937 (F-G), 374 'Shell' Tank Wagon, 388 'Gambrinus' Wagon (lacks roof) and post-war Log Wagon £170-200

Maroon LMS Passenger Coach, Cat. Ref. 342, late 1930's (P-F, scratching, rust to one end, lacks one buffer).....................£170-200

Maroon LMS Passenger Coach, Cat. Ref. 342, late 1930's (P-F, paint crazing to carriage sides, wheels slightly rusty)...................£250-300

Green and yellow LNER electric Pullman Coach, Cat. Ref. 349E, late 1930s (F, slight scratching, paint slightly sticky, lacks pick-up £200-300
A green / cream 349E LNER Pullman Corridor Coach, in original box, circa 1937 (G, some small marks to paintwork, box F).......£632

A red SLR700 LMS 0-4-0 Streamlined Locomotive and Tender, c.1937-1938 (F, some fatigue to body, one front hand rail support fractured, some chipping to paintwork £3,220

An LMS 343 bogie Corridor Coach, circa 1938 (E, some marking to roof) £437

An LMS 342E bogie Corridor Coach, circa 1938 (E, chip to roof) £437

A yellow and brown 416 City Station, with ochre platform, 1935-1936 (G, some small chips, retouch to roof, flag missing).........£575

A red and cream TWE 700 Diesel Railcar, circa 1935 (F-G, some rust patches, some retouching, one coupling broken)..............£1,092

A red R700 0-4-0 LMS Locomotive and Tender, (G, some chips, some small rust patches)..£2,185

A cream and green 349E LNER Passenger Coach (G, rust to wheels) £552
A green R700 LNER 0-4-0 Locomotive and Tender, (P-F, fatigue to casting, paintwork chipped and retouched)..............................£2,070

'HO' GAUGE

A clockwork 0-6-0 LNER Tank Locomotive, Cat. Ref. TM1020, handpainted in green. 1927 (E, repainted by C. Littledale).........£230

A clockwork 4-6-4 Southern Railway 'Stephenson' Tank Locomotive, Cat. Ref TK1020, handpainted in olive green and gold lining. 1930-1934 (F, partly repainted) £920

Collector's notes

Sotheby's

SUMMERS PLACE, BILLINGHURST, WEST SUSSEX

HORNBY DUBLO SALE 25TH SEPTEMBER 1997

Occasional reference has been made to certain well-established abbreviations:
FMC - final metal coupling
EPC - large plastic coupling
NPC - final thin Delrin coupling

PRE-WAR

EDP1 ELECTRIC PASSENGER SET, NE, wrapper dated 10.38, comprising Locomotive 'Sir Nigel Gresley', Tender, Twin-Coach Articulated Unit and controller, with oil bottle, spanner and instructions dated 9.38, in original D103 box............................**£667**

EDL 1 ELECTRIC LOCOMOTIVE 'SIR NIGEL GRESLEY', NE, chipped section to bogie chassis, in rare original D153 box dated 1.40, box stained and formerly taped, complete with Tender, in box dated 11.38 ....**£690**

D1 CORRIDOR COACH, slight scuffs, in original box dated 11.38
....**£80**

D2 TWIN-COACH ARTICULATED UNIT, in original D252 box dated 8.38 ....**£552**

DG7 CLOCKWORK TANK GOODS SET, LMS, wrapper dated 10.38, comprising Tank Locomotive 6917, Open Wagon, chassis and one wheel fatigued, Goods Van and Brake Van, slight rust to one side, with key, oil bottle and instructions, in original D102 box **£460**

EDG 7 ELECTRIC TANK GOODS SET, LMS, wrapper dated 10.38, comprising Tank Locomotive, 6917, buffer beams retouched, Open Wagon, Goods Van, Brake Van, controller, oil bottle, spanner and instructions, in original D104 box. **ESTIMATE:** **£600-800**

DL7 CLOCKWORK TANK LOCOMOTIVE, 6917, LMS, in original D152 box dated 9.38...**£345**

EDL 7 ELECTRIC TANK LOCOMOTIVE, 6917, LMS, in original D154 box dated 9.38, bearing Service Dept. label, with wrapper **£253**

FREIGHT STOCK, LMS D1 12-Ton Goods Van, D302 box, 12-Ton Open Goods Wagon, D303 box, D1 Coal Wagon, D305 box, with extra coal load, and D2 High-Sided Coal Wagon, D312 box together with empty boxes, D308 and D311, wearing throughout **£57**

FREIGHT STOCK, LMS, rare D1 Cattle Truck, D306 box, code BW5661 7.5M 4.39, D1 Meat Van, D308 box, code BW5661 7.5M 4.39, D2 High-Sided Wagon, buffers damaged, D311 box, code BW7877 7.5M 8.39 and D2 High-Sided Wagon with coal, D312 box, code BW9838 8M 12.39 ....**£115**

DG7 CLOCKWORK TANK GOODS SET, GWR, comprising Tank Locomotive 6699, chipped paint at winding arbour, Open Wagon, Goods Van and Brake Van, all green, with oil bottle and key, in original D102 box, repairs to lid-flaps.............................**£1,150**

A VERY RARE EDG7 ELECTRIC TANK GOODS SET, GWR, comprising Tank Locomotive 6699, Open Wagon, Goods Van, Brake Van and No. 1A controller for use with accumulator, with oil bottle and spanner in original D106 box, replacement wrapper, lid with repaired section to one end. (This type of set was designed for use within homes not supplied with electricity)................................**£517**

FREIGHT STOCK, GWR, D1 Goods Brake Van, D301 box, code BW678 3M 8.38, D1 Coach Wagon, D305 box, cde BW5221 10M 3.39 and D1 Cattle Truck, D306 box code BW 5661 7.5M 4.39, rusted staples **£115**

EDG7 ELECTRIC TANK GOODS SET, NE, wrapper dated 10.38, comprising Tank Locomotive 2690, Open Wagon, Goods Van, Brake Van and controller, with oil bottle and spanner, in original D104 box, lid with repaired section and damp damage to one end..............**£575**

DL7 CLOCKWORK TANK LOCOMOTIVE, 2690, NE, in original D152 box dated 9.38, with keeps, excellent condition...**£713**

EDG7 ELECTRIC TANK GOODS SET, SR, wrapper dated 10.38, comprising Tank Locomotive 2594, Open Wagon, Goods Van, Brake Van and controller, with oil bottle, spanner, keeps and instructions dated 9.38, in original D104 box, very good **£1,667**

DL7 CLOCKWORK TANK LOCOMOTIVE, 2594, SR, in original box with wrapper and key...**£943**

D1 TANK WAGONS, 'Royal Daylight', 'Power Ethyl' and 'Esso', some wear, all in original D304 boxes, code BW5221 10M 3.39
....**£161**

D1 MAINLINE STATION, RED ROOF, in D407 box, code BW1047 1M 8.38, together with six gummed printed Station Name Panels
....**£874**

D1 ISLAND PLATFORM, red roof, in original D403 box, dated 8.38, together with a D1 Signal Cabin with red roof and applied label, 'Pennith', unboxed...**£713**

D1 GOODS DEPOT, red roof, in original D402 box, code MW1780 3.250 8.38, together with a D1 Signal Cabin with red roof, unboxed, and six printed, gummed Station Name Labels, 'Ashford', 'Pennith' and 'Berwick' **£483**

D1 ENGINE SHED, green roof, in original box, code BW8530 1M 10.39, ends lacking, worn..**£195**

D1 MAINLINE STATION, green roof, architectural recesses to fence, in D407 box, code MW1780, 3250 8.38, box probably not original, no lid **£299**

D1 GOODS DEPOT, green roof, D402 box, code MW1780 3.250 8.38, box probably not original **£805**

D1 BUILDINGS, green roofs, 1939, Island Platform, slight chip, Goods Depot, Harley's Marmalade advertisement missing, and Signal Cabin, all unboxed...**£161**

D2 CITY STATION SET, comprising Station Building with green roof, Canopy with Side Platforms and six green removal advertising panels, arched, printed cellophane roof, four Centre Platforms, two Centre Ramps, three Side Ramps and Single and Double Platform Buffers **£828**

2 x D1 SHORT TUNNELS AND D2 LONG TUNNEL, each with applied red label, remnant label only to one D1 short tunnel........**£80**

Sotheby's (continued)

D1 MINIATURE RAILWAY STAFF AND PASSENGERS, a complete set of six, in original green box with pale green printed label, together with unboxed passengers, Man carrying raincoat, Man reading newspaper, Golfer, Woman in fur coat, slight chips **£138**

POST WAR, PRE-NATIONALISATION

EDP 1 LNER 'SIR NIGEL GRESLEY' PASSENGER SET, First Issue 1948, Locomotive with horseshoe magnet motor, split pin and washer to pony truck, slight corrosion to hand rails. Tender with plated bogies, First/Third and Brake/Third Corridor Coaches, oil, spanner, controller, four green wire coils, instructions dated 5.48, cover strip and keeps **£874**

D2 LNER TWO-COACH ARTICULATED UNIT, in box, code BW 10199 2M 5.48.................**£621**

EDL 7 GOODS TRAN, LMS, Locomotive with gold label, some wear, D1 Tank Wagon 'Royal Daylight', D1 Cattle Truck, D1 Goods Brake Van (2).D1 Open Goods Wagon (2), D1 Goods Van, D1 Meat Van and D2 High-Sided Wagon, all boxed, dates from 3.48 to 5.49, goods van box with tape damage **£253**

EDG 7 TANK GOODS SET, LMS, Locomotive with sans serif lettering, gold label and small windows, lightweight pony truck, slight corrosion to hand-rails and wear, Goods Van, Open Wagon and Goods Brake Van, oil bottle, controller, instructions dated 5.49 and cover strip, in mid-blue box, interior inscribed, box-lid torn and tape repaired **£172**

EDG 7 TANK GOODS SET, GWR, Locomotive 6699, with lightweight pony truck, gold label, small windows, Open Wagon, Goods Van, Goods Brake Van, cover strip, torn and inscribed, oil bottle, controller and instructions dated 9.47, in 'Royal Scot' box, box poor.................**£241**

EDL 7 GOODS TRAIN, GWR, Locomotive with large windows, gold label, smoke box door chipped, in No.3217 BR Tank Locomotive box, D1 Coal Wagon with coal load, box dated 4.50, D1 Cattle Truck, box 7.50, another, box 10.51, both Cattle Trucks with four windows to each side and two further D1 Cattle Trucks, three windows to each side, boxes 8.52 ....**£207**

EDL 7 GOODS TRAIN, GWR, Locomotive with gold label, large windows, box with cover strip, date obscured by tape damage, and boxed D1 stock. Open Goods Wagon, 3.48 (2), Cattle Truck, 3.48 (2), Goods Brake Van, 5.48 and Goods Van, 9.48 (7) **£368**

EDG 7 TANK GOODS SET, GWR, Locomotive with silver label and small windows, Open Wagon, Goods Van and Goods Brake Van, oil bottle, tag, controller, instructions dated 4.50 and cover strip, in mid-blue box, fair-good.................**£356**

EDL 7 GOODS TRAIN, LNER Locomotive, 9596 in black livery with gold label, large windows, 6.48, box inscribed 3.48, D1 Fish Van, 3.48, D1 Open Goods Wagon, 3.48, D2 High-Sided Wagon, D1 Tank Wagon 'Power Ethyl', 3.48, D1 Goods Van 9.48 and D1 High Capacity Wagon.................**£414**

EDG 7 TANK GOODS SET, SR, comprising Tank Locomotive 2594, serif lettering, large windows, gold label and number to rear of bunker, Open Wagon, Goods Van and Good Brake Van, cover strip, oil bottle, controller and instructions dated 9.47 in 'Royal Scot' box, general wear, box-lid good, base torn **£690**

EDG 7 TANK GOODS SET, SR, Locomotive in malachite green with silver label and thin black-lined yellow numbers and lettering, some paint loss, Open Wagon, Goods Van, and Goods Brake Van, oil bottle, controller, instructions dated 2.51, and cover strip, in mid-blue, good condition.................**£598**

FREIGHT STOCK, SR, D1 Meat Van, D1 Open Goods Wagon, boxes 3.48 and D1 Goods Brake Van, box 5.48, together with NE Fish Van, roof chipped, High-Sided Wagon and LMS Coal Wagon, slight corrosion, and Coal Wagon with coal, in pre-war pale blue boxes **£437**

EDG 7 TANK GOODS SET, SR, Locomotive in malachite green with gold label and thick black-lined yellow numbers and lettering, lightweight pony truck, smokebox door rubbed, Open Wagon, Goods Van and Goods Brake Van, oil bottle, controller, instructions dated 5.48 and cover strip, in mid-blue box, wear to corners.................**£391**

D1 TANK WAGONS, 'Power Ethyl' with hand, 'Esso' and 'Royal Daylight', boxes dated 11.49, tape damage to 'Power Ethyl' **£218**

D1 TANK WAGONS, 'Power Petrol', box 10.52, silver 'Esso' with silver tank ends, box 10.52 and 'Royal Daylight' (2) in boxes 1.53 and 6.53 (4) **£115**

D1 TANK WAGONS, 'Power Petrol', box 32080, silver 'Esso' with silver tank ends, silver 'Esso' with grey tank ends, boxes 32081 and 'Royal Daylight' box 32070, all boxes undated (4) **£63**

EDL 2 LMS 'DUCHESS of ATHOLL' PASSENGER TRAIN, first issue, Locomotive with horseshoe magnet motor and lightweight pony and bogie truck, fine buffer head, in box code BW 11 2.5M 6.48, box worn and tabbed, Tender, two chips, tabbed, not rivetted, in box dated 4.48, D3 Corridor Coaches First/Third with silver-grey roof and pre-war matt sides, two scratches, box dated 4.48, First/Third, gloss sides, box dated 6.49 and Brake/Third, box dated 6.49 ....**£356**

EDP 2 LMS 'DUCHESS OF ATHOLL' PASSENGER SET, Locomotive with EDL 2 under cab roof, Tender with rivetted chassis, First/Third and Brake/Third, silver-grey roofs, oil, spanner, controller, instructions dated 4.50 and cover strip, excellent condition throughout **£690**

RARE EDL 2 LMS 'DUCHESS OF ATHOLL' LOCOMOTIVE, with raised moulded section beneath nameplate instead of recessed slot, instructions dated 1.50, Tender with rivetted chassis, First/Thirds (2), boxes 4.51 and 8.52 and Brake/Third, box 2.50 (5).................**£253**

EDP 2 LMS 'DUCHESS OF ATHOLL' PASSENGER SET, Locomotive with EDL 2 under cab roof, Tender with rivetted chassis, First/Third and Brake/Third, grey roofs, oil, spanner, four insulating tabs, controller, instructions dated 2.51 and cover strip, excellent condition, box fair **£333**

POST NATIONALISATION

EDP 10 PASSENGER SET IN RARE LONG BOX, Tank Locomotive, N. 69567, D14 Suburban Coaches First/Third and Brake/Third, tube of lubricant and instructions dated 1.56, yellow box interior, very good condition, box with slight scuffs **£368**

EDL 11 BR(E) PASSENGER TRAIN, 'Silver King', earlier gloss finish to Locomotive, instructions dated 10.53, cover strip, oil and spanner, in mid-blue box, Tender, in dark blue box dated 4.53, D11 Corridor Coaches First/Third (2) and Brake/Third (2), two in dark blue boxes, 6.53 and two in mid blue boxes 11.53 ....**£138**

EDP 11 BR(E) PASSENGER SET, 'Silver King', earlier gloss finish to Locomotive and Tender, D11 Corridor Coaches First/Third and Brake/Third, tube of lubricant, spanner and instructions dated 2.54, slight corrosion to First/Third, otherwise very good **£149**

EDL 11 LOCOMOTIVE AND D11 TENDER, 'Silver King', matt finish, Locomotive in blue-striped box, slight wear to edges, with blue cover strip and instructions dated 9.54, Tender with wheel totem, in blue-striped box **£138**

L11 LOCOMOTIVE, 'Mallard' N. 60022, mid-blue box with cover strip, tube of lubricant, spanner and instructions dated 3.57, and Tender, lion wheel totem, in blue-striped box, together with one other D11 Tender, wheel totem in blue striped boxes **£241**

D11 AND D12 BR CORRIDOR COACHES, D11 (BR(E)) First/Third and Brake/Third and D12 BR(M) First/Third, Brake/Third and First/Second, various in blue striped boxes, some boxes not matching contents.....................**£161**

3211 BR(E) LOCOMOTIVE AND TENDER, 'Mallard', No. 60022, matt finish with L11 cast under cab roof, nickel-plated driving wheels, plastic bogie and pony wheels, metal coupling, metal Tender with plastic wheels and lion and crown totems facing opposite directions, in blue-striped picture box, very good **£345**

3211 LOCOMOTIVE AND TENDER, 'Mallard' No. 60022, Locomotive with 'Flying Scotsman' headboard label, Tender with lion on crown totem, instructions dated 3.57, mid-blue box with yellow lining.....................**£184**

EDL 12 BR(LMR) PASSENGER TRAIN, 'Duchess of Montrose', earlier gloss finish to Locomotive, cover strip, ol and spanner, instructions dated 12.53, and Tender, mid-blue boxes, and D12 Corridor Coaches First/Third (2) and Brake/Third, dark blue boxes dated 12.52 and 6.53 ....**£115**

EDL 12 BR(M) PASSENGER TRAIN, 'Duchess of Montrose', matt finish to Locomotive, in blue-striped box with cover strip and instructions dated 9.54, Tender with wheel totem, in blue-striped box, and D12 Corridor Coaches First/Second (2), one with plastic wheels, and Brake/Third, in blue-striped boxes **£138**

EDP 12 BR(M) PASSENGER SET, 'Duchess of Montrose', earlier gloss finish to Locomotive and Tender, D12 Corridor Coaches First/Third and Brake/Third, oil bottle, spanner and layout suggestions dated 10.53, excellent condition throughout, one corner box-lid torn **£276**

ACCESSORIES AND TRACK, in plain blue boxes, including D1 Through Stations (2), D1 Island Platform, D1 Footbridge, D1 Signal Cabin, signals, switches, points etc., some wear (qty)................**£460**

ACCESSORIES, in blue-striped boxes, D1 Turntable with instructions, card insert spacer, tag and guarantee, 3475 TPO Lineside Apparatus, TPO Mail Van, D1 Girder Bridge, D1 Signal Cabin, D1 Island Platform, Platform Extension with Wall Platform Extension, slight corrosion, D1 Through Station and 3460 Level Crossing, generally near excellent, boxes with some signs of wear **£368**

RARE EDG 3 'CANADIAN PACIFIC' FREIGHT TRAIN SET, Locomotive, No. 1215, with EDL 2 under cab roof, number above smokebox light and cabside, six-wheeled Tender, High Capacity Brick Wagon, 'Empty to Fletton', black chassis, Caboose and Bogie Bolster Wagon, oil bottle, spanner, tag, instructions dated 7.53, guarantee, CPR sheet leaflet code 16/9. 57/30 and rail layout pamphlet, 6.53, in box, excellent condition throughout.......................**£1,265**

RARE EDP 2 'CANADIAN PACIFIC' PASSENGER TRAIN SET, Locomotive, No. 1215, with EDL 2 under cab roof, number above smokebox light and cabside, six-wheeled Tender, D12 Corridor Coaches BR(M) First/Third 4183 and BR (M) Brake/2nd, 26133, with oil bottle, spanner, instructions dated 7.53, rail layout pamphlet, 6.53 and CPR sheet leaflet, code 16/957/30, in box, excellent condition throughout, one keep repaired, box lid with two corners repaired **£1,092**

'CANADIAN PACIFIC' CABOOSE AND TENDER, Caboose in 32049 box, stamped 9.54, wear to one flap, Tender in 32004 box, stamped 9.53, excellent **£368**

EDP 14 PASSENGER SET, Standard 2-6-4 Tank Locomotive, 80054, D14 Suburban Coaches First/Third and Brake/Thirds (2), tubed lubricant and instructions dated 1.56, yellow box interior, together with EDL 14 Tank Locomotive, 80054, in EDP 14 set box, blue base with lubricant, track and First/Third Coach, Brake/Thirds lacking, one corner to box-lid torn...............................**£241**

EDP 15 PASSENGER SET, 'Silver King', No. 60016, matt finish to Locomotive and Tender, D12 Corridor Coaches First/Third and Brake/Third, tube of lubricant and spanner, instructions dated 1.56, yellow box interior, box fair-good.................................**£253**

P15 'FLYING PASSENGER SET', 'Mallard', No. 60022 and Tender, D12 Corridor Coaches First/Third and Brake/Third, tubed lubricant, spanner, instructions dated 2.59, yellow box interior, box-lid worn.... **£483**

EDG 16 BR(E) TANK GOODS SET, Locomotive, No. 69567, D1 Open Wagons (2) and Goods Brake Van, instructions 10.56.......**£149**

G 16 BR(W) TANK GOODS SET, Locomotive, No. 69567, and Super Detail Plastic Open Wagons (2) and Goods Brake Van, tubed lubricant, instructions dated 2.58, yellow box interior, slight wear to box-lid.................................**£97**

A RARE RETAILER'S DISPLAY CABINET, probably early post-war, light solid oak frame with printed frieze, 'Hornby Dublo', in green with black lining, the top and three sides glazed and with four enclosed glass shelves, 81cm wide; 61cm; 23cm depth **£529**

EDL17 GOODS TRAIN, Locomotive No. 69567, gloss finish, with oil bottle, keeps, cover strip and instructions (2.53), in mid-blue box, tears to two flaps, BR (E) goods stock D1 High Capacity Wagons (2), D1 Open Wagon, D1 Coal Wagon, D1 Horsebox, D1 Goods Brake Vans (2) and D1 Fish Van, dark blue boxes, dated 1952/53 (9).....**£97**

EDG 17 BR(E) TANK GOODS SET, Locomotive, No. 69567, earlier issue with gloss finish, D1 Open Wagon, Goods Van, Brake Van with smooth roof, and 'Royal Daylight' Tank Wagon, oil bottle and instructions dated 2.54, box good **£109**

EDG 17 TANK GOODS SET IN RARE LONG BOX, Locomotive, No. 69567, (later matt finish), 'Mobil Oil' Tank Wagon, Southern Region Meat Van, Eastern Region Open Wagon and Brake Van with chimney and roof gutters, tube of lubricant and instructions dated 1.56, yellow box interior, good condition throughout.................**£172**

3217 BR 0-6-2 TANK LOCOMOTVE, N. 69567, old BR totem with long-tail lion, metal pony truck, wheels and couplings, no coal in bunker, L17 cast to underside, fair, instructions dated 2.59, in blue-striped picture box with hinged cover strip.........................**£115**

Sotheby's (continued)

RARE 3217 BR 0-6-2 TANK LOCOMOTIVE, No. 69567, L17 cast to underside, nickel silver wheels, new BR totem, coal in bunker, blue-grey lining, plastic pony wheels and couplings, excellent, tubed lubricant, instructions dated 2.59, in blue-striped picture box with hinged cover strip and keeps, Beatties retailer label to lid, very good throughout **£299**

RARE 3217 BR 0-6-2 TANK LOCOMOTIVE, No. 69567, in plain blue box, early-type fore and aft-facing long-tail lion totems, coal in bunker, L17 cast to underside, nickel silver wheels, plastic pony wheels and couplings, excellent, instructions dated 2.59, box, code 34217, with orange-yellow cover strip with keeps, keeps inscribed, tear to one lid corner **£437**

D1 TANK WAGONS, blue-striped boxes, 'Royal Daylight', rare in 1st issue box, 'Esso', Shell Lubricating' (2) and 'Vacuum' (5).....**£57**

EDG 18 BR(E) TANK GOODS SET, Locomotive, No. 80054, High Capacity Wagon, Bogie Bolster Wagon and Brake Van, oil bottle and instructions dated 9.54 good condition, box-lid repaired **£74**

EDL 18 BR(M) TANK GOODS SET, Locomotive, No. 80054, 'Weltrol' Bogie Well Wagon, High Capacity Wagon, and LMR Brake Van, tubed lubricant and instructions dated 1.56, yellow box interior, near-excellent..**£195**

EDL 18 TANK GOODS TRAIN, Locomotive, No. 80054, in blue-striped box with yellow interior and cover strip, instructions dated 2.58, Low Sided Wagon with Furniture Container, 32087 box, Low-Sided Wagons (5), Furniture Containers (2), Insulated Meat Containers (2), and a Western Region Goods Brake Van, all in blue-striped boxes..**£149**

RARE 3218 BR 2-6-4 TANK LOCOMOTIVE, no. 8005, circa 1961, nickel-silver wheels, plastic couplings and pony and bogie trucks, forward facing totems, excellent, instructions, probably not original, dated 2.59, in blue-striped picture box, with keeps and hinged cover strip **£598**

TANK WAGONS, in blue-striped boxes, 'Power Petrol', rare in first-issue 'Power Ethyl' box with restraining tabs, 'Esso', Shell Lubricating' and 'Vacuum', all first-issue boxes, and 'Mobil', in second-issue box..**£63**

RARE G19 BR TANK GOODS SET, Locomotive, No. 80054, tinplate 'Mobil' Tank Wagon, die-cast Double Bolster Wagon and Super Detail plastic stock WR Brake Van, 8-Ton Cattle Wagon and Steel-Type Goods Wagon, metal couplings throughout, tubed lubricant and instructions dated 2.59, yellow box interior, small tape repair, box-lid with stained and worn edges **£356**

EDP 20 'BRISTOLIAN' PASSENGER SET, 'Bristol Castle', No. 7013, D21 Coaches with plastic wheels, First/Second and Brake/Second, tube of lubricant and instructions dated 8.57, very good, box good **£287**

P20 'BRISTOLIAN' PASSENGER SET, 'Bristol Castle', No. 7013, D21 Coaches with plastic wheels and nameboard stickers, First/Second and Brake/Second, tubed lubricant and instructions dated 7.58, very good, box-lid with repaired corners, slight scuffs to interior **£322**

3221 BR LOCOMOTIVE AND TENDER, 'Ludlow Castle', N. 5002, with Ring Field motor and early plastic coupling, very good, instructions dated 2.61 and Amended Instructions, 6.61, in blue-striped picture box, box scarred by chimney tape repairs ...**£425**

P22 'ROYAL SCOT' PASSENGER SET, Locomotive EDL 12 'Duchess of Montrose', with named headboard, D22 Coaches with plastic wheels, First/Second and Brake/Second, each with applied nameboard stickers, tubed lubricant, spanner, instructions (2.58) and rare exhibition-type price label, £7/3/6, excellent, in box with hinged cover strip, yellow box interior, tape repairs to lid corners **£322**

RARE G25 LMR FREIGHT SET, Locomotive 2-8-0F, No. 48158, 'Shell' Tank Wagon, Standard Wagon, Mica Refrigerator Van, 'Weltrol' Bogie Well Wagon and Brake Van all stock with plastic wheels, tubed lubricant and instructions dated 3.57, yellow box interior, excellent, box very good...**£345**

LT25 LMR 8F 2-8-0 FREIGHT LOCOMOTIVE AND TENDER, No. 48158, excellent, in blue-striped picture box with hinged cover strip, box good...**£138**

RARE 3224 LMR 2-8-0 8F GOODS LOCOMOTIVE AND TENDER No. 48094, with Ring Field motor, very good, instructions dated 7.58, in blue-striped picture box, one lid corner tape repaired **£437**

3226 BR LOCOMOTIVE AND TENDER, 'City of Liverpool', No. 46247, tiny chips cab-side, instructions dated 2.59, in blue-striped picture box **£379**

L30 BR BO-BO DIESEL-ELECTRIC LOCOMOTIVE, No. D8000, nickel silver wheels, two with rubber tyres, excellent, tubed lubricant, instructions dated 10.58, in blue-striped picture box...**£103**

3231 BR 0-6-0 DIESEL-ELECTRIC SHUNTING LOCO, No. D3763, single coupling rod variant, excellent, instructions dated 8.60, in blue-striped picture box with hinged cover strip **£184**

3231 BR 0-6-0 DIESEL-ELECTRIC SHUNTING LOCO, No. D3763, split coupling rods, excellent, instructions dated 8.60 and Amended Instructions, tubed lubricant, in blue-striped picture box with hinged cover strip **£276**

BR CO-CO DIESEL-ELECTRIC LOCOMOTIVE, nickel-silver wheels, four with rubber tyres, excellent, instructions dated 8.60, in blue-striped picture box with hinged cover strip........................**£230**

CO-BO DIESEL-ELECTRIC LOCOMOTIVE, No. D5713, nickel-silver wheels, four with rubber tyres, excellent, instructions dated 3.61, in blue-striped picture box with hinged cover strip and two card restraining tabs in addition to usual keeps **£299**

3234 DELTIC DIESEL-ELECTRIC LOCOMOTIVE, 'St Paddy', nickel-silver wheels, four with rubber tyres, metal bogie side frames, untouched, tubed lubricant, instructions dated 3.61, in blue-striped picture box with hinged cover strip and card restraining tabs, roof with minor spots due to corrosion...**£943**

3235 BR(S) WEST COUNTRY LOCOMOTIVE and TENDER, 'Dorchester', No. 34042, nickel-silver driving wheels, all other wheels plastic, excellent, instructions dated 3.61, in blue-striped picture box with hinged cover strip..**£322**

BR PASSENGER COACHES, D14 1st/2nd and Brake/2nd, D20 Restaurant Cars (4) and D21 1st/2nd and Brake/2nd, very good throughout, in blue-striped boxes (8) **£138**

MORE FINE TRAINS at Christie's South Kensington

A selection of pre-war Hornby-Dublo
from the record-breaking Bianco Reference Collection.
Sold on 24 & 25 October 1996 at Christie's South Kensington.

Fine collections continue to pour into Christie's South Kensington
and go out again to buyers from around the world. No other auction room offers such
a large variety of material and expertise in so many fields.

Christie's hold up to twelve auctions annually, with fine material reserved
for special sales in May, September and the annual 'Trains Galore' in December,
with special collections widely advertised beforehand. As well as Hornby-Dublo, the sales also
include other 00 Gauge by Triang and Wrenn, 0 Gauge by Hornby and Bassett-Lowke,
and railways by Märklin, Bing and Carette and other makers up to Gauge IV.

Many auctions also include diecast toys by Dinky, Corgi, Matchbox and other leading makers
as well as tinplate toys. Whether buying or selling, Christie's offers a comprehensive service, with detailed
catalogues giving the condition of each lot. We are always pleased to help with any enquiries
about selling, condition of lots, absentee bidding and shipping arrangements.

For further information please contact Hugo Marsh on (0171) 321 3274,
Nigel Mynheer on (0171) 321 3410 or Daniel Agnew on (0171) 321 3335.

CHRISTIE'S
SOUTH KENSINGTON

85 Old Brompton Road, London SW7 3LD Tel: (0171) 581 7611 Fax: (0171) 321 3321 *Internet:* http://www.christies.com

Top Down 1st shelf - Lot 5, 2nd - Lot 28,3rd - Lot 29, 4th - Lot 30, 5th - Lot 31, 5th - Lot 12

Top Down – prices for main lots.
1st shelf - Lot 8, 2nd Lots 1 & 10, 3rd - Lot 14, 4th - Lot 18, 5th - Lot 22, 6th - Lot 25

(For prices realised see the 'Reference Auction Results' in the Hornby Dublo section)

Christie's Hornby Dublo – Bianco Auction

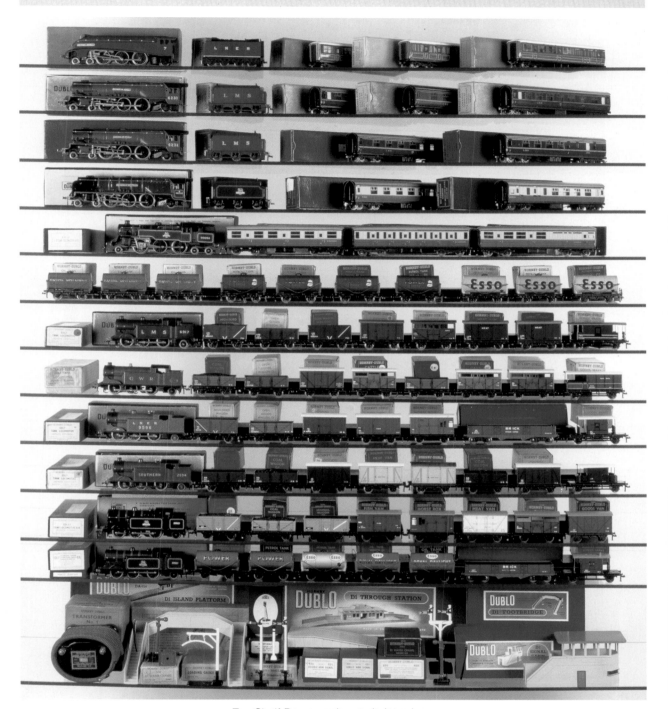

Top Shelf Downwards - main lot prices.
1st Shelf Lots 72 & 73, 2nd 103, 4th 173, 5th 175, 6th 156 & 157, 7th 124 (L.M.S. tank), 8th - 134, 9th - 81, 10th - 147, 11th - 178, 12th - 178. Bottom shelf 191 D1 station set.

(For prices realised see the 'Reference Auction Results' in the Hornby Dublo section)

L - R Top Down Lots 98, 143, 137, 131, 138

(For prices realised see the 'Reference Auction Results' in the Hornby Dublo section)

Christie's Hornby Dublo – Bianco Auction

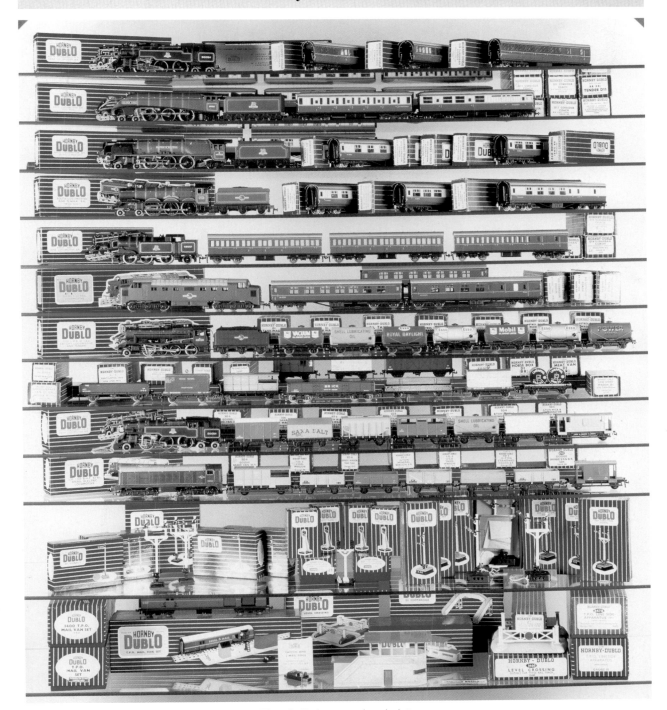

Top shelf downward main lots
1st shelf - Lot 210, 2nd - 213, 3rd - 215, 4th - 216, 5th - 219, 6th - 229 (Co-Co), 7th - 244, 8th - 242, 9th - 258, 10th - 256 (Bo-Bo) & 259

(For prices realised see the 'Reference Auction Results' in the Hornby Dublo section)

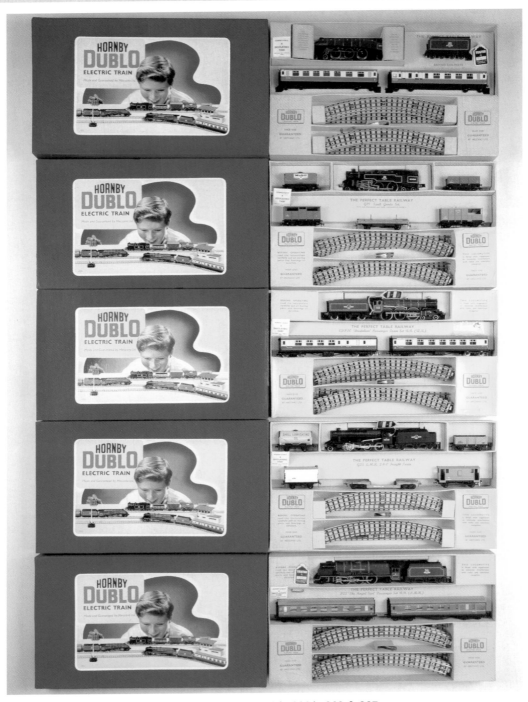

Top down Lots 228,269A, 230A, 269 & 267

(For prices realised see the 'Reference Auction Results' in the Hornby Dublo section)

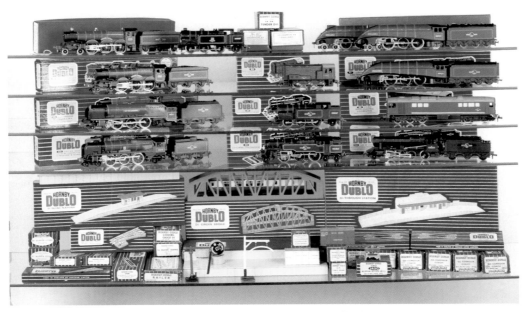

L-R Top shelf downwards main prices for lots.
1st shelf Lot 273, 270, 271, 272
2nd - 281, 280, 282, 3rd - 279, 277, 278, 4th - 275, 274, 276, 5th 295, 296, 300

L - R Top shelf downwards main prices
1st shelf - 286, 2nd - 390, 3rd - 392, 4th 393, 5th - 395, 6th 566

(For prices realised see the 'Reference Auction Results' in the Hornby Dublo section)

Christie's Hornby Dublo – Bianco Auction

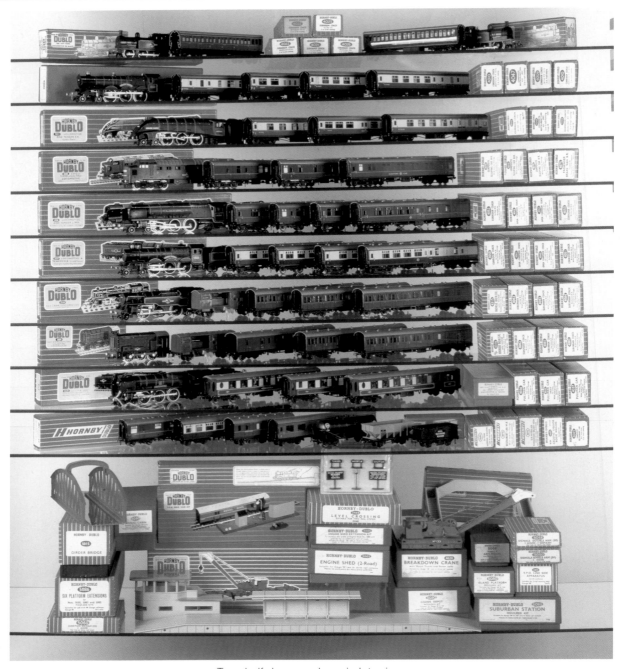

Top shelf downwards main lot prices
1st shelf - 335, 336, 2nd - 338, 339, 3rd - 340, 4th - 334, 5th - 347, 6th - 356, 7th - 367, 8th 373 (Shunter), 9th - 400, 10th - 488, Bootom shelf - 495, 499

(For prices realised see the 'Reference Auction Results' in the Hornby Dublo section)

Top row downwards L - R Lots 556, 557,555, 2nd 553, 561, 3rd - 381, 4th - 330, 5th - 334

(For prices realised see the 'Reference Auction Results' in the Hornby Dublo section)

Top Down Lots 570, 568, 567 & 407

(For prices realised see the 'Reference Auction Results' in the Hornby Dublo section)

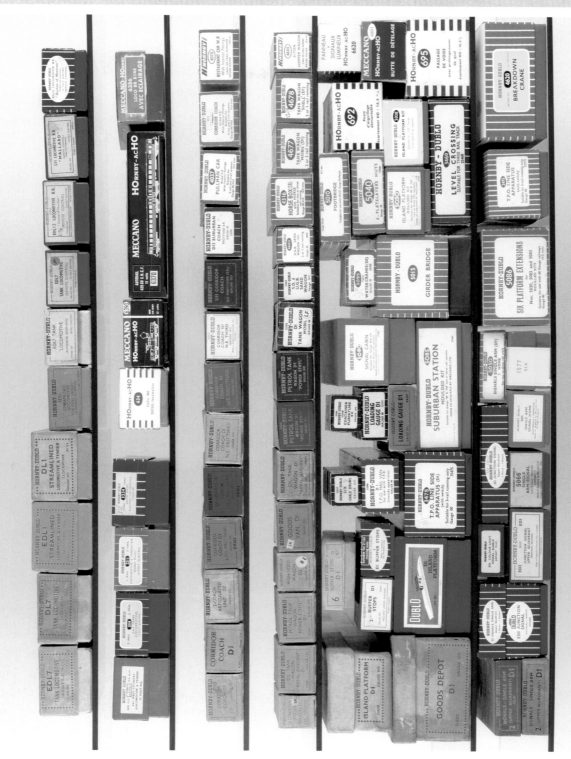

Reference collection of box ends

D1 'ESSO' Petrol Tank Wagon D304
box code BW5221 10m 3.39 sold for £140

Rare EDL7 SR Tank Locomotive, horseshoe magnet, thick sans-serif 'SOUTHERN' lettering, thin sans-serif cabside numbers, silver label, small windows, disc wheels, instructions dated 4.49, powder blue cover strip, two keeps and box dated 5.49 (sold for £1100)

(For prices realised see the 'Reference Auction Results' in the Hornby Dublo section)

Rare L11 single chimney 'Mallard' locomotive and tender, repair locomotive box,
cover strip, two keeps, Tender (sold for £950)

Rare 4685 diamond bogie caustic liquor Bogie Wagon

(For prices realised see the 'Reference Auction Results' in the Hornby Dublo section)

Tri-ang Railways

Introduction

In 1950, Rovex Plastics Ltd., of Richmond introduced a new 'OO' gauge train set to the market place. It was a two-rail electric powered set and featured a black plastic 'Princess' locomotive and two short red coaches. The plastic bodies were made by Rovex and the electric motor by a Birmingham manufacturer named Zenith Ltd. Also appearing in shops at this time were some 'OO' gauge plastic vans and wagons made by a firm called Trackmaster.

In 1951 the three firms mentioned above were acquired by the Lines Bros. Group and so the Tri-ang Railways system was born. It was launched at the British Industries Fair in 1952.

Early issues included the original Rovex set which was issued in 'B.R.' and subsequently 'S.R.' liveries. In addition, the famous 0-6-0 'Jinty' tank locomotive was produced – the first Tri-ang engine. New issues in the period leading up to 1964 included the 'Transcontinental Series' of U.S. and Canadian liveries and aimed at the export market.

In addition, three Victorian locomotives were introduced – the G.W.R. 'Lord of the Isles', the 'Rocket' and the 'Caledonian' Single No. 123. The 'TT' (Table Top) system was introduced while new inventions included overhead electric wires for locomotives with pantographs, plus a system which enabled some locomotives to puff out real smoke!

In 1964 Meccano Ltd., makers of Hornby Dublo, were in financial difficulty and were acquired by the Tri-ang Group and hence 'Tri-ang–Hornby' was formed. However, despite amalgamating the old Hornby Dublo models into Tri-ang, the Tri-ang Group went into liquidation in 1969.

The Rovex part of Tri-ang was bought by the Dunbee, Combex, Mark amalgamation and the firm Rovex Scale Models Ltd. was organised to operate the Margate factory. The name of the trains now became 'Hornby Railways'. At the same time, the G. & R. Wrenn subsidiary set up their own business, and holding some of the original Hornby Dublo tools, re-introduced many of the old lines.

The models listed date from 1958 and the Editor will be pleased to receive any further information.

Tri-ang Locomotives

Ref	Description	Colour	Number	Intro	Deleted	Used	Mint	

Steam Outline Locomotives (Electrically powered)

Ref	Description	Colour	Number	Intro	Deleted	Used	Mint	
33	BR CL 7MT 'Morning Star'	Green	70021	1981	1983	£25	£75	❑
37	BR CL 8F 'Princess Patricia'	Blue	46210	1989	1991	£25	£65	❑
41	GWR 0-6-OPT	Green	8571	1975	1989	£15	£35	❑
42	LNER CL A1 'Royal Lancer'	Green	4476	1989	1991	£25	£60	❑
48	London Transport 0-6-0 PT	Red	L90	1978		£15	£35	❑
50	BR CL 8F 'Princess Elizabeth'	Green	46201	1957	1958	£12	£50	❑
50	BR CL 8F 'Princess Victoria'	Black	46205	1959	1962	£12	£50	❑
50	BR CL 8F 'Princess Victoria'	Black	46205	1974		£15	£50	❑
50	LMS 'Princess Royal'	Crimson	6200	1984	1985	£25	£80	❑
51	GWR 0-6-0 PT	Green	8571	1972	1974	£12	£35	❑
52	BR Fowler 3F 0-6-0 T	Black	47606	1957	1958	£10	£30	❑
52	BR Fowler 3F 0-6-0 T	Black	47606	1959	1975	£10	£30	❑
52	LMS Fowler 3F 0-6-0 T	Black	47606	1959	1975	£10	£30	❑
52	LMS Fowler 3F 0-6-0 T	Maroon	7606	1971	1972	£15	£35	❑
52	LMS Fowler 3F 0-6-0 T	Maroon	16440	1978	1979	£15	£35	❑
52	P/O Fowler 3F 0-6-0 T (from Sets)	Black	2021	1973		£18	NGPP	❑
53	BR CL 8F 'Princess Elizabeth'	Green	46201	1957	1961	£15	£45	❑
53	BR Fowler 3F 0-6-0 T	Black	47556	1988	1991	£15	£35	❑
53	LNER CL B17/4 'Manchester United'	Green	2862	1980	1982	£25	£65	❑
55	LMS CL 4P 2-6-4 T	Maroon	2300	1981	1982	£20	£40	❑
56	BR 'Iron Duke'	Green	70014	1975		£20	£65	❑
57	CR CL OF 0-4-0 ST	Blue		1980	1982	£12	£18	❑
57	SR Schools, 'Charterhouse'	Green	903	1989	1990	£35	£65	❑
58	BR Fowler 3F 0-6-0 T	Black	47458	1978	1979	£12	£30	❑
59	BR CL 3MT 2-6-2 T	Black	82004	1957	1960	£20	£50	❑
59	BR CL 3MT 2-6-2 T	Green	82004	1960	1972	£20	£55	❑
59	GWR CL 2721 0-6-0PT	Green	2744	1980	1984	£15	£30	❑
60	BR CL B17/4 4-6-0 'Leeds United'	Green	61656	1982	1985	£25	£90	❑
61	LMS CL 5	Black	5112	1976		£25	£55	❑
62	BR CL 4P 2-6-4 T	Black	42308	1982	1985	£20	£35	❑
63	BR CL 7P 'Britannia'	Green	70000	1976	1979	£20	£65	❑
65	BR CL 9F 2-10-0 'Evening Star'	Green	92220	1977	1979	£20	£65	❑
66	LMS 'Duchess of Sutherland'	Maroon	6233	1977	1979	£20	£65	❑
68	BR CL 5 4-6-0	Black	45021	1984	1985	£25	£55	❑
70	GWR 'King George V' (Limited Edition)	Green		1985		£25	£65	❑
72	LMS 'City of Bristol'	Maroon	6237	1985	1986	£25	£90	❑
74	BR BoB '41 Squadron'	Malachite Green	34076	1985	1986	£30	£125	❑
77	GWR Holden 0-4-0 T	Green	101	1978	1979	£8	£25	❑
77	LNER CL A4 'Mallard'	Green	4468	1984	1985	£25	£75	❑
78	GWR 'King Edward I'	Green	6024	1978	1979	£25	£65	❑
80	BR CL 8F 'Princess Elizabeth'	Green	46201	1984	1985	£25	£80	❑
84	BR Schools 'Clifton'	Black	30927	1984	1985	£35	£125	❑
88	LMS CL 4P 2-6-4 T	Black	2345	1984	1985	£20	£65	❑
99	LNER CL A4 'Silver Fox'	Grey	2512	1985	1989	£25	£125	❑
103	SR CL M7 4-4-0 T	Green	249	1985	1986	£35	£75	❑
130	LNER 0-6-0 T	Green	8400	1988	1989	£15	£30	❑
150 S	BR CL B12	Black	61573	1962	1963	£20	£45	❑
150	BR CL B12	Black	61572	1966	1970	£20	£45	❑
150	L & Y 0-4-0 ST	Black	627	1986	1992	£12	£20	❑
150	LNER CL B12	Black	1577	1976		£20	£45	❑
150	LNER CL B12	Black	7476	1977		£20	£45	❑
152	LMS 0-4-0 ST	Maroon	16031	1990	1993	£12	£20	❑
153	BR CL 2F 0-6-0 ST	Black	748	1957	1961	£20	£30	❑
153	P/O 'Tolgus Tin' 0-4-0 T	Grey	No 1	1986	1988	£10	£35	❑
154	SR CL N15 'Sir Dinidan'	Green	795	1976	1978	£25	£70	❑

No.	Description	Colour	Number	From	To	Price	Value	
155	P/O Colmans 0-4-0 (from Sets)	Yellow	21	1984	1985	**£10**	NGPP	❏
157	SR CL E2 0-6-0 T	Black	103	1985		**£16**	**£100**	❏
158	GWR 0-6-0 PT	Green	2747	1985	1988	**£15**	**£30**	❏
159	'Mr. Robbie Burns' 0-4-0 (from Sets)	Red		1986	1987	**£10**	NGPP	❏
161	P/O 'William Mansfield' 0-4-0 (from Sets)	Blue	No 3	1986	1987	**£10**	NGPP	❏
162	P/O 'NCB Dunraven' 0-4-0 PT	Cream	112	1984	1985	**£10**	**£25**	❏
163	P/O 'Ford Motor Co.' 0-4-0 T	White	45	1984	1985	**£10**	**£35**	❏
164	P/O 'Industrial Iron Horse'	Light Grey		1984	1985	**£10**	**£35**	❏
165	GWR 0-6-0 PT	Green	2783	1989	1991	**£18**	**£30**	❏
165	GWR 0-6-0 PT	Green	2873	1990	1993	**£18**	**£30**	❏
173	GWR 0-4-0 T (GWR 150)	Green	101	1985		**£15**	**£75**	❏
174	P/O 'Huntley and Palmers' 0-4-0 ST	Red	4	1985		**£10**	**£25**	❏
175	BR CL 4P Compound	Black	41043	1986	1988	**£20**	**£65**	❏
251	BR Fowler 3F 0-6-0	Black	43775	1958	1965	**£15**	**£35**	❏
251	BR Fowler 3F 0-6-0	Maroon	43620	1966	1967	**£15**	**£35**	❏
251	LMS Fowler 3F 0-6-0	Maroon	3775	1968		**£15**	**£85**	❏
252	LNER CL J83 0-6-0 T	Green	8477	1976	1978	**£12**	**£30**	❏
254	P/O U.S. Tank 0-4-0 T	Black	254	1976		**£8**	**£25**	❏
255	HR 0-4-0 ST 'Loch Ness'	Blue	8	1989	1992	**£12**	**£30**	❏
255	P/O 0-4-0 T	Blue	7178	1976	1977	**£10**	**£25**	❏
256	P/O U.S. Tank 0-4-0 T	Black	256	1977		**£8**	**£25**	❏
257	BR Schools, 'Dover'	Green	30911	1983		**£35**	**£125**	❏
258 S	BR CL 8P 'Princess Royal'	Maroon	46200	1959	1963	**£18**	**£45**	❏
258	BR CL 8P 'Princess Royal'	Maroon	46200	1969	1974	**£18**	**£45**	❏
258 G	LMS 'Princess Elizabeth'	Maroon	6201	1970	1971	**£15**	**£45**	❏
258 NS	LMS 'Princess Elizabeth'	Maroon	6201	1971	1974	**£15**	**£45**	❏
259	BR CL D49/1 'Yorkshire'	Black	62700	1983	1985	**£25**	**£65**	❏
259 S	BR CL 7P6F 'Britannia'	Green	70000	1960	1972	**£20**	**£65**	❏
261	SR CL E2 0-6-0 T	Green	104	1982	1985	**£16**	**£75**	❏
262	BR CL 8P 'Duchess of Atholl'	Green	46231	1982	1985	**£25**	**£75**	❏
264	BR CL 9F 2-10-0	Black	92200	1982	1983	**£25**	**£75**	❏
292	GWR 'King Richard'	Green	6027	1988	1990	**£25**	**£65**	❏
300	GWR CL 57XX 0-6-0 PT	Green	8773	1980	1982	**£12**	**£30**	❏
301	LMS Fowler 3F 0-6-0 T	Maroon	16440	1980	1989	**£12**	**£30**	❏
302	BR Fowler 3F 0-6-0 T	Black	47480	1980	1982	**£12**	**£30**	❏
303	BR CL 9F 'Evening Star' 2-10-	Green	92220	1980	1982	**£25**	**£75**	❏
305	LMS 'Duchess of Abercorn'	Crimson	6234	1980	1982	**£25**	**£75**	❏
309	BR CL A4 'Mallard'	Green	60022	1980	1983	**£25**	**£55**	❏
309	BR CL A4 'Mallard' (from Sets)	Green	60022	1989	1993	**£25**	NGPP	❏
311	LMS 'Duke of Sutherland'	Crimson	5541	1980	1983	**£25**	**£55**	❏
312	LNER CL A4 'Silver Link'	Silver and Grey	2509	1990	1993	**£25**	**£120**	❏
313	GWR 'Hagley Hall' 4-6-0	Green	4930	1980	1983	**£20**	**£55**	❏
313	LNER CL A4 'Golden Eagle'	Green	4482	1990	1994	**£25**	**£65**	❏
314	BR CL 5	Black	44871	1990	1991	**£25**	**£65**	❏
315	LBSC CL E2 0-6-0 T	Umber	100	1980	1982	**£16**	**£35**	❏
315	LMS CL 8F	Black	8193	1988	1990	**£25**	**£65**	❏
320	LMS CL 5 4-6-0	Black	5138	1981	1985	**£25**	**£55**	❏
322	BR CL 8F	Black	48758	1988	1989	**£25**	**£65**	❏
322	LNER CL A3 'Flying Scotsman'	Green	4472	1980		**£25**	**£55**	❏
324	BR 'Lady Godiva' 4-6-0	Black	45519	1983		**£25**	**£75**	❏
324	BR CL 8F	Black	48774	1990	1993	**£25**	**£65**	❏
325	LMS CL 8F	Black	8027	1990	1992	**£25**	**£65**	❏
325	LMS CL 8F	Black	8118	1990	1992	**£25**	**£65**	❏
325	LMS CL 8F	Black	8233	1990	1992	**£25**	**£65**	❏
327	LNER CL A4 'Mallard'	Blue	4468	1988	1989	**£25**	**£65**	❏
329	BR CL 7P 'William Shakespeare'	Green	70004	1990	1991	**£25**	**£75**	❏
330	BR CL 9F 'Evening Star'	Black	92220	1990		**£25**	**£75**	❏
330	BR CL 9F 2-10-0	Black	92207	1990	1991	**£25**	**£75**	❏
330	BR CL 9F 2-10-0	Black	92222	1990	1991	**£25**	**£75**	❏
330	BR CL 9F 2-10-0	Black	92231	1990	1991	**£25**	**£75**	❏
333	GWR 0-4-0T	Green	101	1980	1983	**£10**	**£25**	❏
346	Stephenson's 'Rocket'	Yellow		1965	1968	**£25**	**£150**	❏
349	GWR 'King Henry VIII'	Green	6013	1980	1985	**£25**	**£65**	❏

350	BR CL A4 'Mallard'	Green	60022	1979		£20	£55	❏
350	BR CL L1 4-4-0	Green	31757	1960	1967	£25	£75	❏
350	SR CL L1 4-4-0	Green	1757	1972		£25	£85	❏
353	LBSC CL E2 0-6-0 T	Umber	100	1979		£16	£35	❏
354	GWR 'Lord of the Isles'	Green	3046	1961	1963	£30	£85	❏
354	GWR 'Lord of the Isles'	Green	3046	1971	1973	£30	£85	❏
355	MR 4-4-0 Compound	Crimson	1000	1983	1985	£20	£85	❏
355	P/O 0-4-0 T 'Connie'	Yellow	No 6	1963	1965	£10	£50	❏
355 B	P/O 0-4-0 T 'Nellie'	Blue	No 7	1961	1972	£10	£50	❏
355 G	P/O 0-4-0 T	Green	27	1970	1971	£10	£50	❏
355	P/O 0-4-0 T 'Connie'	Blue	No 6	1962		£10	£50	❏
355 R	P/O 0-4-0 T 'Polly'	Red	No 9	1963	1970	£10	£50	❏
356 S	BR BoB 'Winston Churchill'	Green	34051	1961	1969	£25	£120	❏
357	LMS 'Duke of Sutherland'	Maroon	5541	1979		£25	£55	❏
359	BR 0-4-0 T	Black		1961	1962	£10	£30	❏
372	LNER CL A4 'Seagull'	Blue	4902	1981	1982	£20	£70	❏
373	BR CL 9F 'Evening Star'	Green	92220	1988	1991	£25	£65	❏
374	SR BoB 'Spitfire' 4-6-2	Malachite Green	21C166	1981	1985	£30	£100	❏
376	LMS CL 4P Compound 4-4-0	Maroon	1000	1981	1983	£20	£75	❏
378	LNER CL D49/1 Cheshire 4-4-0	Green	2753	1981	1983	£20	£65	❏
380	BR Saint 'Clevedon Court'	Black	2937	1988	1991	£25	£60	❏
380	SR Schools 'Stowe' 4-4-0	Green	928	1981	1982	£35	£65	❏
390	GWR 'County of Oxford'	Green	3830	1984	1985	£20	£75	❏
392	GWR 'County of Bedford' 4-4-0	Green	3621	1981	1983	£20	£65	❏
396	GNR CL J13 0-6-0 ST	Green	1247	1981	1983	£12	£30	❏
398	LNER CL A1 'Flying Scotsman'	Green	4472	1981	1994	£25	£65	❏
450	LMS Fowler 2P 4-4-0	Black	690	1973	1974	£25	£65	❏
452	LMS Fowler 3F 0-6-0 T	Maroon	7606	1973	1974	£15	£30	❏
453	P/O 0-4-0	Red	25550	1973	1975	£10	£25	❏
455	P/O 0-4-0 T (Limited Edition)	Red	25550	1966		£10	£25	❏
455	P/O 0-4-0T 'Silver Dome' (Limited Edition)	Red	25550	1966		£10	£25	❏
550	BR CL 9F 2-10-0	Black	92166	1973		£20	£75	❏
552	BR CL 7P 'Oliver Cromwell'	Green	70013	1973	1975	£20	£65	❏
553	CR 4-2-2	Blue		1963	1967	£25	£85	❏
553	CR 4-2-2	Blue		1973		£25	£85	❏
651	Stephenson's 'Rocket'	Yellow		1963		£25	£150	❏
653 S	Prairie Tank 2-6-2	Black		1963	1969	£25	£65	❏
659	BR 0-4-0 T	Black		1962		£10	£30	❏
683	SR Schools 'Repton'	Green	926	1983	1985	£35	£75	❏
685	LMS 'Coronation'	Blue	6220	1983	1985	£25	£85	❏
752	P/O 0-4-0ST 'Stewarts & Lloyd'	Dark Red	205	1984	1985	£10	£25	❏
754	BR CL M7 0-4-4	Black	30021	1968		£25	£75	❏
754	BR CL M7 0-4-4	Black	30027	1969	1970	£25	£75	❏
759	BR 'Albert Hall'	Green	4983	1967	1977	£18	£50	❏
761	GWR 'Kneller Hall'	Green	5934	1978	1979	£18	£55	❏
763	LMS CL 1P 4-2-2 (Ex CR) (Limited Edition box)	Crimson	14010	1983		£30	£75	❏
765	'Lord Westwood'	Red	25555	1973	1974	£18	£45	❏
766	Super S (from Sets)	Red		1984		£8	NGPP	❏
767	LMS 'George VI' (Limited Edition BTS)	Maroon	6244	1982		£30	£225	❏
768	LMS PUG 0-4-0 ST (Limited Edition BTS)	Black	16032	1982		£10	£25	❏
768	LMS PUG 0-4-0ST 'Monty' (Limited Edition BTS)	Black	16030	1982		£10	£25	❏
779	P/O 'Desmond' 0-4-0 ST	Red		1981	1983	£10	£25	❏
782	BR 0-4-0 ST 'Smokey Joe'	Black	56025	1983	1994	£10	£20	❏
795	'Lord of the Isles' (Limited Edition box)	Green		1984		£45	£150	❏
796	'Rocket' Set (With Coaches) (Limited Edition box)	Yellow and Black		1985		NGPP	£150	❏
812	LNER CL A3 'Silver Link'	Silver	2509	1990		£30	£120	❏
817	SR Schools, 'Eton'	Green	900	1986	1987	£35	£75	❏
830	GWR 'Saint David'	Green	2920	1986	1987	£30	£70	❏
832	LMS 'Princess Elizabeth'	Maroon	6201	1986	1988	£25	£65	❏
834	LMS 'Queen Mary'	Maroon	6222	1986	1988	£25	£95	❏
840	LMS CL 5	Black	5112	1977	1978	£25	£50	❏
842	LMS CL 5	Maroon	4657	1978	1981	£25	£55	❏

Tri-ang Locomotives

845	LNER CL A3 'Flying Scotsman'	Green	4472	1978	1979	£25	£55	❑
850	BR CL A3 'Flying Scotsman'	Green	60103	1968	1971	£25	£55	❑
852	BR CL 2 'Ivatt' 2-6-0	Green	46521	1978	1981	£20	£50	❑
855	LNER CL A3 'Flying Scotsman'	Green	4472	1969	1977	£25	£55	❑
857	BR CL 2 'Ivatt' 2-6-0	Black	46400	1975	1977	£20	£50	❑
858	LMS CL 5	Black	5241	1987	1989	£30	£55	❑
859	BR CL 5	Black	45158	1974	1975	£25	£55	❑
859	BR CL 5	Green	45192	1973		£25	£55	❑
859	LNER Hunt CL 'Fitzwilliam'	Green	359	1987	1989	£30	£65	❑
860	BR Hunt CL D49/2 'Pytchley'	Black	62750	1987	1989	£30	£65	❑
861	BR CL 9F 2-10-0 'Evening Star'	Green	92220	1971	1975	£25	£65	❑
861	LNER CL J52	Black	3980	1987	1988	£12	£65	❑
862	BR CL M7 0-4-4	Black	30111	1987	1988	£25	£75	❑
864	LMS 'Coronation'	Blue	6220	1970	1973	£25	£85	❑
866	LNER CL B12/3	Green	8509	1970	1974	£18	£45	❑
866	LNER CL B12/3	Green	8509	1978	1979	£18	£45	❑
866	SR BoB 'Fighter Pilot'	Green	21C155	1987	1989	£30	£150	❑
868	SR CL M7 0-4-4	Green	328	1970	1971	£25	£75	❑
868	SR CL M7 0-4-4	Green	245	1972	1974	£25	£75	❑
869 S	BR BoB 'Fighter Command' (Renamed)	Malachite Green	21C164	1971		£25	NGPP	❑
869 S	BR BoB 'Hurricane' (Renamed)	Malachite Green	21C165	1971		£25	NGPP	❑
869	SR BoB 'Winston Churchill'	Malachite Green	21C151	1970	1973	£25	£1,200	❑
871	LMS CL 8P 'King George VI'	Maroon	6244	1971	1974	£25	£85	❑
888	LNER CL A4 'Sir Nigel Gresley' (from Sets)	Blue	4498	1987	1988	£25	£75	❑
9811	LMS 'Lady Patricia' (Kays Limited Edition)	Maroon	6210	1990		£25	£120	❑
9812	BR A4 'Mallard' (Kays Limited Edition)	Blue	60022	1990		£25	£120	❑

Diesel and Electric Locomotives

54	BR CL 08 Intercity 'Piccadilly'	Intercity Grey	08673	1988	1992	£15	£30-£35	❑
60	BR CL 47	Green	D1520	1976		£14	£25-£30	❑
68	BR CL 25	Blue	25247	1977	1979	£12	£25-£30	❑
69	BR CL 253 (PWR)	Blue	43002	1979		£12	NGPP	❑
70	BR CL 253 (DMY)	Blue		1979		£8	NGPP	❑
72	BR CL 25	Green	7596	1977	1979	£12	£25-£30	❑
73	BR CL 47 Mammoth	Green	D1670	1979		£15	£25-£30	❑
74	BR CL 35 Hymek	Green	D7063	1977	1979	£12	£25-£35	❑
75	BR CL 47	Blue	47421	1977	1978	£12	£25-£30	❑
80	BR CL 29	Blue	6124	1978	1979	£12	£25-£30	❑
84	BR CL 29	Green	D6110	1978	1979	£12	£25-£30	❑
152	BR CL 08 0-6-0	Black		1957	1958	£8	£25-£30	❑
152	BR CL 08 0-6-0	Blue	D3035	1969	1975	£12	£25-£30	❑
152	BR CL 08 0-6-0	Green	13035	1959	1960	£10	£25-£30	❑
152	BR CL 08 0-6-0	Green	D3035	1961	1968	£10	£25-£30	❑
156	BR CL 12 0-6-0	Green	13012	1977	1979	£12	£25-£30	❑
156	BR CL 12 0-6-0	Green	13005	1976		£12	£25-£30	❑
156	BR SR Surburban Motor Coach	Green	S1057S	1957	1959	£18	£75-£95	❑
156	BR SR Surburban Motor Coach	Green	S1057S	1960	1963	£18	NGPP	❑
157	BR DMU Railcar (PWR)	Blue	M79079			£12	NGPP	❑
157	BR DMU Railcar (PWR)	Green	M79079	1958	1966	£12	NGPP	❑
157	BR DMU Railcar (PWR)	Green	M79628	1960		£12	NGPP	❑
157	BR DMU Railcar (PWR)	Green	M79632	1975		£12	NGPP	❑
157	BR DMU Railcar (PWR)	Green	M79079	1976	1977	£12	NGPP	❑
158	BR DMU Railcar (DMY)	Blue	M79079			£8	NGPP	❑
158	BR DMU Railcar (DMY)	Green	M79632	1959	1966	£8	NGPP	❑
158	BR DMU Railcar (DMY)	Green	M79629	1960		£8	NGPP	❑
158	BR DMU Railcar (DMY)	Green	M59120	1975		£8	NGPP	❑
209	BR CL 110 DMU (PWR)	Blue	E51819	1989	1991	£16	NGPP	❑
210	BR CL 110 DMU BRK 2ND	Blue	E51846	1989	1991	£12	NGPP	❑
219	BR CL 47 'County of Herts'	NSE Blue	47583	1990		£18	£30-£35	❑
219	BR CL 47 'James Nightall'	NSE Blue	47579	1989		£18	£30-£35	❑

No.	Description	Colour	Number	Year	Year	Price	Price	
225	BR SR Suburban Motor Coach DM	Green	S1052S	1957	1959	£12	NGPP	❏
225	BR SR Suburban Motor Coach DM	Green	S1052S	1960	1963	£12	NGPP	❏
240	BR CL 91 Intercity	Intercity Grey	91001	1988	1989	£18	£30-£35	❏
240	BR CL 91 Intercity	Intercity Grey	91008	1990	1992	£18	£30-£35	❏
242	BR CL 90 Intercity	Intercity Grey	90001	1988	1990	£18	£30-£35	❏
245	BR CL 47 'Silcock Express'	R/F Grey	47231	1989	1992	£18	£30-£35	❏
250	BR CL 58	Blue	58007	1982	1983	£15	£30-£35	❏
250	BR CL 58 R/F	R/F Grey	58001	1984	1987	£15	£30-£35	❏
253	Dock Shunter 0-4-0	Black	5	1958	1961	£10	£30-£35	❏
253	Dock Shunter 0-4-0	Black	3	1972	1977	£10	£30-£35	❏
253	Dock Shunter 0-4-0	Red	3	1962	1971	£10	£30-£35	❏
253	Dock Shunter 0-4-0	Red	5	1963		£10	£30-£35	❏
254	BR Steeple Cab Pantograph 0-4-0	Green		1960		£25	£65-£85	❏
267	BR CL 110 DMU Pack	Blue	E51819	1989	1991	NGPP	£35-£40	❏
268	BR MK 4 Driving Van Trailer	I/city Dark Grey		1990	1994	NGPP	NGPP	❏
283	BR CL 58 'Bassetlaw' R/F	R/F Grey	58034	1988	1989	£18	£30-£35	❏
284	BR CL 37	Green	D6721	1988		£18	£30-£35	❏
284	BR CL 37	Green	D6713	1989		£18	£30-£35	❏
284	BR CL 37	Green	D6796	1990		£18	£30-£35	❏
285	BR CL 37	Blue	37202	1988		£18	£30-£35	❏
285	BR CL 37	Blue	37166	1989	1990	£18	£30-£35	❏
286	BR CL 37	R/F Grey	37677	1988		£18	£30-£35	❏
286	BR CL 37	R/F Grey	37518	1989	1990	£18	£30-£35	❏
287	BR CL 47	Blue	47409	1988		£18	£30-£35	❏
287	BR CL 47	Blue	47353	1989		£18	£30-£35	❏
287	BR CL 47	Blue	47124	1990		£18	£30-£35	❏
288	BR CL 47 'North Star' Intercity	Intercity Grey	47613	1989		£18	£30-£35	❏
288	BR CL 47 'Royal Mail' Intercity	Intercity Grey	47549	1990		£18	£30-£35	❏
288	BR CL 47 'Windsor Castle' Intercity	Intercity Grey	47620	1988		£18	£30-£35	❏
289	BR CL 86 'Vulcan Heritage'	Intercity Grey	86228	1988		£18	£25	❏
289	BR CL 86 Intercity 'The Kingsman'	Intercity Grey	86417	1988	1989	£18	£45-£50	❏
297	BR CL 142 Pacer	Orange		1988	1990	£18	£40-£45	❏
307	BR 'County of Norfolk'	Blue	47170	1982	1983	£15	£30-£35	❏
316	BR CL 47 'Lady Diana Spencer' (Limited Edition)	Blue	47712	1982		£20	£30	❏
319	BR CL 47 'Queen Mother'	Blue	47541	1983	1985	£20	£30	❏
326	BR CL 25	Blue	25241	1980	1985	£12	£25-£30	❏
327	BR CL 25	Green	D7571	1980	1983	£12	£25-£30	❏
328	BR CL 47 'Mammoth'	Green	D1670	1980	1982	£12	£25-£30	❏
332	BR CL 253 Intercity (Pack)	Intercity Blue		1980	1983	£18	£25	❏
332	BR CL 58 R/F S/S Coal	R/F Grey	58006	1990	1994	£18	£30-£35	❏
332	BR CL 58 R/F S/S Coal	R/F Grey	58025	1990	1994	£18	£30-£35	❏
332	BR CL 58 R/F S/S Coal	R/F Grey	58044	1990	1994	£18	£30-£35	❏
333	BR CL 86 Intercity	Intercity Grey	86405	1990	1992	£18	£30-£35	❏
333	BR CL 86 Intercity	Intercity Grey	86419	1990	1992	£18	£30-£35	❏
333	BR CL 86 Intercity	Intercity Grey	86431	1990	1992	£18	£30-£35	❏
335	BR CL 35 Hymek	Green	D7097	1980	1983	£12	£35-£40	❏
335	BR CL 86 'Halleys Comet' Intercity	Intercity Grey	86504	1990	1994	£18	£30-£35	❏
337	BR CL 29	Blue	6142	1980	1983	£18	£30	❏
338	BR CL 29	Green	D6103	1980	1983	£18	£30	❏
342	BR CL 47 R/F S/S Construction	R/F Grey	47079	1990	1992	£18	£30-£35	❏
347	BR CL 37	Green	D6736	1986	1987	£18	£30-£35	❏
348	BR CL 37 R/F	R/F Grey	37063	1986	1989	£18	£30-£35	❏
351	BR CL EM2 'Electra'	Blue	27000	1966	1971	£45	£85-£100	❏
351	BR CL EM2 'Electra'	Green	27000	1960	1965	£45	£85-£100	❏
352	BR CL 52 'Western Courier'	Maroon		1979		£12	£30-£35	❏
354	BR CL 08	Green	D3010	1980	1981	£12	£25-£30	❏
354	BR CL 47 'Rail Riders'	Blue	47406	1985		£18	£40-£45	❏
357 B	BR CL 31 A1A-A1A	Blue	D5578	1962	1971	£20	£30	❏
357 R	BR CL 31 A1A-A1A	Green	D5572	1963	1967	£12	£25-£30	❏
357	BR CL 31 A1A-A1A	Green	D5572	1972	1976	£12	£25-£30	❏
359	BR CL 37	Blue	37071	1984	1985	£15	£30-£35	❏
360	BR CL 86 'Phoenix'	Blue	86219	1981	1983	£15	£30-£35	❏
367	BR CL 86/2 'The Boys Brigade'	Blue	86243	1984	1985	£15	£45-£50	❏

No.	Description	Colour	Number	From	To	Price	Price	
368	BR CL 52 'Western Courier'	Maroon	D1062	1980	1982	£15	£30-£35	❏
368	BR CL 86 NSE	NSE Blue	86401	1988	1989	£18	£30-£35	❏
369	BR CL 37	Blue	37073	1980	1983	£15	£30-£35	❏
370	BR CL 253 I/C (PWR)	Blue	253005	1980	1982	£15	£30-£35	❏
371	BR CL 253 I/C (DMY)	Blue		1980	1982	£15	NGPP	❏
388	BR CL 86 'Frank Hornby' (Limited Edition)	Intercity Grey	86414	1988	1988	£25	£65	❏
397	BR CL 253 Intercity Pack	Intercity Grey	43072	1988	1989	NGPP	£35	❏
401	BR CL 253 Intercity Pack	Intercity Grey		1984	1987	NGPP	£35	❏
402	BR CL 37 'William Cookworthy'	Blue	37207	1984	1986	£15	£30-£35	❏
403	BR CL 110 DMU Pack	Blue		1984	1985	£20	£45	❏
404	BR CL 47	Blue	47568	1984	1987	£15	£30-£35	❏
428	BR CL 163 DMU Trailer 2nd Class	Blue		1984	1985	£15	NGPP	❏
555	BR DMU Pullman (PWR)	Blue and Grey		1963	1968	£15	NGPP	❏
555	BR DMU Pullman (PWR)	Grey and Blue		1969	1971	£15	NGPP	❏
556	BR DMU Pullman (DMY)	Blue and Grey		1963	1968	£10	NGPP	❏
556	BR DMU Pullman (DMY)	Grey and Blue		1969	1971	NGPP	NGPP	❏
559	BR Diesel 0-4-0 Shunter	Green	D2907	1963	1967	£10	£25	❏
687	BR CL 110 DMU	Green		1983	1985	£15	NGPP	❏
688	BR CL 163 Trailer 2nd	Green		1983	1985	£10	NGPP	❏
698	BR CL 110 DMU Pack	White		1982	1983	NGPP	£40	❏
700	BR CL 110 DMU Motor BRK Composite	White		1982	1983	£16	NGPP	❏
701	BR CL 110 DMU Motor Composite	White		1982	1983	£10	NGPP	❏
702	BR APT CL 370 Driving Trailer	Intercity Grey		1982	1985	NGPP	NGPP	❏
703	BR APT Van Trailer	Intercity Grey		1982	1985	NGPP	£150-£175	❏
704	BR APT Power Car	Intercity Grey		1982	1985	NGPP	NGPP	❏
705	BR CL 58 R/F S/S Coal	Grey	58050	1988	1989	£18	£35	❏
706	BR APT Driving Trailer	Intercity Grey		1982	1985	NGPP	NGPP	❏
706	BR CL 253 Intercity (PWR)	Intercity Dk Grey	43036	1990	1994	£18	NGPP	❏
707	BR APT Van	Intercity Grey		1982	1985	NGPP	NGPP	❏
707	BR CL 253 Intercity (DMY)	Intercity Dk Grey	43050	1990	1994	£10	NGPP	❏
708	BR CL 253 Intercity 125 (PWR)	Intercity Grey	43126	1984	1987	£18	NGPP	❏
709	BR CL 253 Intercity 125 (DMY)	Intercity Grey		1984	1987	£10	NGPP	❏
741 A	XPT HST (PWR), (Limited Edition export)	Silver and Red		1983		NGPP	£125-£150	❏
742 A	XPT HST (DMY), (Limited Edition export)	Silver and Red		1983		NGPP	£125-£150	❏
751	BR CL 37	Blue	D6830	1968	1977	£12	£30-£35	❏
751	BR CL 37	Blue	37130	1978	1979	£12	£30-£35	❏
751	BR CL 37	Green	D6830	1965	1967	£12	£30-£35	❏
753	BR CL 81 BO-BO	Blue	E3001	1965	1971	£35	£50	❏
757	BR CL 35 Hymek	Green	D7063	1967		£12	£30-£35	❏
758	BR CL 35 Hymek	Blue	D7063	1968	1976	£12	£30	❏
768 A	CIE CL 35 Hymek, (Limited Edition export)	Black and Orange		1976		NGPP	£75	❏
769	BR CL 47 'Robin Hood', (Limited Edition BTS)	Blue	47601		1982	£15	£45	❏
778	BR CL 52 'Western Harrier'	Blue	D1008	1981	1982	£15	£35	❏
780	BR CL 08 (from Sets)	Blue	08201	1981	1988	£15	NGPP	❏
794	BR APT Pack	Intercity Grey		1982	1985	£40	£150-£175	❏
797	BR CL 253 Intercity (PWR)	Intercity Grey	43072	1988	1989	£15	NGPP	❏
798	BR CL 253 Intercity (DMY)	Intercity Grey		1988		£10	NGPP	❏
800	BR CL 86 'Royal Anglian Regiment'	Intercity Grey	86246	1986	1987	£15	£45-£50	❏
802	BR CL 47 Intercity	Intercity Grey	47487	1986	1987	£15	£35	❏
803	BR CL 08 Shunter Intercity	Intercity Grey	08938	1986	1988	£12	£35	❏
836	BR CL 43 Intercity	Intercity Grey		1990		NGPP	£25	❏
863	BR CL 47	Green	D1738	1974	1975	£12	£35	❏
867	BR CL 142 Pacer	Blue		1987	1992	£15	£45	❏
874	BR CL 06 Barclay 0-4-0	Blue	06005	1987	1991	£12	£25	❏
875	BR CL 06 0-4-0	Green	D2428	1987	1989	£12	£25	❏
876	BR CL 47 'Evening Standard'	NSE Blue	47573	1987	1988	£15	£35	❏
877	BR CL 25	Blue	25218	1987	1989	£12	£30	❏
877	BR CL 25	Blue	25071	1990		£12	£30	❏
878	BR CL 25	Green	D5177	1987	1988	£12	£30	❏
886	BR CL 47 Intercity 'Greyfriars Bobby'	Intercity Grey	47711	1988		£18	£35	❏
887	BR CL 47 S/R 'Duke of Edinburgh's Award' Scotrail	Grey	47716	1988		£18	£40	❏
898	BR CL 47 R/F (from Sets)	Intercity Grey	47378	1988		£18	NGPP	❏

Railway Coaches

No.	Name	Colour	Number	From	To	Price	Price	
23	BR Mail Coach	Crimson		1957	1959	£3	£6	❏
24	LNER Composite Clerestory	Teak		1973		£5	£8	❏
25	LNER Brake Third Clerestory	Teak		1973		£5	£8	❏
26	GWR 1st/3rd Composite	Brown / Cream		1972	1973	£5	£8	❏
27	GWR Brake Composite	Brown / Cream		1972	1973	£5	£8	❏
28	BR Mk.1 Brake 3rd (9 in)	Crimson / Cream	34002	1957	1962	£3	£6	❏
28	BR Mk.1 Brake 3rd (9 in)	Crimson / Cream	M34000	1957	1962	£3	£6	❏
29	BR Mk.1 First (9 in)	Crimson / Cream	M24001	1959	1962	£3	£6	❏
98	Permanent Way Coach	Yellow		1987	1991	£5	£8	❏
120	BR Brake 2nd Suburban	Maroon	M43171	1957	1962	£4	£8	❏
120	BR Brake 2nd Suburban	Maroon	53171	1960		£4	£8	❏
121	BR Composite Suburban	Maroon	M41006	1959	1961	£6	£10	❏
121	BR Composite Suburban	Maroon	41006	1962		£6	£10	❏
122	GWR Clerestory Composite	Brown and Cream		1982	1985	£5	£8	❏
123	GWR Clerestory BRK 3rd	Brown and Cream		1982		£5	£8	❏
212	S and D J R 4 Wheel Coach	Blue		1976	1977	£3	£5	❏
213	GWR 4 Wheel Coach	Brown and Cream		1978	1983	£3.50	£5	❏
219	C.R. Coach 4 Wheels	Crimson / White		1980	1982	£3.50	£5	❏
220	SR Mk.1 BRK 2nd	Green	S34243	1958	1962	£5	£8	❏
22	SR Mk.1 Composite	Green	S15033	1958	1962	£5	£8	❏
222	SR Suburban BRK 2nd	Green	S4212S	1958	1962	£4	£6	❏
223	Pullman Parlour 1st Class	Brown and Cream		1981	1994	£6	£9	❏
223	SR Suburban Composite	Green	S3153S	1958	1963	£6	£12	❏
224	BR Mk.1 Buffet	Crimson / Cream	2401	1958		£3	£5	❏
224	BR Mk.1 Buffet	Crimson / Cream	M2001	1959	1962	£3	£5	❏
226	BR Utility Van	Blue	S2357S	1968	1970	£8	£12	❏
226	SR Utility Van	Green	S2355S	1958		£10	£15	❏
226	SR Utility Van	Green	S2357S	1959	1967	£10	£15	❏
226	Utility Van Red Doors (from Sets)	Green		1965		£12	NGPP	❏
227	BR Utility Van	Maroon		1959	1961	£8	£12	❏
228	BR Pullman 1st Class	Brown and Cream		1958	1973	£6	£9	❏
229	BR Pullman 1st Class	Brown and Cream		1974	1979	£6	£9	❏
229	SR Buffet Car	Green	S1007	1959	1962	£6	£9	❏
230	BR Coach	Red		1960	1961	£3	£5	❏
230	BR Pullman Golden Arrow	Blue and Grey	S309S	1974	1978	£7	£10	❏
231	BR Coach	Green		1960	1961	£3	£5	❏
233	Pullman BRK 3rd Class	Brown and Cream		1981	1994	£6	£9	❏
320	BR Brake 2nd	Maroon		1959	1961	£3	£6	❏
321	BR Composite	Maroon	24010	1959	1961	£3	£6	❏
322	BR Restaurant Car	Maroon	11005	1959	1961	£3	£6	❏
328	BR Pullman Brake 2nd 'Car 79'	Brown and Cream		1960	1973	£5	£8	❏
329	WR Brake 2nd	Brown and Cream	W34149	1960	1962	£3	£6	❏
330	WR Composite	Brown and Cream		1960	1962	£3	£6	❏
331	WR Restaurant Car	Brown and Cream	W302	1960	1962	£3	£6	❏
332	GWR 3rd Class Clerestory	Brown and Cream		1961	1963	£5	£8	❏
332	GWR 3rd Class Clerestory	Brown and Cream		1970	1972	£5	£8	❏
333	GWR Brake 3rd Clerestory	Brown and Cream		1961	1963	£5	£8	❏
333	GWR Brake 3rd Clerestory	Brown and Cream		1970	1972	£5	£8	❏
334	BR DMU Centre Car	Green		1961	1967	£8	£12	❏
334	BR DMU Centre Car	Green	M59120	1976	1977	£8	£12	❏
339	BR Sleeping Car 2nd Class	Blue		1968	1971	£5	£8	❏
339	BR Sleeping Car 2nd Class	Maroon		1962	1965	£5	£8	❏
339	BR Sleeping Car 2nd Class Intercity	Blue		1974	1975	£5	£8	❏
339	LMS Sleeping Car	Maroon		1966	1967	£5	£8	❏
384	LMS Clerestory Composite	Maroon	4863	1987	1989	£5	£8	❏
385	LMS Clerestory Brake	Maroon	6438	1987	1989	£5	£8	❏
391	LNER Clerestory 1st/3rd Composite	Teak		1990	1994	£5	£8	❏
395	BR Mk.3a 1st Class Intercity TF	Intercity Grey		1988	1989	£4	£7	❏
401	Mail Coach Set Intercity	Intercity Blue		1974	1977	£6	£15	❏

No.	Description	Colour	No.	From	To	Price	Price	
402	Mail Coach Set	Blue		1969		£6	£15	❑
402	Mail Coach Set	Maroon		1962	1968	£6	£15	❑
405	BR Mk.4 Intercity 1st Open	Intercity Grey	11208	1990	1994	£5	£8	❑
407	BR Mk.4 Intercity Tourist Open	Intercity Grey	12408	19990	1994	£5	£8	❑
408	BR Mk.4 Catering Car	Intercity Grey	10305	1990	1994	£5	£8	❑
409	BR (Ex LNER) Composite	Crimson / Cream		1988	1992	£5	£8	❑
410	BR (Ex LNER) BRK Composite	Crimson / Cream		1988	1992	£5	£8	❑
412	LMS Mail Coach Set	Maroon		1983	1985	£5	£8	❑
413	LMS Royal Mail Coach	Maroon	30250	1978	1979	£5	£8	❑
413	LNER 1st Class Sleeping Car	Teak		1988	1990	£5	£8	❑
416	BR Mail Coach TPO	Blue		1980	1982	£5	£8	❑
416	BR Royal Mail TPO Set	Red		1988	1992	£6	£9	❑
417	BR Mk.2 2nd Class Open Intercity SO	Intercity Blue		1980	1983	£4	£7	❑
418	BR Mk.2 2nd Class BRK Intercity BSK	Intercity Blue		1980	1983	£4	£7	❑
419	BR (Ex LNER) Sleeping Car	Crimson / Cream		1988	1991	£5	£8	❑
419	BR Mk.1 Buffet Car Intercity RMB	Intercity Blue		1980	1982	£4	£7	❑
420	BR Mk.1 2nd Cl Sleeping Car Intercity	Intercity Blue		1980	1982	£5	£8	❑
420	BR Mk.3a 2nd Class Intercity	Intercity Grey		1988	1989	£4	£7	❑
421	BR Ex LMS Composite	Crimson / Cream		1980	1983	£5	£8	❑
422	BR 1st/2nd Composite	Maroon	15865	1962	1969	£5	£8	❑
422	LMS Composite	Maroon	2257	1970	1975	£5	£8	❑
422	LMS 1st Class Corridor	Silver and Blue		1983	1987	£5	£8	❑
423	BR Mk.1 Brake 2nd	Maroon	35024	1962	1969	£5	£8	❑
423	LMS Brake 1st	Maroon	5051	1970	1975	£5	£8	❑
423	LMS Brake 3rd	Silver and Blue		1983	1987	£5	£8	❑
424	BR Buffet Car	Maroon	1807	1962	1967	£5	£8	❑
424	BR Ex LMS Brake 3rd	Crimson / Cream		1980	1983	£5	£8	❑
425	BR Full Parcels Brake	Blue		1968	1971	£5	£8	❑
425	BR Full Parcels Brake	Maroon		1962	1965	£5	£8	❑
425	BR Mk.3a 1st Class Open Intercity TF	Blue		1980	1985	£4	£7	❑
425	LMS Full Parcels Brake	Maroon		1966	1967	£5	£8	❑
426	BR Mk.3a 2nd Class Open Intercity TS	Blue		1980	1985	£4	£7	❑
426	BR Pullman Type 6	Blue and Grey		1963	1966	£7	£11	❑
426	BR Pullman Type 6	Grey and Blue		1969	1971	£7	£11	❑
427	BR Composite	Crimson / Cream	M4329			£5	£8	❑
427	BR Mk.3 Buffet Car Intercity TRUB	Blue		1980	1988	£5	£8	❑
427	CR 1st/3rd Composite	Red and White		1963	1967	£5	£8	❑
427	CR 1st/3rd Composite	Red and White		1973		£5	£8	❑
428	BR Mk.3 1st Class Intercity	Blue		1979		£4	£7	❑
428	CR 1st/3rd Composite Brake	Red and White		1963	1967	£5	£8	❑
428	CR 1st/3rd Composite Brake	Red and White		1973		£5	£8	❑
429	GWR Composite	Brown and Cream		1977	1979	£5	£8	❑
430	BR Mk.3 Restaurant Car Intercity	Intercity Grey		1988	1989	£5	£8	❑
430	GWR Brake 3rd	Brown and Cream		1977	1979	£5	£8	❑
431	BR Mk. 3a 1st Open Intercity TF	Blue		1985	1988	£5	£8	❑
431	SR 1st/3rd Composite	Brunswick Green	1384	1977	1979	£5	£8	❑
432	BR Mk.3a 2nd Class Open Intercity TS	Blue		1985	1988	£5	£8	❑
432	SR Brake 3rd	Brunswick Green	1405	1977	1979	£5	£8	❑
433	BR Mk.3a 1st Class Open Intercity TF	Intercity Grey		1985	1987	£5	£8	❑
433	LMS Composite	Maroon	3934	1977	1979	£5	£8	❑
434	BR Mk.3a 2nd Class Open Intercity TS	Intercity Grey		1985	1987	£5	£8	❑
434	LMS Brake 3rd	Maroon	5644	1977	1979	£5	£8	❑
435	GWR Clerestory 3rd Class	Brown and Cream		1985	1987	£5	£8	❑
435	LNER Composite	Teak	22357	1977	1979	£5	£8	❑
436	GWR Clerestory Brake	Brown and Cream		1985	1987	£5	£8	❑
436	LNER Composite Brake	Teak	22652	1979	1979	£5	£8	❑
437	BR Composite	Crimson / Cream	M4329	1977	1979	£5	£8	❑
437	BR Ex SR Composite	Green		1985	1986	£5	£8	❑
438	BR Brake 3rd	Crimson / Cream	M26545	1977	1979	£5	£8	❑
438	BR Ex SR Brake 3rd	Green		1985	1986	£5	£8	❑
439	BR Mk.2a 2nd Class Open NSE TSO	NSE Blue		1987	1991	£5	£8	❑
439	BR Mk.3 Open 2nd Intercity	Blue		1977	1979	£5	£8	❑
440	GWR Mail Coach Set	Brown and Cream		1985	1987	£8	£15	❑

No.	Description	Colour	Number	From	To	Price	Price	
441	SR Composite	Brunswick Green		1980	1990	£5	£8	❏
442	BR (Ex LMS) Composite	Crimson / Cream	M4330	1985	1994	£5	£8	❏
443	BR (Ex LMS) Brake	Crimson / Cream	M26548	1985	1994	£5	£8	❏
444	BR Mk.2 1st Class Brake NSE BFK	NSE Blue		1987	1990	£5	£8	❏
445	SR Brake 3rd	Brunswick Green	1405	1980	1990	£5	£8	❏
446	GWR 4 Wheel Coach	Brown and Cream		1987	1994	£3	£5	❏
448	LNER Sleeping Car	Teak	1316	1978	1979	£5	£8	❏
449	LNER Clerestory Brake 3rd	Teak		1990	1994	£5	£8	❏
451	Royal Train HM Queen Elizabeth's Saloon			1984	1985	£6	£10	❏
452	LMS Clerestory Composite	Maroon		1983	1985	£5	£8	❏
453	LMS Clerestory Brake	Maroon		1983	1985	£5	£8	❏
454	BR Mk.3a Open 'Hoverspeed'	NSE Blue		1986	1987	£6	£10	❏
454	GWR Restaurant Car	Brown and Cream		1978	1979	£5	£8	❏
455	Royal Train, Duke of Edinburgh's Coach			1984	1985	£6	£10	❏
456	GWR Composite	Brown and Cream		1980	1993	£5	£8	❏
457	GWR Brake 3rd	Brown and Cream		1980	1993	£5	£8	❏
458	GWR Restaurant Car	Brown and Cream		1980	1991	£5	£8	❏
459	Royal Train, Sleeper/Brake			1984	1985	£6	£10	❏
467	BR Mk.3a Brake Intercity TGS	Blue		1984	1985	£5	£8	❏
468	LMS 4 Wheel Coach	Maroon		1986	1994	£3	£5	❏
469	Pullman Parlour Orient Express	Brown and Cream		1984	1985	£7	£10	❏
474	LMS 1st/3rd Composite	Maroon	3934	1980	1985	£5	£8	❏
474	LMS 1st/3rd Composite	Maroon	4120	1986	1994	£5	£8	❏
475	LMS Brake 3rd	Maroon	5644	1980	1985	£5	£8	❏
475	LMS Brake 3rd	Maroon	5714	1986	1994	£5	£8	❏
477	LNER Composite	Teak		1980	1994	£5	£8	❏
478	LNER Brake	Teak		1980	1994	£5	£8	❏
479	LNER 1st Class Sleeping Car	Teak		1980	1985	£5	£8	❏
483	BR Composite (Ex LNER)	Maroon		1983	1985	£5	£8	❏
484	BR Brake (Ex LNER)	Maroon		1983	1985	£5	£8	❏
485	BR 1st Class Sleeper (Ex LNER)	Maroon		1983		£5	£8	❏
486	SR 1st/3rd Composite	Malachite Green	5117	1981	1983	£5	£8	❏
487	SR Brake 3rd	Malachite Green		1981	1983	£5	£8	❏
488	BR Mk.3a 1st Class Intercity TF	Intercity Grey		1984	1985	£5	£8	❏
489	BR Mk.3 Open 2nd Intercity	Intercity Grey		1984	1985	£5	£8	❏
490	BR Mk.3a Restaurant Car Intercity TRUB	Intercity Grey		1984	1987	£5	£8	❏
620	BR Engineering Dept. Coach	Black	20	1963	1965	£8	£12	❏
620	SR Engineering Dept. Coach	Green	20	1966	1967	£8	£12	❏
621	Liverpool-Manchester	Yellow and Black		1963	1966	£8	£15	❏
622	BR Mk.1 Composite	Green	S15873	1963	1969	£5	£8	❏
622	SR Mk.1 Composite	Brunswick Green	5740	1970	1971	£6	£9	❏
622	SR Mk.1 Composite	Malachite Green	5015	1974		£6	£9	❏
623	BR Mk.1 BRK 2nd	Green	S34936	1963	1969	£5	£8	❏
623	SR Mk.1 BRK 3rd	Brunswick Green	4351	1970	1971	£6	£9	❏
623	SR Mk.1 BRK 3rd	Malachite Green	4351	1974		£6	£9	❏
624	BR Buffet Car	Green	S1851	1963	1967	£7	£10	❏
626	BR Mk.2 Composite CK	Crimson / Cream	15605	1963	1965	£5	£8	❏
626	BR Mk.2 Composite CK	Crimson / Cream	15210	1972	1975	£5	£8	❏
627	BR Brake 2nd BSK	Crimson / Cream		1963	1965	£5	£8	❏
627	BR Brake 2nd BSK	Crimson / Cream	34100	1972	1975	£5	£8	❏
628	BR 2nd Buffet RMB	Crimson / Cream	1801	1963	1965	£5	£8	❏
628	BR 2nd Buffet RMB	Crimson / Cream	1805	1972	1975	£5	£8	❏
699	BR DMU Trailer 2nd	White		1982	1983	£5	£8	❏
704	BR Mk.3a Open 2nd Intercity TS	Intercity Dk Grey		1990	1994	£5	£8	❏
713	BR Mk. 3 1st Buffet Intercity TRFB	Intercity Dk Grey		1990	1992	£5	£8	❏
719	BR Mk. 3a Open 1st Intercity TF	Blue		1990	1992	£5	£8	❏
722	BR Brake 1st Intercity	Blue	M14031	1968		£5	£8	❏
722	BR Brake 1st Intercity + Lights	Blue	M14031	1969	1972	£5	£8	❏
723	BR 2nd Class Intercity	Blue	M5032	1968		£5	£8	❏
723	BR 2nd Class Intercity + Lights	Blue	M5032	1969	1972	£5	£8	❏
724	BR Mk.2 2nd Cl Intercity CRW	Blue	M5120	1973	1975	£5	£8	❏
726	BR Mk.2 BRK 2nd Intercity CRW	Blue	M14052	1973	1975	£5	£8	❏
727	BR Composite	Blue		1966	1969	£5	£8	❏

728	BR Brake 2nd	Blue	35024	1966	1970	£5	£8	❏
728	BR Mk.2 Brake 2nd	Blue		1980	1982	£5	£8	❏
729	BR Buffet Car	Blue		1967	1970	£5	£8	❏
730	BR Composite CKD	Blue		1967	1971	£5	£8	❏
731	BR Brake 2nd CKD	Blue		1967	1971	£5	£8	❏
732	BR Buffet Car CKD	Blue		1967	1969	£5	£8	❏
740	Departmental Breakdown Coach	Red		1971	1973	£6	£10	❏
743	GWR Composite	Brown and Cream		1970	1971	£5	£8	❏
743	GWR Composite	Brown and Cream	5015	1974	1975	£5	£8	❏
744	GWR Brake 3rd	Brown and Cream		1970	1971	£5	£8	❏
744	GWR Brake 3rd	Brown and Cream	5104	1974	1975	£5	£8	❏
745	LNER Full 3rd	Teak		1970	1975	£5	£8	❏
746	LNER Brake 3rd	Teak		1970	1975	£5	£8	❏
747	LMS 1st/3rd Composite Ex CR	Maroon	2640	1971	1973	£5	£8	❏
748	LMS Brake 1st/3rd Ex CR	Maroon	2643	1971	1973	£5	£8	❏
749	SR Maunsell 1st/3rd	Green	1750	1971	1973	£6	£9	❏
750	SR Maunsell Brake 1st/3rd	Green	1774	1971	1973	£6	£9	❏
844	BR Buffet Car Intercity CRW	Green	1805	1973	1975	£5	£8	❏
895	Scotrail Mk.3 1st Class Open	Scotrail Grey	11909	1988	1989	£5	£8	❏
896	Scotrail Mk.3 2nd Class Open	Scotrail Grey	12030	1988	1989	£5	£8	❏
921	BR Mk.2 Open Intercity CRW	Blue	M5120	1976	1979	£5	£8	❏
922	BR Mk.2 BRK 2nd Intercity CRW	Blue	M14052	1976	1978	£5	£8	❏
922	BR Mk.2 BRK 2nd Intercity CRW	Blue	M9439	1979		£5	£8	❏
923	BR Buffet Car Intercity	Blue	1805	1976	1979	£5	£8	❏
924	BR Sleeping Car Intercity	Blue	2510	1976	1979	£5	£8	❏
928	BR Composite CK	Crimson / Cream	15210	1976	1977	£5	£8	❏
929	BR Mk.1 Brake 2nd	Crimson / Cream	34100	1976	1977	£5	£8	❏
930	GWR Composite	Brown and Cream	5015	1976	1977	£5	£8	❏
931	GWR Brake 3rd	Brown and Cream	5104	1976	1977	£5	£8	❏
933	SR Composite	Green	5015	1976	1977	£6	£9	❏
934	SR Brake 3rd	Green	4351	1976	1977	£6	£9	❏
935	LMS Full 3rd	Maroon	2257	1976	1977	£5	£8	❏
936	LMS Brake 1st	Maroon	5051	1976	1977	£5	£8	❏
937	LNER Full 3rd	Teak	1010	1976	1977	£5	£8	❏
938	LNER Brake 3rd	Teak	1870	1976	1977	£5	£8	❏

R.402 Operating Royal Mail Coach Set. 'Mailbag' is suspended from pick-up hook. As train speeds past, a scoop in the side of the coach automatically opens and grabs the 'mailbag'. Further along the track a door in the opposite side of the coach automatically ejects the bag into the receiving bin.

37

R.55 Transcontinental Diesel. Introduced in 1954 for the Canadian market together with non-powered version R.57 to represent the back-to-back double heading so familiar across the Atlantic. The 'B' unit R.58 (inset) followed in 1956. The model has been made in Canadian Pacific and Santa Fe colours as well as the Canadian National illustrated.

R.54 4-6-2 Pacific (below). Also designed in 1954 for overseas markets. The model was based on a Canadian Pacific prototype and although withdrawn from sale in Britain in 1964, continues in production for export. Later models incorporate a front coupling, smoke generator, 'see-through' wheels and Magnadhesion.

R.56 4-6-4T. This was a compromise design for South Africa, India, New Zealand and Australia and introduced in 1955. The original was black (inset) but was changed to maroon livery in 1961 at the same time as a smoke generator was fitted. The locomotive was withdrawn at the end of 1962.

R.59 2-6-2T. A model of British Railways Class 3 Mixed Traffic Locomotive. First produced by Tri-ang in 1956 in lined out black livery, it was changed to green livery as run on the Western Region of B.R. in 1961. Temporarily withdrawn from production in 1966.

19

Tri-ang Vans and Wagons

Guards / Brake Vans

No.	Description	Colour	Code	From	To	Price	Price	
16	BR Brake Van LWB (Grey roof)	Red Brown		1968	1973	£2	£3.50	❏
16	BR Brake Van LWB (White roof)	Red Brown		1974	1975	£2	£3.50	❏
16	Brake Van	Brown	M73031	1959	1960	£2	£3.50	❏
16	Brake Van	Grey	M73031			£2	£3.50	❏
16	ER Brake Van	Red Brown	M73031	1961	1967	£2	£3.50	❏
18	GWR Brake Van	Grey		1976	1979	£2.50	£3.50	❏
19	LBSC Guards Van	Brown	43	1980	1982	£3	£4.50	❏
29	SR 20 Ton Brake Van	Brown	55918	1982	1990	£3	£4.50	❏
30	BR 20 Ton Brake Van	Red Brown		1982	1985	£3	£4	❏
31	LNER Brake Van LWB	Grey		1982	1985	£3	£4.50	❏
48	BR 20T Brake Van Car	Grey and Red		1986	1992	£3	£4	❏
49	BR Brake Van S/S Car	Grey and Yellow		1990	1992	£3	£4	❏
89	BR 20T Brake Van Service Dept	Grey and Yellow		1989	1990	£3	£4	❏
98	LMS Brake Van	Brown		1977	1979	£2	£3.50	❏
107	LMS Brake Van + Lamp (Grey roof)	Red Brown		1974		£3	£5	❏
107	LMS Brake Van + Lamp (White roof)	Red Brown		1975	1976	£3	£5	❏
114	NE Brake Van	Grey		1973	1975	£2	£3.50	❏
124	GWR Brake Van	Brown	W6297	1959	1961	£2	£3.50	❏
124	GWR Brake Van	Brown	W6297	1962	1970	£2	£3.50	❏
124 A	GWR Brake Van	Grey		1971	1975	£2	£3.50	❏
215	NE Brake Van	Grey		1976	1979	£2	£3.50	❏
218	BR Brake Van	Red Brown		1976	1979	£2	£3.50	❏
313 A	NSWR Brake Van (Export)	Red Brown		1974	1975	£3.50	£5	❏
314 A	VR Brake Van (Export)			1974	1975	£3.50	£5	❏
389 A	NSWR Brake Van (Export)	Red Brown		1976		£3.50	£5	❏
390 A	VR Brake Van (Export)			1976		£3.50	£5	❏
636	BR Brake Van LWB	Red Brown		1967		£2	£3.50	❏
714	GWR 20T Brake Van	Grey		1980	1991	£3	£4	❏
718	LMS 20T Brake Van	Red Brown		1980	1994	£3	£4	❏
729	BR Brake Van	Red Brown		1980	1982	£2	£3.50	❏

Hoppers and Bulk Carriers

No.	Description	Colour	Code	From	To	Price	Price	
13	Procor Hopper, Tarmac	White		1988	1992	£3	£4.50	❏
15	Procor Hopper, Yeoman	Grey and Blue		1988	1992	£3	£4.50	❏
19	Procor Hopper, Tilbury	Orange		1988	1989	£2.50	£4	❏
23	BRT Hopper, Bulk Grain	Blue	7799	1989	1994	£3	£4.50	❏
26	Procor Hopper, Redland	Green		1990	1992	£3	£4.50	❏
33	BR MGR Hopper, R/F Coal S/S	Silver and Orange		1990	1994	£2.50	£4	❏
39	BR MGR Hopper S/S HAA	Silver and Yellow		1988	1989	£2.50	£4	❏
52	English China Clay CDA	Silver and Blue		1988	1992	£3.50	£5	❏
103	Hopper Wagon Roberts	Black		1973	1974	£2.50	£4	❏
214	BR Hopper Wagon	Grey		1969	1973	£2.50	£4	❏
214	Consett Iron Co. Hopper	Red		1975		£2.50	£4	❏
214	BR Hopper Wagon	Grey		1959	1965	£2.50	£4	❏
215	Bulk Grain Hopper	Green		1959		£2.50	£4	❏
215	Bulk Grain Hopper	Grey	B85040	1960	1968	£2.50	£4	❏
232	Consett Iron Co. Hopper	Green		1976	1979	£2	£3.50	❏
237	Blue Circle Cement	Yellow		1976		£2	£3.50	❏
238	BR MGR Hopper HAA	Silver and Red		1980	1981	£2.50	£4	❏
238	Bulk Grain, Heygates	White		1986	1988	£2.50	£4	❏
249	BR MGR Hopper R/F S/L HAA	Silver and Red		1981	1994	£2.50	£4	❏
309 A	Readymix Bulk Cement Wagon (Export)	Grey		1974	1975	£3.50	£5	❏
347	Engineering Dept. Hopper	Black		1963	1966	£3.50	£5	❏
347	Engineering Dept. Hopper	Green		1966	1968	£3.50	£5	❏
385 A	'Readymix' Bulk Cement Wagon	Grey		1976		£2.50	£4	❏
647	Bulk Grain, 'Dewars'	Blue		1968		£3	£4	❏
648	Bulk Grain, 'Johnnie Walker'	Blue		1968	1973	£3	£4	❏
649	Bulk Grain, 'VAT 69'	Blue		1968	1971	£3	£4	❏
650	Bulk Grain, 'Haig Whisky'	Blue		1968		£3	£4	❏
732	'Consett Iron Co.' Hopper	Green		1980	1982	£2.50	£4	❏

Transcontinental Series

No.	Description	Colour	Number	From	To	Price	Price	
24	TC Coach	Red and Silver		1957	1960	£3	£6	❑
25	TC Coach Vista Dome	Red and Silver		1957	1961	£3	£6	❑
54 S	TC 'Hiawatha' 4-6-2	Black	TR 2335	1957	1964	£15	£30	❑
55	CNTC BO-BO	Black/Red/White	4008	1968	1969	£15	£25	❑
55	TC Canadian Pacific BO-BO	Grey and Maroon	4008			£15	£25	❑
55	TC Trans' Railways BO-BO	Red and Silver	4008	1962	1965	£12	£25	❑
55	TC 'Tria-ng Railways' BO-BO	Red and Silver	4008	1957	1961	£12	£25	❑
56	TC 4-6-4T (For AUS, NZ, SA)	Black		1957	1962	£20	£40	❑
56	TC 4-6-4T (For AUS, NZ, SA)	Maroon		1961	1962	£20	£40	❑
57	TC Diesel AS R55 (DMY)	AS R55		1959	1962	£6	£10	❑
58	TC 'BZ' UNIT	Red and Silver		1959	1960	£6	£10	❑
111	TC Hopper Wagon	Green	174421			£2.50	£4	❑
111	TC Hopper Wagon	Yellow	174421	1959	1960	£2.50	£4	❑
111	TC Tri-ang Hopper Wagon	Red	174421	1961	1965	£2.50	£4	❑
114	TC Box Car Sliding Doors	Yellow		1957	1960	£3	£5	❑
115	TC Caboose	Maroon	7482	1957	1961	£3	£5	❑
115	TC Caboose	Brown		1962	1965	£3	£5	❑
116	TC Gondola	Blue	3576	1957	1960	£3	£5	❑
116	TC Gondola	Green	3576	1959		£3	£5	❑
116	TC Gondola 'Express Delivery'	Blue	3576	1962	1963	£3	£5	❑
116	TC Gondola 'Rock Island Lines'	Grey				£3	£5	❑
117	TC Bogie 'Shell Oil' Tanker	Blue		1959		£5	£8	❑
117	TC Bogie 'Shell Oil' Tanker	Yellow		1959		£5	£8	❑
117	TC Bogie 'Shell Oil' Tanker	Blue		1961	1963	£5	£8	❑
117 C	TC Bogie Tanker	Black		1968	1969	£6	£9	❑
119	TC Mail Coach	Maroon		1957	1959	£3.50	£5	❑
125	TC Observation Car	Red and Silver		1959	1961	£4	£8	❑
126	TC Stock Car	Yellow		1959		£3	£6	❑
126	TC Stock Car	Brown				£3	£6	❑
126	TC Stock Car	Yellow	742	1961	1965	£3	£6	❑
129	TC Refrigerator Car	Cream	2690	1961		£3	£6	❑
129	TC Refrigerator Car	White	2690	1959	1960	£3	£6	❑
129	TC Refrigerator Car	White	2690	1961	1965	£3	£6	❑
130	TC Baggage Car	Red and Silver		1957	1961	£3	£6	❑
131	TC Coach	Blue and Yellow		1958	1961	£3	£6	❑
132	TC Vista Dome Coach	Blue and Yellow		1959	1961	£3	£6	❑
133	TC Observation Coach	Blue and Yellow		1958	1961	£3	£6	❑
134	TC Baggage Car	Blue and Yellow		1959	1961	£3	£6	❑
136	TC Box Car Speedy Service	Brown		1959	1960	£3	£6	❑
136	TC Box Car Speedy Service	Grey		1961	1965	£3	£6	❑
137	TC Cement Car	Grey		1959	1960	£3	£6	❑
137	TC Cement Car	Grey		1961	1965	£3	£6	❑
137	TC Wabash Hopper Wagon	Grey				£3	£6	❑
138	TC Snow Plough	Green and Black		1959	1965	£8	£12	❑
139	TC Pickle Wagon	Black and Cream		1960	1965	£8	£15	❑
155	TC Diesel Switcher BO-BO	Black			1963	£15	£25	❑
155	TC Diesel Switcher BO-BO	Yellow	7005	1957	1963	£15	£25	❑
159	TC Diesel DBL-END	Blue and Yellow		1958	1969	£12	£20	❑
232	TC Budd Rail Car (DMY)	Grey		1961		£20	£35	❑
234	TC Flat Car	Grey		1960	1963	£3	£6	❑
235	TC Pulp Wood Car	Grey		1960	1969	£3	£6	❑
236	TC Bogie Well Wagon	Blue	TR 1371	1960		£3	£6	❑
236	TC Bogie Well Wagon	Green	TR 1371	1961	1963	£3	£6	❑
237	TC Well Wagon + Low Loader	Green		1960	1961	NGPP	£35	❑
238	TC Well Wagon + Cable Drum	Blue		1960	1961	NGPP	£30	❑
248	TC Ambulance Car	Green and White		1963	1971	£4	£6	❑
250	TC Diesel Loco as R159 (DMY)	Blue and Yellow		1959	1962	£6	£10	❑
252	TC Steeple Cab Pantograph 0-4-0	Maroon		1961		£30	£45	❑
254	TC Steeple Cab Pantograph 0-4-0	Green		1959	1963	£30	£45	❑
257	TC BO-BO Pantograph	Green		1959	1963	£25	£40	❑

262	TC Continental Fourgon	Red		1963	1965	£12	£20	❏
307 A	A-1-A Diesel (Export)			1974	1975	NGPP	NGPP	❏
308 A	Diesel Switcher VR (Export)	Blue	T336	1974	1975	£18	£30	❏
316 A	0-6-0 Diesel (Export)			1974	1975	NGPP	NGPP	❏
317 A	VR S-Class Diesel (Export)			1974	1975	NGPP	NGPP	❏
318 A	Commonwealth Diesel (Export)			1974	1975	NGPP	NGPP	❏
319	TC Mail Coach Set	Dark Red		1961		NGPP	£15	❏
324	TC Diner	Red and Silver		1960	1961	£4	£6	❏
325	TC Diner	Blue		1960	1961	£4	£6	❏
335	TC Coach	Green		1961	1963	£6	£9	❏
336	TC Observation Car	Green		1961	1963	£6	£9	❏
337	TC Baggage/Kitchen	Green		1961	1963	£6	£9	❏
338	TC Diner	Green		1961	1963	£6	£9	❏
344	TC Track Cleaner Car	Olive Green		1961	1976	£6	£9	❏
352	Budd Diesel Rail Car	Grey		1960	1965	£25	£40	❏
353	TC 0-4-0 Diesel Switcher	Red	TR20071	1963	1965	£10	£18	❏
353	TC 0-4-0 Diesel Switcher	Yellow	TR20071	1962		£15	£30	❏
358 S	Old Time Loco 2-6-0	Yellow		1962	1965	£30	£50	❏
400	TC Mail Coach Set	Blue		1962		NGPP	£15	❏
400	TC Mail Coach Set	Red		1962	1963	NGPP	£15	❏
440	TC Coach Silver/Red	Red and Silver		1962	1963	£3	£6	❏
441	TC Observation Car Silver/Black	Silver and Black	304	1962		£3	£6	❏
441	TC Observation Car Silver/Red	Red and Silver		1962	1963	£3	£6	❏
442	TC Baggage/Kitchen Silver/Red	Red and Silver		1962	1963	£3	£6	❏
443	TC Diner Silver/Red	Red and Silver		1962	1963	£3	£6	❏
444	TC Coach Blue	Blue		1962	1966	£3	£6	❏
444	TC Coach Silver/Black	Silver and Black		1968	1969	£3	£6	❏
445	TC Observation Coach Blue	Blue		1962	1966	£3	£6	❏
445	TC Observation Coach Silver/Black	Silver and Black		1968	1969	£3	£6	❏
446	TC Baggage/Kitchen Blue	Blue		1962	1966	£3	£6	❏
447	TC Diner Blue	Blue		1962	1966	£3	£6	❏
448	TC Old Time Coach	Yellow and Brown		1962	1965	£6	£8	❏
449	TC Caboose Red	Red	449	1963		£6	£10	❏
450	TC NSW Suburban Motor Coach	Red Brown		1960		NGPP	NGPP	❏
560	Well Wagon and Crane	Green and Red		1963	1965	£15	£25	❏
625	TC Wagon-Lits Sleeping Car	Blue		1963	1965	NGPP	NGPP	❏

Closed Vans

1	'KP Nuts' Van	Blue		1982	1985	£2	£3.50	❏
2	'Birds' Van	Yellow		1982	1985	£2	£3.50	❏
9	'Golden Shred' Van	Red		1982	1985	£2	£3.50	❏
11	BR Ventilated Van	Red Brown		1968	1975	£2	£3.50	❏
11	Goods Van	Green	W8755	1961	1967	£2	£3.50	❏
11	Goods Van	Brown	W8755	1960		£2	£3.50	❏
11	Goods Van	Green	W8755	1959		£2	£3.50	❏
11	Goods Van	Grey	W8755			£2	£3.50	❏
11	Goods Van GW	Brown	87204			£2	£3.50	❏
13	Fine Fish Van	Blue		1973		£2	£3.50	❏
13	Fine Fish Van (new printing)	Blue		1974	1975	£2	£3.50	❏
14	Insulfish Van	Blue	6301	1966	1972	£2	£3.50	❏
14	Insulfish Van	Blue	6307	1973		£2	£3.50	❏
14	Insulfish Van	White	N6301	1961	1965	£2	£3.50	❏
14	Fish Van	White	N6301	1959	1960	£2	£3.50	❏
15	'Canterbury Lamb' Van	Yellow		1982		£2.50	£4	❏
16	BR 45T Van Speed-Link S/S VDA	Grey and Yellow		1989		£3.50	£5	❏
17	R/F 45 Ton Van S/S VDA	Grey and Yellow		1990	1994	£3.50	£5	❏
21	NE Refrigerator Van	White		1972	1973	£2	£3.50	❏
27	BR Ferry Van R/F VIX	Red and Grey		1982	1990	£4	£5.50	❏
34	Ventilated Van R/F S/S VEA	Grey and Yellow		1990	1992	£2.50	£4	❏

No.	Description	Colour	No.	From	To	Price	Price	
40	'Eastbourne Model Shop' Van (Limited Edition)	White				£3	£5	❏
42	Railmail Wedding Van (Limited Edition)	Grey		1981		£3	£5	❏
56	'Astra Fireworks' Van	Yellow		1987	1988	£2	£3.50	❏
63	'Yellow Pages' Van	Yellow		1987	1988	£2	£3.50	❏
105	'Birds Eye Fish Fingers' Van	Blue		1974	1979	£2	£3.50	❏
109	'Cadbury's' Van LWB	Blue		1974		£2	£3.50	❏
109	'Cadbury's' Van LWB	Purple and Gold		1975		£2	£3.50	❏
111	'Yorkshire Pudding Co.' Van (Limited Edition)	Yellow		1972		£4	£6.50	❏
114	'Wimpy' Van	Red		1983	1989	£2	£3.50	❏
117	BR Ventilated Van R/F VEA	Grey and Red		1983	1992	£2	£3.50	❏
130	'Lyons Maid' Van	White		1974		£2.50	£4	❏
132	'Baxters' Van	Blue		1983	1985	£2	£3.50	❏
134	'Callard & Bowser' Van	Cream		1983		£2	£3.50	❏
135	'Smiths Crisps' Van	White		1978	1979	£2	£3.50	❏
137	'McVities' Van LWB	Blue		1978	1979	£2	£3.50	❏
138	'Silver Spoon' Van	Blue		1984	1985	£2	£3.50	❏
141	'Campbells Soups' Procor	Red		1984	1985	£3.50	£5	❏
145	'Red Arrows' Van LWB	Blue		1984	1985	£2	£3.50	❏
146	'Oxo' Van	Silver		1984	1985	£2	£3.50	❏
147	NE Refrigerator Van (White roof)	White	151275	1984	1987	£2	£3.50	❏
149	'Prima Pet Foods' Van	Yellow		1984	1985	£2.50	£4	❏
162	Prime Pork Van	Green		1974	1975	£2	£3.50	❏
200	'ETC Frozen Foods' Van	White		1985	1986	£2.50	£4	❏
201	'Terry's' Van	Yellow		1985	1986	£2.50	£4	❏
202	'Reconofork' Van LWB	Grey Brown		1985	1986	£3	£5	❏
205	Ventilated Van Sliding Doors	Red Brown		1976	1978	£2	£3.50	❏
206	Fine Fish Van	Blue		1976	1977	£2	£3.50	❏
206	Fine Fish Van	Blue				£2	£3.50	❏
216	Prime Pork Van	Green		1976	1977	£2	£3.50	❏
216	Prime Pork Van, (new printing)	Green		1978	1979	£2	£3.50	❏
216	Procor Van PVA	Blue		1986	1988	£3.50	£5	❏
217	'Anglian Windows' Van LWB	Cream		1986	1987	£3	£5	❏
218	Closed Van	Green		1959	1962	£2	£3.50	❏
222	'Kelloggs' Van LWB	Blue		1977		£2	£3.50	❏
22	'Kelloggs' Van LWB	White		1976		£2	£3.50	❏
234	BR 45T Van R/F	Red Brown		1980	1981	£3.50	£5	❏
241	'Yorkshire Dales' 'Fridge Van	Brown		1982		£3.50	£5	❏
242	BR Ventilated Van	Red Brown		1979	1982	£2	£3.50	❏
243	'Rest Assured' Van	White		1986	1988	£2	£3.50	❏
247	BR 45 ton Van R/F S/L VDA	Red and Grey		1981	1992	£3.50	£6	❏
574	'Kelloggs' Van LWB	White		1968		£2	£3.50	❏
670	'Palethorpes' 6 Wheel	Dark Red		1976	1979	£3.50	£5	❏
671	Insulated Milk 6 Wheel	White		1976	1979	£3.50	£5	❏
722	'Kit Kat' Van	Red		1980	1982	£2	£3.50	❏
725	'Smith's Food' Van	Grey		1980	1982	£2	£3.50	❏
727	'McVitie's' Van	Blue		1980	1982	£2	£3.50	❏
728	'Weetabix' Van	Yellow		1980	1982	£2	£3.50	❏
733	'Palethorpe's' 6 Wheel	Dark Red		1980	1982	£3.50	£5	❏
734	LMS Insulated Milk Van	White		1980	1981	£3.50	£5	❏
738	BR Anglo Ferry Van	Red Brown		1970	1971	£3.50	£5	❏
738	BR Anglo Ferry Van	Red Brown		1978	1979	£3.50	£5	❏
740	BR Anglo Ferry Van	Red Brown		1980	1981	£3.50	£5	❏
741	'Transfesa' Ferry Van	Blue		1971	1974	£4	£6	❏
742	'Interfrigo' Ferry Van	White		1972	1973	£4	£6	❏
780	Express Parcels Van	Blue	E12080	1971	1973	£2	£3.50	❏
786	'Fyffe's' Ferry Van (from Sets)	White		1973		£4.50	NGPP	❏
787	'Ford' Ferry Van (from Sets)	Blue		1973		£4.50	NGPP	❏

Open Wagons

4	'Colgate' Open	Red		1982		£2	£3.50	❏
6	'Barrow Coke' Open	White		1982	1984	£2	£3.50	❏
9	7 Plank Ocean	Brown		1975		£2	£3.50	❏
10	'Pugh & Co.' Open (Limited Edition)	Red				£2.50	£4	❏
10	7 Plank Mineral Open	Brown	W1005	1959	1960	£2	£3.50	❏
10	7 Plank Mineral Open	Brown	NE76853	1961		£2	£3.50	❏
10	7 Plank Mineral Open	Green		1963	1970	£2	£3.50	❏
10	7 Plank Mineral Open	Grey	W1005	1962	1965	£2	£3.50	❏
10	7 Plank Mineral Open	Grey	NE76853			£2	£3.50	❏
10	7 Plank Open NE	Red	83670			£2.50	£4	❏
10	7 Plank Open SR	Blue	12530			£2.50	£4	❏
10 A	7 Plank Open SR	Brown	12530	1971	1973	£2	£3.50	❏
10	7 Plank Open SR	Red	12530	1974		£2.50	£4	❏
12	'Bodell & Co.' Open (Limited Edition WHS)	Grey				£2.50	£4	❏
13	7 Plank NE with Coal	Grey				£3.50	£5	❏
13	7 Plank with Coal	Grey		1959	1961	£3.50	£5	❏
16	'Perfection' (+ Rail) Open	Red		1982	1983	£2.50	£4	❏
21	'Black and Reoch'	Blue	22	1984	1985	£2.50	£4	❏
21	'Black and Reoch'	Red	22	1982	1985	£2.50	£4	❏
22	Cory LWB Open	Dark Red		1972	1974	£2	£3.50	❏
24	5 Plank 'Crook & Greenaway' OPE	Blue		1988	1994	£2	£3.50	❏
32	'Hargreaves' End Tipper	Blue Grey		1982	1985	£3	£4.50	❏
67	BR 45T Open Wagon R/F S/S OAA	Grey and Yellow		1990	1994	£3.50	£5	❏
79	BR Mineral Open MSV	Red Brown		1987	1993	£2	£3.50	❏
81	Iron Ore Open MSV	Grey		1990	1992	£2	£3.50	❏
90	7 Plank 'Princess Royal'	Maroon	250	1975		£2	£3.50	❏
93	Norstand Open LWB	Blue	480	1975		£2	£3.50	❏
94	5 Plank 'Pilkington Glass' (Limited Edition WHS)	Red				£2.50	£4	❏
96	5 Plank 'Bestwood'	Brown	655	1977	1979	£2	£3.50	❏
97	5 Plank 'Arnold Sands'	Brown	803			£2	£3.50	❏
97	5 Plank 'Arnold Sands'	Black	803			£2	£3.50	❏
97	5 Plank 'Arnold Sands'	Grey	803			£2	£3.50	❏
97	5 Plank 'Arnold Sands'	Red	803	1977		£2	£3.50	❏
100	7 Plank 'Lancashire' Open	Red	322	1973	1974	£2	£3.50	❏
101	'Bannockburn Coke' Open	Grey	No 4	1973	1979	£2	£3.50	❏
102	NCB Mineral Wagon LWB	Black	3471	1973	1977	£2	£3.50	❏
104	5 Plank 'A.W. Day' Open	Green	320	1973	1974	£2	£3.50	❏
112 A	LMS Open Wagon Drop Doors	Dark Red	12527			£2.50	£4	❏
112 A	LMS Open Wagon Drop Doors	Red	12527	1971	1972	£2.50	£4	❏
112 A	LMS Open Wagon Drop Doors	Brown	12527			£2.50	£4	❏
112	NE Open Wagon Drop Doors	Grey	47205			£2.50	£4	❏
112	Open Wagon Drop Doors	Red	M2313	1959	1961	£2	£3.50	❏
112	Open Wagon Drop Doors	Red	M2313	1962	1970	£2	£3.50	❏
113	Drop Side Wagon	Red	B4593	1962	1972	£2	£3.50	❏
113	Drop Side Wagon	Red	B4597	1973		£2	£3.50	❏
113	Drop Side Wagon	Red	B4593	1959	1961	£2	£3.50	❏
116	5 Plank 'Amos Benbow' Open	Light Blue		1983	1985	£2	£3.50	❏
118	5 Plank Open 'Emlyn'	Green	813	1986	1994	£2	£3.50	❏
136	Bolsover Open LWB	Black	6390			£2	£3.50	❏
136	Bolsover Open LWB	Blue	6390			£2	£3.50	❏
136	Bolsover Open LWB	Dark Blue	6390			£2	£3.50	❏
136	Bolsover Open LWB	Red	6390			£2	£3.50	❏
136	Bolsover Open LWB (new printing)	Red and Black	6390	1978	1982	£2	£3.50	❏
139	5 Plank 'William Shaw'	Red		1984	1986	£2	£3.50	❏
142	7 Plank 'Evans & Bevan'	Brown	288	1989	1994	£2	£3.50	❏
163	5 Plank 'Spiers'	Grey		1974		£2	£3.50	❏
204	7 Plank 'Ocean'	Brown		1976		£2	£3.50	❏
206	7 Plank 'Chance & Hunt'	Red	142	1985	1994	£2	£3.50	❏

No.	Description	Colour	Running No.	From	To	Price 1	Price 2	
208	5 Plank 'Texas' Open	White		1985	1986	£2	£3.50	❑
209	7 Plank 'Princess Royal'	Dark Red	250		1976	£2	£3.50	❑
210	5 Plank 'General Refracts'	Grey			1973	£2	£3.50	❑
211	'British Steel' Open LWB	Blue		1985	1994	£2	£3.50	❑
217	Mineral Wagon	Blue				£2	£3.50	❑
217	Mineral Wagon	Grey		1976	1978	£2	£3.50	❑
217	Mineral Wagon	Yellow				£2	£3.50	❑
217	Open Wagon	Grey		1959	1962	£2	£3.50	❑
219	Bogie Brick Wagon	Dark Red	NE451004		1967	£3	£5	❑
219	Bogie Brick Wagon	Red		1959	1967	£3	£5	❑
219	'London Brick' Wagon	Red Brown		1970	1973	£3	£5	❑
220	'Norstand' Open	Blue	480	1976	1979	£2	£3.50	❑
222	'Jif' Open	Yellow		1983	1985	£2	£3.50	❑
235	BR 45T Wagon R/F OBA	Red Brown		1979	1981	£3	£4.50	❑
235	BR 45T Wagon R/F OBA	Red Brown			1987	£3	£4.50	❑
239	BR Minerals Wagon MSV	Red		1979	1985	£2	£3.50	❑
240	Brick Wagon with Bricks	Red		1960	1961	£5	£8	❑
240	GW Open (+ Rail)	Grey		1979	1984	£2.50	£4	❑
243	Mineral Wagon	Grey	B75201	1960	1961	£2	£3.50	❑
243	Mineral Wagon	Grey	B75201	1962	1975	£2	£3.50	❑
244	BR Mineral Wagon + Coal	Grey		1960	1961	£3.50	£5	❑
244	Open Wagon 'Beatties'	Yellow			1973	£3	£4.50	❑
245	BR Open Wagon + Oil Drums	Grey		1960	1961	£4	£6	❑
246	BR Open Wagon + Timber	Green		1960	1961	£4	£6	❑
248	BR 45 Ton Open R/F S/L OAA	Red and Grey		1981	1990	£4	£5.50	❑
310 A	'R.W. Miller' Coal Wagon (export)			1974	1975	£3	£5	❑
312 A	'C & A Mineral' Open (export)	Black		1974	1975	£3	£5	❑
386 A	'R.W. Miller' Coal Wagon				1976	£3	£5	❑
388 A	'C & A' Mineral Open	Black			1976	£3	£5	❑
577	'Tri-ang-Hornby' Converter Wagon	Black		1966	1969	£3	£5	❑
716	5 Plank 'Scarwood'	Grey		1980	1983	£2	£3.50	❑
717	5 Plank 'Arnold Sands' (new chassis)	Red Brown		1980	1982	£2	£3.50	❑
717	5 Plank 'Arnold Sands' (new chassis)	Grey		1980	1982	£2	£3.50	❑
719	Coke Wagon, 'Roberts Davy'	Blue Grey		1980	1982	£2	£3.50	❑
719	Coke Wagon, 'Roberts Davy'	Light Grey		1980	1982	£2	£3.50	❑
730	SC Open LWB	Light Green	25506	1980	1982	£2	£3.50	❑
781	NER Coke Wagon	Blue Grey	52220	1971	1974	£2	£3.50	❑
781	NER Coke Wagon	Dark Blue	52220		1974	£2	£3.50	❑
781	NER Coke Wagon	Grey	52220			£2	£3.50	❑

Tankers

No.	Description	Colour		From	To	Price 1	Price 2	
3	'Polo' Tanker	Green		1982	1985	£2	£3.50	❑
7	'United Dairies' Tanker	White		1976	1982	£2	£3.50	❑
8	'Esso' Tanker	Silver		1976	1979	£2	£3.50	❑
12	'BP' Tanker	Silver		1961	1962	£2	£3.50	❑
12	'BP' Tanker	Silver		1966	1969	£2	£3.50	❑
12	'Shell' Tanker	Grey		1970	1971	£2	£3.50	❑
12	'Shell' Tanker	Silver		1963	1965	£2	£3.50	❑
12	'Shell/BP' Tanker	Red and Silver		1959	1960	£2	£3.50	❑
14	'Esso' Tanker	Silver and Red		1982	1985	£2	£3.50	❑
15	'UD' Milk Tanker	White		1959	1960	£2	£3.50	❑
15	'UD' Milk Tanker	White		1961	1973	£2	£3.50	❑
15	'UD' Milk Tanker (lined letters)	White		1974	1975	£2	£3.50	❑
20	'Shell' Tanker LWB	Grey		1973	1979	£2.50	£4	❑
23	'Pfizer Chemicals' Tanker	Green		1982	1983	£2.50	£4	❑
25	'Regent' Tanker	Blue and Silver		1988	1991	£2.50	£4	❑
26	'Allbright and Wilson Acid' LWB	Light Blue		1982	1983	£2.50	£4	❑
28	'Esso' 100T Tanker	Grey and Red		1988	1990	£5	£7.50	❑

No.	Description	Colour		From	To		
71	'Duckhams QXR' Tanker LWB	Blue		1987	1988	£3	£4.50	❑
108	'Esso' Tanker (with Ladder)	Silver		1974	1975	£2	£3.50	❑
111	'National Benzole' Tanker LWB	Black		1989	1992	£3	£4.50	❑
115	'Fina' Tanker LWB	Silver		1983	1985	£3	£4.50	❑
127	'Castrol' Tanker	Green	65	1987	1994	£2.50	£4	❑
129	'Redline' Tanker	Blue		1987	1990	£2.50	£4	❑
132	'Shell' Tanker LWB	Yellow		1974	1975	£2	£3.50	❑
133	'Milk' Tanker	Chrome		1983	1985	£3.50	£5	❑
140	'Duracell' Tanker	Gold and Black		1984	1990	£2.50	£3.50	❑
143	'Carlsberg' Tanker LWB	Green and White		1984	1985	£2.50	£4	❑
144	'Jet/Conoco' 100T Tanker	Grey		1984	1985	£5	£7.50	❑
184	'Texaco' Tanker LWB	Red		1975		£2	£3.50	❑
203	'Trimite' Tanker	Black		1985	1988	£2.50	£4	❑
210	'Shell BP' Tanker Fuel Oil	Black		1959	1961	£2	£3.50	❑
210	'Shell BP' Tanker Fuel Oil	Black		1962	1965	£2	£3.50	❑
211	'Shell Oil' Tanker	Yellow		1959	1961	£2	£3.50	❑
211	'Shell Oil' Tanker	Yellow		1962	1968	£2	£3.50	❑
218	'BP Chemicals' LWB	Grey		1986	1994	£2.50	£4	❑
221	'National Benzole' Tanker	Cream		1981	1983	£2.50	£4	❑
227	'Shell' Tanker LWB	Yellow		1976	1979	£2	£3.50	❑
231	'Texaco' Tanker LWB	Red		1976	1982	£2	£3.50	❑
231	'Texaco' Tanker LWB (Ladder)	Red				£2	£3.50	❑
236	'Gulf' 100T Tanker	Black		1986	1987	£5	£7.50	❑
245	'BP/Shell' Tanker	Silver		1980		£2.50	£4	❑
247	'ICI' Caustic Tanker	Red		1962	1966	£6	£9	❑
311 A	'Peters Milk' Tanker (Export)	White		1974	1975	£3.50	£5	❑
349	'Murgatroyd Chlorine' Tanker	White		1963	1970	£5	£9	❑
387 A	'Peters Milk' Tanker (Export)	White		1976		£3.50	£5	❑
667	'BOC' 100 Ton Tanker	White		1973	1974	£5	£7.50	❑
669	'Shell' 100 Ton Tanker	Grey		1970	1973	£4.50	£6	❑
669	'Shell/BP' 100T Tanker	Grey		1982	1983	£5	£7.50	❑
713	'Esso' Tanker	White and Blue		1984	1991	£2	£3.50	❑
713	'Esso' Tanker	White and Red		1984	1988	£2	£3.50	❑
713	'Esso' Tanker Silver (Crossed B)	Silver		1980	1982	£2	£3.50	❑
715	'Shell' Tanker LWB	Grey		1980	1982	£2.50	£4	❑
731	'Gulf' Tanker LWB	Grey		1980	1982	£2.50	£4	❑

Miscellaneous Goods Wagons

No.	Description	Colour		From	To		
5	Flat Truck and Car	Orange		1982	1991	£2	£3.50	❑
11	'Fisons' Silo Wagon	White		1982	1985	£2.50	£3.50	❑
17	Bolster Wagon 1 SPPT	Brown		1962	1965	£2	£3.50	❑
17	Bolster Wagon 2 SSPTS	Grey	M59015	1959	1960	£2	£3.50	❑
17	Bolster Wagon 2 SPPTS	Grey		1961		£2	£3.50	❑
17 C	Flat Wagon + Car 'Viva'	Red Brown		1973		£3.50	£5	❑
17 C	Flat Wagon + Car 'Anglia'	Red Brown		1966	1968	£3.50	£5	❑
17 C	Flat Wagon + Car 'Cortina'	Red Brown		1969	1970	£3.50	£5	❑
17 C	Flat Wagon + Car 'BMC 1100'	Red Brown		1971		£3.50	£5	❑
17	Wagon + Freightliner Container	Red/Brown/White		1982	1983	£3.50	£4	❑
18	Bolster, 'AEI Cables'	Brown		1965		£2.50	£4.50	❑
18	Bolster, 'AEI Cables'	Brown		1969	1971	£2.50	£4.50	❑
18	Bolster, 'J and P Cables'	Brown	B913011	1963		£2.50	£4.50	❑
18	Bolster, 'J and P Cables'	Grey		1962		£2.50	£4.50	❑
18	Bolster, 'Liverpool'	Grey	M59015	1959	1960	£2.50	£4.50	❑
18	Bolster, 'Pirelli'	Brown	M59015	1966	1968	£2.50	£4.50	❑
18	Bolster, 'Pirelli'	Grey	M59015	1961		£2.50	£4.50	❑
18	Silcock Express + 16 Cars	Orange		1989	1992	£10	NGPP	❑
19	Bolster Wagon with Load	Grey	M59015	1959		£2	£3.50	❑
19	Plate Wagon with Load	Red Brown		1972	1973	£4	£7.50	❑

No.	Description	Colour	Number	From	To		
20	BR Cont's P and O/RMP/Metal Box			1988	1991	£6	£12
22	Cattle Truck	Grey		1982	1985	2.50	£4
23	Bogie Wagon 'Salmon' + Rails	Black		1972	1973	£4	£6
28	Shunter's Wagon	Grey		1973	1975	£2	£3.50
35	BR Cont's Freightliner x 3			1982	1985	£6	£12
36	BR Cont's CP Ships/IFF			1982	1985	£6	£12
95	Prestwin Bulk Powder Silo	Yellow		1989	1990	£2.50	£4
106	SR Sheep Wagon	Beige	51915	1984	1985	£3.50	£4.50
106	SR Sheep Wagon	Brown	51915	1973	1982	£2.50	£4
106	SR Sheep Wagon	Grey	51915			£2.50	£4
110	Bogie Bolster 3 SPPTS	Grey	M13127	1959	1961	£2	£3.50
110	Bogie Bolster 4 SPPTS	Grey		1962	1965	£3.50	£4.50
110	Bogie Bolster 4 SPPTS (from Sets)	Orange	B940092	1967	1971	£3	NGPP
118	Bogie Well Wagon	Green	41917	1959	1961	£2	£3.50
118	Bogie Well Wagon	Green	41917	1962	1967	£2	£3.50
118	Bogie Well Wagon	Grey	41917	1960	1961	£2	£3.50
118	Bogie Well Wagon	Orange	41917	1958		£2	£3.50
122	Cattle Truck LWB	Brown	M3712	1959	1960	£2	£3.50
122	Cattle Truck LWB	Brown	M3712	1961	1972	£2	£3.50
123 A	GWR Horse Box	Brown	505	1972	1975	£3	£4
123	Horse Box	Red	B542	1959	1960	£2	£3.50
123	Horse Box	Red	B542	1961	1966	£2	£3.50
123	Horse Box	Red	B547	1967	1971	£2	£3.50
123	Horse Box (White roof)	Red	B547	1971		£2.50	£3.50
124	Car Transporter + 3 cars	Orange		1982	1990	£4	£6
125	Prestwin Silo Wagon	Brown		1978	1979	£2.50	£4
126	Transporter + 3 cars	Orange		1977	1981	£4	£6
127	Crane Truck	Red		1963	1979	£4	£6
131	Wagon with Wheel Load	Green		1974		£3	£4
131	Wagon with Wheel Load	Red		1975		£2.50	£3.50
133	Wagon with Boat Load	Green		1974		NGPP	NGPP
142	Crane Truck	Yellow		1984	1985	£4	£6
204	BR Cont's RML/Scan Dutch/OCL			1985	1987	5.50	£12
208	Shunter's Wagon	Grey		1976	1978	£2	£3.50
211	'Mineral Lime Co.'	Brown		1973	1977	£2	£3.50
212	Bogie Bolster + Log	Grey	M13127	1959	1961	£3.50	£5
213	Bogie Well Wagon and Crane	Green and Cream		1959	1961	£5	£8
215	Cattle Truck, Harvey Bros	Grey		1986	1989	£3	£4
224	Wagon with Wheel Load	Red		1976		£2	£3.50
225	BR 45Ton Steel Carrier R/F	Red Brown		1980	1981	£3	£4.50
236	BR 45T Steel Carrier	Red Brown		1979		£3	£4.50
241	Well Wagon + Tank Load	Grey and Green	41917	1960	1963	£8	£12
242	Trestrol Wagon	Green		1962		£3	£5
242	Trestrol Wagon	Grey		1961	1965	£3	£5
242	Trestrol Wagon with Girders	Green		1972	1973	£8	£15
244	BR Bogie Bolster + Load R/F	Grey and Red		1986		£5	£8
246	BR 45 ton Steel Carrier R/F S/	Red and Grey		1981	1994	£3	£4.50
296	Track Cleaning Car	Yellow		1982	1994	£3.50	£5
315 A	'CIG Oxygen' Wagon (Export)			1974	1975	NGPP	£20
340	3 Containers Wagon (dark grey)	Brown		1963	1972	£4.50	£6
340	2 Containers Wagon (light grey)	Red Brown		1963	1972	£3	£4.50
342	Car Transporter	Grey		1965	1974	£3	£6
345	Side Tipping Wagon Log Load	Grey		1963	1969	£6	£15
345	Side Tipping Wagon Pipe Load	Black and Red		1974		£6	£15
348	Giraffe Car	Yellow		1963	1971	£10	£20
391 A	'CIG Oxygen' Wagon			1976		NGPP	£20
561	'Tri-ang' Container Wagon	Brown and Blue		1963	1971	£2.50	£4
563	Bogie Bolster + 3 Vans	Orange		1967	1971	£8	£25
564	Blue Circle Cement	Grey		1966	1971	£2	£3.50
564	Blue Circle Cement	Yellow		1972	1975	£2	£3.50
578	TR-HD Converter - Horse Box	Red Brown		1967	1969	£4.50	£6

632	BR Cont's Freightliner Open x 3			1969	1973	£4.50	£6.50	❏
633	BR Cont's Freightliner x 3			1967	1981	£4.50	£6	❏
634	BR Cont's 'Pickfords' / 'Containerway'			1969	1971	£5.50	£12	❏
635	BR Cont's 'BP Chemicals' x 3			1969	1973	£5.50	£12	❏
637	BR Cont's 'Harold Wood' x 3			1969	1973	£6	£12	❏
666	Motorail + 16 Cars	Blue		1969	1970	£8	NGPP	❏
666	Motorail Cartic + 12 Cars	Blue		1971	1973	£8	NGPP	❏
666	Silcock Express + 16 Cars	Orange		1990	1991	£8	NGPP	❏
668	China Clay Wagon, 'Bowaters'	Blue		1969	1973	£3	£5	❏
676	Bolster Wagon	Green		1971	1974	£2	£3.50	❏
676	Bolster Wagon	Red Brown				£2	£3.50	❏
677	BR Cont's Manch'Liners/Fyffes			1971	1971	£6	£12	❏
678	BR Cont's 3 Off Various			1970	1971	£5.50	£12	❏
719	BR Cont's Ford/Scotch Beef			1969	1973	£5.50	£12	❏
723	Prestwin Silo	Brown		1980	1982	£2.50	£4	❏
739	BR 75 Ton Crane	Red		1971	1982	£15	NGPP	❏
749	BR 75 Ton Crane	Yellow		1982	1994	NGPP	NGPP	❏
922 RM	Car Transporter 'Minic'	Grey and Orange		1967	1969	£3	£5	❏

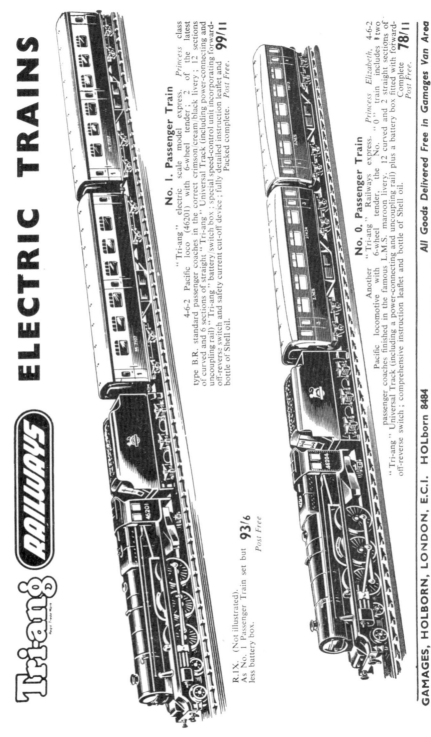

ELECTRIC TRAINS

Tri-ang RAILWAYS

No. 1. Passenger Train

Princess class 4-6-2 Pacific "Tri-ang" electric scale model express. loco (46201) with 6-wheel tender; 2 of the latest type B.R. standard passenger coaches in the correct crimson/cream/black livery; 12 sections of curved and 6 sections of straight "Tri-ang" Universal Track (including power-connecting and uncoupling rail) "Tri-ang" battery/switch box; special speed-control unit incorporating forward-off-reverse switch and safety current cut-off device; fully detailed instruction leaflet and bottle of Shell oil. *Post Free.* Packed complete. **99/11**

R.IX. (Not illustrated).
As No. 1 Passenger Train set but **93/6** *Post Free*
less battery box.

No. 0. Passenger Train

Another "Tri-ang" Railways express. *Princess Elizabeth*, 4-6-2 Pacific locomotive with 6-wheel tender; the No. "0" train includes two "Tri-ang" passenger coaches finished in the famous L.M.S. maroon livery. 12 curved and 2 straight sections of "Tri-ang" Universal Track (including a power-connecting and uncoupling rail) plus a battery box fitted with forward-off-reverse switch; comprehensive instruction leaflet and bottle of Shell oil. Complete **78/11** *Post Free.*

GAMAGES, HOLBORN, LONDON, E.C.I. HOLborn 8484   *All Goods Delivered Free in Gamages Van Area*

20

Picture taken from the 1959 Gamages catalogue.

Tri-ang RAILWAYS

WAGONS and BRAKE VANS

Accurate scale models of typical British Railways' goods rolling stock. Each has a perfectly moulded body mounted on a die-cast chassis fitted with automatic couplings. Incorporating all external details from brake pads to rivet heads.

Complete "TRI-ANG" range always in stock at Gamages

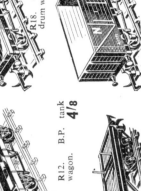

R18. Cable drum wagon. **4/8**

R10. Open "12 ton" goods truck. **3/9**

R13. Open "12 ton" coal truck. **3/11**

R12. B.P. tank wagon. **4/8**

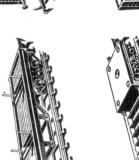

R110. Bogie bolster wagon. **6/3**

R118. Bogie well wagon **5/10**

R15. Milk tank Wagon. **4/8**

R14. Fish Van. **3/11**

FAMOUS BRITISH TRAINS

"ATLANTIC COAST EXPRESS"

First ran from Waterloo to the West of England in 1925. The "Atlantic Coast Express" has the longest run on the Southern Region—260 miles Waterloo to Padstow.

The service operates daily throughout the year and is usually formed of nine coaches with seating accommodation for 396 passengers. Frequently in the summer and at other holiday times it is necessary to run this train in as many as five portions to carry all the passengers. Locomotives of the Southern Region's powerful "Merchant Navy" class usually haul this train between Waterloo and Exeter.

For all Tri-ang Products

GAMAGES, HOLBORN, LONDON, E.C.I. HOLborn 8484

26

Picture taken from the 1959 Gamages catalogue.

BATTERY OPERATED Tri-ang RAILWAYS

Regd. Trade Mark

No. 2 Passenger Train

Comprising 0-6-0 class 3F electric tank loco, 2 L.M.S. coaches, battery box, 12 curved rails, 1 straight rail, 1 power connecting rail, instruction leaflet and supply of Shell oil: packed in full colour labelled box. Complete. **71/-** *Post Free.*

No. 2X. PASSENGER TRAIN not illustrated). As set No. 2, but with speed control unit in place of battery box. Complete. **78/6** *Post Free.*

Exclusive to Gamages!

No. 3G. Goods Train

As No. RG3X. As above, with battery box. Complete. **73/-** *Post Free.*

See back page of cover for full details and coloured illustration.

No. R 3GX. As above, but with speed control unit in place of battery box. Complete. **79/11** *Post Free.*

21

DO YOU KNOW? The British Railways telephone and telegraph system is second only in size to that of the Post Office!

Picture taken from the 1959 Gamages catalogue.

Tri-ang RAILWAYS TRANSCONTINENTAL SERIES

The "TRI-ANG" RAILWAYS System consists of "00" gauge scale models, either ELECTRIC (12 volts D.C.) or Precision CLOCKWORK powered, together with all the track, rolling stock, lineside buildings, control units and other accessories which go to form a complete and "true-to-life" model railway.

Each component is considered as a precision instrument and, therefore, design, construction and finish are of the very highest standards.

No. R. 8X Transcontinental Freight Set.
American type freight train, hauled by Pacific type 4-6-2 loco (fitted with Walshaerts gear) with eight-wheeled bogie tender, box car (sliding doors), gondola, caboose. 12 curved, 5 straight and 1 power connecting rail.   Complete   **£5.19.6** with speed control unit.   *Post Free.*

No. R. 7X Transcontinental Passenger Set
American transcontinental express.   Similar to R. 8X above, but with two passenger coaches, one featuring Vistadome.   **£5.19.6** Complete
Post Free.

Model Railway Dept. First Floor

GAMAGES, HOLBORN, LONDON, E.C.1.   HOLborn 8484

22

Picture taken from the 1959 Gamages catalogue.

'Battlespace' Range

128	Helicopter Wagon	Green and Yellow		1966	1971	£6	£25	❑
128	Helicopter Wagon (from Sets)	White and Yellow		1982	1985	£6	NGPP	❑
128	Helicopter Wagon	Yellow and Red		1974		£6	£25	❑
128	Helicopter Wagon NATO	Grey/Green+Red		1962	1965	£6	£20	❑
130	Tank Transporter (from Sets)	Yellow		1982	1983	£8	NGPP	❑
131	Exploding Rocket Car (from Sets)	Red		1982	1983	£6	NGPP	❑
216	Rocket Launcher	Grey		1959	1965	£5	£15	❑
216	Rocket Launcher	Olive Green		1966	1971	£5	£15	❑
239	Trestrol + Bomb Load	Olive Green		1966	1971	£10	£25	❑
239	Trestrol + Bomb Load NATO	Green		1962	1965	£10	£25	❑
249	B/S Exploding Car	Olive Green		1966	1971	£8	£25	❑
249	B/S Exploding Car	Red		1982	1983	£6	£15	❑
249	Exploding Car	Red		1963	1965	£6	£15	❑
339	WD CL 08 0-6-0 (from Sets)	Green	WD 17	1982	1983	£25	NGPP	❑
341	Searchlight Wagon	Olive Green		1966	1971	£8	£25	❑
341	Searchlight Wagon NATO	Green		1962	1965	£8	£25	❑
343	Four Rocket Launcher	Olive Green		1966	1968	£10	£35	❑
343	Four Rocket Launcher NATO	Green	TR 7191	1962	1965	£10	£35	❑
558	Battle Space 0-6-0T Jinty (from Sets)	Olive Green		1966	1970	£15	NGPP	❑
562	Catapault Launcher	Olive Green		1966	1971	£4	£25	❑
566	Satellite Launcher	Red and Blue		1966	1971	£6	£25	❑
567	Radar Tracking Car	Blue		1966	1971	£8	£25	❑
568	Tank Transporter	Olive Green		1966	1971	£6	£25	❑
568	Tank Transporter (from Sets)	Yellow Brown		1982	1983	£6	NGPP	❑
571	G10 'Q' Car	Olive Green		1967	1969	£8	£150	❑
630	POW Car	Olive Green		1967	1971	£4	£35	❑
631	Tank Recovery Crane	Olive Green	901	1967	1971	£6	£25	❑
639	Sniper Car	Olive Green		1967	1971	£10	£35	❑
725	Command Car	Green		1967	1971	£6	£25	❑
752	Battle Space Turbo Car	Red		1966	1971	£20	£40	❑
756	Battle Space Diesel 0-4-0 (from Sets)	Red		1966	1970	£20	NGPP	❑

'Thomas the Tank Engine and Friends'

91	'James' Composite Coach	Red and White		1988	1991	£4	£7	❑
94	'James' Brake Coach	Red and White		1988	1991	£4	£7	❑
104	'Thomas' Cattle Wagon	Cream and Brown	51915	1986	1991	£2.50	£4	❑
105	'Thomas' Tidmouth Milk	White		1985	1994	£2.50	£3.50	❑
107	Open Wagon	Brown		1985	1994	£2	£3.50	❑
108	Closed Van	Brown		1985	1992	£2	£3.50	❑
109	Brake Van LWB	Red Brown		1985	1994	£3	£4.50	❑
110	'Annie' Coach	Yellow		1985	1994	£3.50	£5	❑
112	'Clarabel' Coach	Yellow		1985	1994	£3.50	£5	❑
120	'Gordon's' Composite Coach	Green and Yellow		1986	1994	£5	£8	❑
121	'Gordon's' Brake Coach	Green and Yellow		1986	1994	£5	£8	❑
305	Tar Tanker	Black		1989	1991	£2.50	£4	❑
306	Breakdown Crane	Grey Brown		1989	1992	NGPP	£75	❑
317	'Devious Diesel'	Black		1987	1989	£15	£35	❑
350	'Percy the Saddle' Tank Engine	Green	6	1985	1994	£12	£30	❑
351	'Thomas the Tank'	Blue	1	1985	1994	£18	£35	❑
382	'Duck' Pannier Tank	Green	8	1986	1991	NGPP	£35	❑
383	'Gordon' Blue Engine	Blue	4	1986	1994	£25	£65	❑
852	'James' The Red Engine	Red	5	1988	1994	£25	£65	❑

Tri-ang 'TT' – Table-Top Railways

Listing taken from the Tri-ang Railways Catalogues T300 (1962) 6th Edition, and RT280 (1963) 9th Edition.
This listing is included as a collector's checklist. Insufficient information is available as yet – hence all NGPP.

Ref.	Model name	Notes, length	Market Price Range	

Rolling Stock

Ref.	Model name	Notes, length	Market Price Range	
T 70	Mineral Wagon	63 cms	NGPP	❑
T 71	Goods Van	63 cms	NGPP	❑
T 72	BR Brake Van	73 cms	NGPP	❑
T 73	Shell-BP Petrol Tank Wagon	63 cms	NGPP	❑
T 74	Milk Tank Wagon	63 cms	NGPP	❑
T 75	Shell-BP Fuel Oil Tank Wagon	63 cms	NGPP	❑
T 76	Shell Lubricating Oil Tank Wagon	63 cms	NGPP	❑
T 77	Cattle Wagon	63 cms	NGPP	❑
T 78	Horse Box	73 cms	NGPP	❑
T 79	Fruit Van	73 cms	NGPP	❑
T 80	BR Suburban Composite Coach	162 cms	NGPP	❑
T 81	BR Suburban Brake 2nd Coach	162 cms	NGPP	❑
T 82	BR Main Line Composite Coach	179 cms	NGPP	❑
T 83	BR Main Line Brake 2nd Coach	179 cms	NGPP	❑
T 84	BR Restaurant Car	with built-in interior fittings, 179 cms	NGPP	❑
T 86	BR 2nd Class Sleeping Car	179 cms	NGPP	❑
T 132	SR Main Line Composite Coach	179 cms	NGPP	❑
T 133	SR Main Line Brake 2nd Coach	179 cms	NGPP	❑
T 134	SR Restaurant Car	with built-in interior fittings, 179 cms	NGPP	❑
T 135	Utility Van	172 cms	NGPP	❑
T 136	Diesel Trailer Car	Non-powered, 186 cms	NGPP	❑
T 137	Diesel Centre Car	For use with the T190 and T136 Diesel Cars to make up multiple units, 186cms	NGPP	❑
T 146	Track Cleaning Car	With 6 charges of Track Cleaning Fluid, 73 cms	NGPP	❑
T 170	Ore Wagon	73 cms	NGPP	❑
T 171	Bulk Grain Wagon	73 cms	NGPP	❑
T 172	Low-Sided Wagon	63 cms	NGPP	❑
T 173	Bogie Well Wagon	176 cms	NGPP	❑
T 175	Meat Van	63 cms	NGPP	❑
T 176	Open Wagon	63 cms	NGPP	❑
T 182	WR Main Line Composite Coach	179 cms	NGPP	❑
T 183	WR Main Line Brake 2nd Coach	179 cms	NGPP	❑
T 184	WR Restaurant Car	With built-in interior fittings 179cms	NGPP	❑
T 185	Pullman 1st Class Kitchen Car	With built-in interior fittings 179cms. Available in the following names: Eagle, Falcon and Snipe.		
T 190	Diesel Power Car	186 cms	NGPP	❑
T 230	Seat Unit	for Suburban Composite and Brake 2nd Coaches	NGPP	❑
T 231	Seat Unit	for Main Line Composite Coaches	NGPP	❑
T 232	Seat Unit	for Main Line Brake 2nd Coaches	NGPP	❑
T 272	Bogie Caustic Tank	98 cms	NGPP	❑
T 275	Bogie Chlorine Tank Wagon	98 cms	NGPP	❑
T 276	Container Wagon with Containers	63 cms	NGPP	❑
T 277	Bogie Bolster Wagon with timber baulk load	146 cms	NGPP	❑
T 278	Cement Wagon	63 cms	NGPP	❑
T 279	Salt Wagon	63 cms	NGPP	❑
T 370	GWR Brake Van	73 cms	NGPP	❑
T 570	Brake Van	73 cms	NGPP	❑
T 571	Grain Wagon	73 cms	NGPP	❑
T 572	Tank Wagon 'Primagaz'	73 cms	NGPP	❑
T 573	Continental Cattle Wagon	73 cms	NGPP	❑
T 574	Continental Mineral Wagon	73 cms	NGPP	❑
T 580	Continental Stainless Steel Passenger Coach	179 cms	NGPP	❑
T 581	Continental Wagon-lits Sleeping Car	188 cms	NGPP	❑
T 582	Continental Wagon-Lits Sleeping Car	179 cms	NGPP	❑
T 583	Continental Wagon-lits Pullman Car	188 cms	NGPP	❑
T 584	SNCF Passenger Coach (Forestiere)	188 cms	NGPP	❑

Tri-ang 'TT'

Locomotives

T 90	0-6-0 Class 3F Tank Locomotive	92 cms	NGPP ❑
T 90	0-6-0 Class 3F Tank Locomotive	Without smoke, 92 cms	NGPP ❑
T 90S	0-6-0 Class 3F Tank Locomotive	With smoke, 92 cms	NGPP ❑
T 91	4-6-0 Castle Class Locomotive 'Tintagel Castle'	Green livery, 13 cms	NGPP ❑
T 92	Tender for 'Tintagel Castle'	81 cms	NGPP ❑
T 93	4-6-2 Merchant Navy Class Locomotive 'Clan Line'	Green livery, 138 cms	NGPP ❑
T 94	Tender for 'Clan Line'	71 cms	NGPP ❑
T 95	0-6-0 Diesel Shunter	Green livery, 92 cms	NGPP ❑
T 96	A1A - A1A Class 2 Diesel Electric Locomotive	Green livery, 178 cms	NGPP ❑
T 97	4-6-2 Britannia Class Locomotive 'Boadicea'	Without smoke. Green livery, Walschaerts Valve Gear	NGPP ❑
T 97S	4-6-2 Britannia Class Locomotive 'Boadicea'	With smoke. Green livery, Walschaerts Valve Gear, 143 cms	NGPP ❑
T 98	Tender for 'Boadicea'	73 cms	NGPP ❑
T 99	2-6-2 Class 4MT Tank Locomotive	13 cms	NGPP ❑
T 590	0-6-0 Tank Locomotive	92 cms	NGPP ❑
T 591	4-6-2 Continental 'Pacific' Locomotive	Without smoke, 146 cms	NGPP ❑
T 591S	4-6-2 Continental 'Pacific' Locomotive	With smoke, 146 cms	NGPP ❑
T 592	Tender for Continental 'Pacific'	88 cms	NGPP ❑
T 594	Continental Suburban Electric Motor Coach	173 cms	NGPP ❑
T 595	Continental Suburban Electric Trailer Coach	Non-powered, 173 cms	NGPP ❑

Train Sets

T 1	Express Train Set	T93 'Clan Line' Loco, T94 Tender, 2 x T132 Composite Coach, T133 Brake 2nd Coach and T164 Power Connecting Clip with 3 x T151 Straight Track, T152 Half Straight Track, 8 x T153 Large Radius Curved Track and T156 Uncoupling Track forming an oval 44" x 26" (112cms x 76cms)	NGPP ❑
T 6	Express Train Set	T91 'Tintagel Castle' Loco, T92 Tender, T182 Composite Coach, 183 Brake 2nd Coach and T164 Power Connecting Clip with 3 x T151 Straight Track, T152 Half Straight Track, 8 x T153 Large Radius Curved Track and T156 Uncoupling Track forming an oval 44" x 26" (112cms x 76cms)	NGPP ❑
T 7	Diesel Railcar Train Set	T190 Power Car, T137 Centre Car, T136 Trailer Car, T164 Power Connecting Clip with 3 x T151 Straight Track, T152 Half Straight Track, 8 x T153 Large Radius Curved Track and T156 Uncoupling Track forming an oval 44" x 26" (112cms x 76cms)	NGPP ❑
T 8	Express Freight Train Set	T96 Diesel Loco, T170 Ore Wagon, T276 Container Wagon, T79 Fruit Van, T272 Caustic Tank Wagon, T72 Brake Van and T164 Power Connecting Clip with 3 x T151 Straight Track, T152 Half Straight Track, 8 x T153 Large Radius Curved Track and T156 Uncoupling Track forming an oval 44" x 26" (112cms x 76cms)	NGPP ❑
T 9	Diesel Goods Train Set	T95 Diesel Shunter, T74 Milk Tank Wagon, T171 Bulk Grain Wagon, T77 Cattle Wagon, T72 Brake Van, T164 Power Connecting Clip with 3 x T151 Straight Track, T152 Half Straight Track, 8 x T153 Large Radius Curved Track and T156 Uncoupling Track forming an oval 44" x 26" (112cms x 76cms)	NGPP ❑
T 10	Goods Train Set	T90 Tank Loco, T172 Low-Sided Wagn, T70 Mineral Wagon, T72 Brake Van and T164 Power Connecting Clip with T151 Straight Track, T152 Half Straight Track, 8 x T153 Large Radius Curved Track and T156 Uncoupling Track forming an oval 35" x 26" (89cms x 76cms)	NGPP ❑
T 501	Continental Freight Train Set	T590 0-6-0 Tank Locomotive, T571 Grain Wagon, T572 Tank Wagon 'Primagaz', T570 Brake Van, T152 Half Straight, 8 x T153 Curves, T156 Uncoupling Track, T164 Power Connecting Clip forming an oval 31" x 26" (79cms x 66cms)	NGPP ❑
T 504	Continental Express Freight Train Set	T591 4-6-2 Class 231D Locomotive, T592 Tender, T573 Cattle Wagon, T571 Grain Wagon, T572 Tank Wagon 'Primagaz', T574 Mineral Wagon, T570 Brake Van, 3 x T151 Straights, T152 Half Straight, 8 x t153 Curves (LR), T156 Uncoupling Track and T164 Power Connecting Clip forming an oval 44" x 26" (112cms x 66cms)	NGPP ❑

1st EDITION
'BRITISH MODEL TRAINS CATALOGUE'

USERS SURVEY

Whether you are a collector or trader we would greatly value your views on this new Edition and would ask you to kindly complete and return this questionnaire.

We hope to publish the results of this survey and for the three most helpful and constructive replies we receive, we shall be giving a years free subscription to the collecting magazine or newspaper of their choice. If necessary do please use a separate sheet for your replies.

1.   What do you MOST like about the Catalogue?

....

....

2.   What do you LEAST like about the Catalogue?

....

....

3.   What improvements would you like to see?

....

....

4.   Would you like the catalogue to be published yearly or every two years?

....

....

If you have model information not currently included in the catalogue, do please send it to us – your costs will be fully refunded.

NAME & ADDRESS (BLOCK CAPITALS PLEASE)

....

....

Kindly return the form to:
Swapmeet Publications, PO Box 47, Felixstowe, Suffolk, England. IP11 7LP.

WHEN REPLYING TO ADVERTISEMENTS PLEASE MENTION JOHN RAMSAY'S CATALOGUE

WHEN REPLYING TO ADVERTISEMENTS PLEASE MENTION JOHN RAMSAY'S CATALOGUE

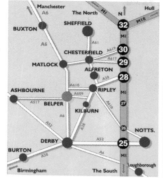

Retailers Shop Sign (£210). 4-2-2 loco & tender 'CR' blue No 123 (part lot.

(RIGHT) R257 Double ended Grren pantograph locomotives (part lot)

Retailer Shop Sign (£250)

No 3231 Diesel Shunter (£190). No 2250 Electric Motor Coach. 'Canadian Pacific 437270' casoose (mint boxed) (£220) and Co-Bo Diesel near mint-boxed (£95).

Models sold by Barry Potter Auctions, 25 The Green, Great Bowden, Leicestershire and pictures reproduced by his kind permission.

Bassett-Lowke and Exley

Top: Gauge/Bing for Bassett-Lowke. Live steam 4-4-0 'COUNTY OF NORTHAMPTON'. (£1,240)
Middle: Bassett-Lowke 2-6-0 loco & tender 'Mogul' No 13000 (£610)
Bottom: Gauge/Carette for Bassett-Lowke Boiler wagon (£610)

'O' Gauge'
Top: Bassett-Lowke 4-6-0 loco & tender. 3 rail AC electric c. 1940 (£2,550)
Middle: Exley 'ROYAL MAIL' coach with dummy side net
Bottom: Bassett-Lowke 2-6-2 Tank. 3 rail AC electric c.1940. Private owners van (£160)

Models sold by Barry Potter Auctions, 25 The Green, Great Bowden, Leicestershire LE16 7EU and pictures reproduced by his kind permission.

'O' Gauge 0-6-0 Tank LMS Black No 78. 3 rail electric Mint Boxed (£520)
"O' Gauge 0-6-0 Tank LNER Black No 335. 3 rail electric Mint Boxed (£510)
"OO' Wrenn 2276/5P 4-6-2 Loco & tender.
Bottom: 4-4-2 Hornby Loco and tender Southern Green No 850 'LORD NELSON'
(part of Hornby Green arrow set which sold for £1,120). Hornby No 1 'SR' Pink
refrigereator Van near mint boxed (£560)

Top: Hornby 4-4-4 South African 'S.A.R.' maroon clockwork with 'HORNBY
SERIES 6027' on cabside (£710), South African wagons (£790), Hornby No 6201
PRINCESS ELIZABETH' in rare matt paint. Excellent Boxed (£2,320) Hornby No 1
special tank LNER 2162, 0-40, 3 rail 20 volt electric, near Mint Boxed (£460).
Hornby 'CRAWFORDS' Biscuit van. Excellent Boxed. Hornby single 'WINE'
wagon (part lot).

Models sold by Barry Potter Auctions, 25 The Green, Great Bowden, Leicestershire and pictures reproduced by his kind permission.

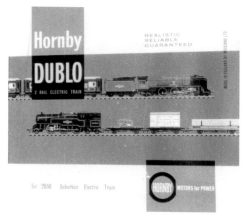

No 2050 Surburban Electric Train Set (£220)

Hornby Dublo No 2049 Breakdown Set (£300)

No RS62 Tri-ang Car-A-Belle Set (£160)

Hornby Dublo No 2049 Breakdown Set (£300)

No RS62 Tri-ang Car-A-Belle Set (£160)

Models sold by Vectis Model Auctions, Fleck Way, Thornaby, Stockton on Tees and the pictures reproduced by their kind permission.

Wrenn Railways

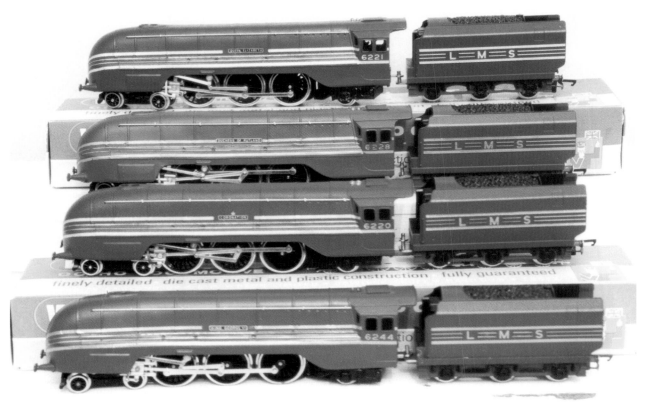

Coronation (7P) class locomotives. Models sold by Romsey Auction Rooms, 86 The Hundred, Romsey, Hampshire SO51 8BX. Picture reproduced by their kind permission.

Models sold in 1997 by Lacy Scott & Knight as part of a superb large Wrenn collection. Pictures reproduced by their kind permission.

Wrenn Railways

Top: W2273 'THE ROYAL AIR FORCE' (£350)
Plus W2265a 'FIGHTER PILOT' (£310)

Top row L-R: W2234 08 Sunter & W2243
08 Shunter 'DUNLOP' (£180 the pair).
Middle row: W2410 0-6-0 'SR' Green
(£530). W2214 'LMS' N2 Tank (£150).
Bottom row: W2230np Bo-Bo Non-
powered, W2230 Bo-Bo D8017

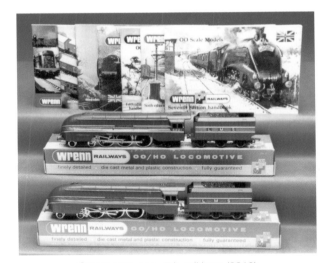

Catalogues 1st - 7th editions (£210)
W2301 'QUEEN ELIZABETH' (£490)
W2302 'KING GEORGE VI' (£420)

Top row:
W2411 'ROYAL MAIL LINE' (£460)
W2407 'TAVISTOCK' (£320)
W2415 'LORD DOWDING' (£290)

Pictures kindly supplied by Barry Potter Auctions, 25 The Green, Great Bowden, Leicestershire LE16 7EU and reproduced by his kind permission. Auction prices realised shown in the auction results.

W2314 'SIR WILLIAM STANIER'
W2237 'LYME REGIS'
W2266a 'CITY OF WELLS G/A'
W2260 'ROYAL SCOT'
W2210 'MALLARD'

W2311 'CITY OF LEEDS'
W2223 'WINDSOR CASTLE'
W2267 'LAMPORT & HOLT LINE'
W2261 'BLACK WATCH'
W2402 'SIR EUSTAGE MISSENDEN'

W2400 'GREAT WESTERN'
W2413 'BITTERN'
W2403 'THE RIFLE BRIGADE'
W2265 'WINSTON CHURCHILL'
W2246 'C.R.'   W2202 'N.T.G.'

W2409 8F 48102
W2414 'CITY OF NOTTINGHAM'
W2407 'TAVISTOCK'
W2315 'CITY OF GLASGOW'
W2245 'SOUTHERN'

Pictures kindly supplied by Barry Potter Auctions, 25 The Green, Great Bowden, Leicestershire LE16 7EU and reproduced by his kind permission. Auction prices realised shown in the auction results.

Wrenn Railways

OO/HO gauge scale models manufactured by
G. and R. Wrenn Ltd., Bowlers Croft, Basildon, Essex, England.

The Editor would like to express his appreciation to Rob Smith of Southampton Model Centre for his assistance in the production of the Wrenn listings.

Steam Outline Locomotives, 1968-1992

Market Price Range

The price range shown reflects both mail order advertised prices and auction price realisations. It must be understood that the top prices shown are in respect of the likely amount one would have to pay for pristine mint boxed examples.

Technical specifications

Wrenn Locomotives are mostly constructed with die-cast metal bodies. The models have fine body detailing, individual hand rails and nickel-plated driving wheels. The locomotives are in a large part hand-finished. Painted parts have been twice stove-enamelled; crests and linings are in authentic colours.

Tri-ang type couplings are fitted as standard but Hornby-Dublo type are included with all locomotives. Wrenn locomotives are modelled in 4mm. to the foot scale (1:76) and are suitable for use on OO/HO track systems of 16.5mm. (0.650.) gauge.

N.B. This introduction has been extracted from the description provided in the first edition Wrenn catalogue (1973).

Abbreviations

BR = British Railways
GWR = Great Western Railway,   GW = Great Western
LMS = London, Midland and Scottish,

LNER = London and North Eastern Railway,
NE = North Eastern, MR = Midland Region, WR = Western Region,
NCB = National Coal Board, NTG = North Thames Gas,

SR = Southern Railways (or Southern Region),
SE & CR = South East and Chatham Railway, R/B = rebuilt
WD = War Department

MPR = market price range, NGPP = no grading possible at present.

wrenn RAILWAYS OO/HO Gauge FIRST EDITION CATALOGUE 15p

Wrenn Railways

Ref.	Livery	Number	Colour	Locomotive name, notes	Market Price Range

Steam Outline Locomotives (Electrically Powered)

Locomotives, 'Castle' Class (4-6-0)

Ref.	Livery	Number	Colour	Locomotive name, notes	Market Price Range	
W 2221	BR	4075	Green	'Cardiff Castle'	**£120-150**	❏
W 2221b	BR	5023	Light Green	'Brecon Castle'	**£150-200**	❏
W 2221k	GWR	4075	Green	'Cardiff Castle', (kit)	**£400-500**	❏
W 2221a	BR	7013	Green	'Bristol Castle'	**£300-350**	❏
W 2222	GWR	7002	Green	'Devizes Castle'	**£140-170**	❏
W 2223	BR	4082	Blue	'Windsor Castle'	**£150-200**	❏
W 2247	GWR	7029	Green	'Clun Castle'	**£140-170**	❏
W 2247a	BR	7029	Green	'Clun Castle'	**£250-300**	❏
W 2284	BR	5090	Green	'Neath Abbey'	**£350-400**	❏
W 2400	BR	7007	Green	'Great Western'	**£400-500**	❏
W 2417	BR	5034	Green	'Corfe Castle'	**£400-500**	❏

Locomotives, 'Coronation' (7P) Class (4-6-2)

Ref.	Livery	Number	Colour	Locomotive name, notes	Market Price Range	
W 2300				'Princess' (unpainted kit)	**£500-700**	❏
W 2301	LMS	6221	Blue	'Queen Elizabeth'	**£600-750**	❏
W 2301a	LMS	6220	Blue	'Coronation'	**£700-800**	❏
W 2302	LMS	6244	Maroon	'King George VI'	**£600-750**	❏
W 2302a	LMS	6228	Maroon	'Duchess of Rutland'	**£750-900**	❏

Locomotives, 'City' (8P) Class (4-6-2)

Ref.	Livery	Number	Colour	Locomotive name, notes	Market Price Range	
W 2226	BR	46245	Maroon	'City of London'	**£120-150**	❏
W 2226m2	BR	46245	Maroon	'City of London', (5-pole)	**£400-500**	❏
W 2226a	BR	46238	Maroon	'City of Carlisle'	**£350-450**	❏
W 2226am2	BR	46238	Maroon	'City of Carlisle', (5-pole)	**£400-500**	❏
W 2227	LMS	6254	Black	'City of Stoke-on-Trent'	**£120-150**	❏
W 2227a	LMS	6256	Black	'Sir William Stanier'	**£275-350**	❏
W 2227am2	LMS	6256	Black	'Sir William Stanier', (5-pole)	**£400-500**	❏
W 2228	BR	46235	Green	'City of Birmingham'	**£150-200**	❏
W 2228m2	BR	46235	Green	'City of Birmingham', (5-pole)	**£400-500**	❏
W 2228a	BR	46241	Green	'City of Edinburgh'	**£250-300**	❏
W 2228am2	BR	46241	Green	'City of Edinburgh', (5-pole)	**£400-500**	❏
W 2229	BR	46242	Blue	'City of Glasgow'	**£150-200**	❏
W 2229a	BR	46246	Blue	'City of Manchester'	**£330-400**	❏
W 2241	LMS	6229	Black	'Duchess of Hamilton'	**£150-200**	❏
W 2241m2	LMS	6229	Black	'Duchess of Hamilton', (5-pole)	**£400-500**	❏
W 2241a	LMS	6225	Black	'Duchess of Gloucester'	**£325-400**	❏
W 2241am2	LMS	6225	Black	'Duchess of Gloucester', (5-pole)	**£400-500**	❏
W 2242	LMS	6247	Maroon	'City of Liverpool'	**£150-175**	❏
W 2264	BR	46229	Maroon	'Duchess of Hamilton'	**£400-500**	❏
W 2285	LMS	6221	Maroon	'Queen Elizabeth'	**£375-450**	❏
W 2286	BR	46252	Black	'City of Leicester'	**£375-450**	❏
W 2294	LMS	6234	Grey	'Duchess of Abercorn'	**£400-500**	❏
W 2299	BR	46221	Green	'Queen Elizabeth'	**£400-500**	❏
W 2304	BR	46244	Maroon	'City of Leeds' (with alternative 'KG VI' plates)	**£400-500**	❏
W 2304	BR	46244	Maroon	'King George V'	**£400-500**	❏
W 2311	BR	46244	Black	'City of Leeds' (unlined, with wrong number)	**£400-500**	❏
W 2312	BR	46245	Green	'City of London'	**£400-500**	❏
W 2313	BR	46234	Green	'Duchess of Abercorn'	**£650-750**	❏
W 2314	BR	46256	Green	'Sir William Stanier'	**£650-750**	❏
W 2315	BR	46242	Maroon	'City of Glasgow'	**£650-750**	❏
W 2316	BR	46242	Green	'City of Glasgow'	**£650-750**	❏
W 2401	LMS	6223	Maroon	'Princess Alice'	**£400-500**	❏
W 2405	BR	46231	Green	'Duchess of Atholl'	**£400-500**	❏
W 2414	BR	46251	Black	'City of Nottingham'	**£400-500**	❏

Locomotives, 'Royal Scot' Class (4-6-0)

W 2260	LMS	6100	Maroon	'Royal Scot'	£225-275 ❏
W 2260-5P	LMS	6100	Maroon	'Royal Scot', (5-pole)	£300-375 ❏
W 2260a	LMS	6141	Maroon	'Caledonian'	£325-400 ❏
W 2261	LMS	6012	Black	'Black Watch'	£225-275 ❏
W 2261-5P	LMS	6102	Black	'Black Watch', (5-pole)	£300-375 ❏
W 2261a	LMS	6160	Black	'Queen Victoria's Riflemen'	£325-400 ❏
W 2262	BR	46110	Green	'Grenadier Guardsman'	£225-275 ❏
W 2262a	BR	46148	Green	'Manchester Regiment', (5-pole)	£325-375 ❏
W 2273	BR	46159	Blue	'The Royal Air Force', (5-pole)	£335-400 ❏
W 2274	LMS	6125	Maroon	'Lancashire Witch', (5-pole)	£250-300 ❏
W 2288	BR	46159	Green	'The Royal Air Force'	£325-400 ❏
W 2293	LMS	6141	Black	'Caledonian' (gloss or matt)	£325-400 ❏
W 2298	BR	46100	Green	'Royal Scot'	£400-500 ❏
W 2403	LMS	6146	Black	'The Rifle Brigade'	£400-500 ❏

Locomotives, 'A4' Class (4-6-2)

W 2209	LNER	4482	Green	'Golden Eagle'	£150-175 ❏
W 2209a	LNER	4495	Green	'Great Snipe'	£250-300 ❏
W 2209am2	LNER	4495	Green	'Great Snipe', (5-pole)	£350-450 ❏
W 2210	LNER	4468	Blue	'Mallard'	£200-250 ❏
W 2210am2	LNER	4495	Blue	'Golden Fleece', (5-pole)	£500-600 ❏
W 2211	BR	60022	Green	'Mallard'	£100-150 ❏
W 2211a	BR	60014	Green	'Silver Link'	£250-300 ❏
W 2212	LNER	7	Blue	'Sir Nigel Gresley'	£100-150 ❏
W 2212a	LNER	4498	Blue	'Sir Nigel Gresley'	£150-200 ❏
W 2212am2	LNER	4498	Blue	'Sir Nigel Gresley', (5-pole)	£400-500 ❏
W 2213	NE	4903	Black	'Peregrine'	£150-200 ❏
W 2213a	NE	4900	Black	'Gannet'	£250-300 ❏
W 2282	NE	4463	Black	'Sparrow Hawk'	£250-300 ❏
W 2283	LNER	4493	Grey	'Woodcock'	£500-600 ❏
W 2295m2	LNER	4489	Blue	'Dominion of Canada'	£500-600 ❏
W 2306	BR	60010	Green	'Dominion of Canada'	£500-600 ❏
W 2310	LNER	4498	Blue	'Sir Nigel Gresley'	£500-600 ❏
W 2413	LNER	4464	Green	'Bittern'	£400-500 ❏

Locomotives, 'West Country/Merchant Navy' (7P) Class (4-6-2)

W 2235	BR	34005 R/B	Green	'Barnstaple'	£150-200 ❏
W 2236	BR	34042 R/B	Green	'Dorchester'	£150-200 ❏
W 2236a	BR	34016 R/B	Green	'Bodmin'	£350-450 ❏
W 2237	SR	21C109 R/B	Green	'Lyme Regis'	£150-200 ❏
W 2238	BR	35028 R/B	Green	'Clan Line'	£250-300 ❏
W 2239	BR	34028 R/B	Green	'Eddystone'	£275-350 ❏
W 2265	BR	34051	Green	'Winston Churchill'	£275-300 ❏
W 2265a	SR	21C155	Green	'Fighter Pilot' (Golden Arrow)	£400-500 ❏
W 2265ax	SR	21C155	Green	'Fighter Pilot'	£500-600 ❏
W 2266	SR	21C103	Green	'Plymouth'	£325-400 ❏
W 2266ax	BR	34092	Green	'City of Wells'	£350-450 ❏
W 2266a	BR	34092	Green	'City of Wells' (Golden Arrow)	£400-500 ❏
W 2267	BR	35026	Blue	'Lamport and Holt Line'	£400-500 ❏
W 2267a	BR	35026	Green	'Lamport and Holt Line'	£700-800 ❏
W 2268	BR	34004	Blue	'Yoevil', (5-pole)	£400-500 ❏
W 2268a	BR	34004	Green	'Yoevil'	£650-750 ❏
W 2269	BR	34053 R/B	Green	'Sir Keith Park' (Golden Arrow)	£400-500 ❏
W 2269x	BR	34053 R/B	Green	'Sir Keith Park'	£350-450 ❏
W 2275	BR	34065	Green	'Hurricane', (5-pole)	£400-500 ❏
W 2276	SR	21C 101	Green	'Exeter' (Golden Arrow), (5-pole)	£800-1,000 ❏

Wrenn locomotives

W 2276x	SR	21C 101	Green	'Exeter', (5-pole)	£800-1,000	❑
W 2277	BR	34066	Green	'Spitfire'	£400-500	❑
W 2278	SR	21C 13	Black	'Blue Funnel Line'	£500-600	❑
W 2278a	SR	21C 13	Green	'Blue Funnel Line'	£800-1,000	❑
W 2287	BR	34036 R/B	Green	'Westward Ho!'	£400-500	❑
W 2289	SR	21C 5	Black	'Canadian Pacific Line'	£500-600	❑
W 2290	SR	21C 5	Green	'Canadian Pacific Line'	£750-850	❑
W 2291	BR	34010	Green	'Sidmouth'	£400-500	❑
W 2296	BR	34021 R/B	Green	'Dartmoor'	£500-600	❑
W 2297	BR	35010 R/B	Green	'Blue Star Line'	£500-600	❑
W 2305	SR	21C 107	Green	'Wadebridge'	£800-1,000	❑
W 2309	BR	34036 R/B	Black	'Westward Ho!' (unlined)	£750-1,000	❑
W 2402	BR	34090 R/B	Green	'Sir Eustace Missenden'	£400-500	❑
W 2407	SR	21C 111	Green	'Tavistock'	£400-500	❑
W 2411	BR	35003	Blue	'Royal Mail Line'	£400-500	❑
W 2412	BR	34020	Green	'Seaton'	£400-500	❑
W 2415	BR	34052 R/B	Green	'Lord Dowding'	£500-600	❑
W 2416	BR	34057	Green	'Biggin Hill'		❑

Tank Locomotives, 'R1' Class (0-6-0)

W 2201	ESSO	38	Blue		£65-85	❑
W 2201a	SE & CR	69	Green		£140-160	❑
W 2202	NTG	56	Yellow		£50-60	❑
W 2203	SHELL		Silver		£50-60	❑
W 2204	LMS	7420	Maroon		£40-50	❑
W 2205	BR	31337	Black		£40-50	❑
W 2205	BR	31340	Black		£50-60	❑
W 2205a	BR	31047	Black		£150-180	❑
W 2206	BR	31340	Green		£40-50	❑
W 2206	BR	31337	Green		£50-60	❑
W 2206a	BR	31128	Green		£150-180	❑
W 2207	SR	1127	Olive Green		£40-50	❑
W 2207a	SR	1152	Olive Green		£150-180	❑
W 2408			Gold plated ...(non-powered)		£300-350	❑
W 2410	SR	1047	Green		£600-900	❑

Tank Locomotives, 'N2' Class (0-6-2)

W 2214	LMS	2274	Maroon		£70-85	❑
W 2215	LMS	2385	Black		£70-85	❑
W 2215a	LMS	2248	Black		£250-300	❑
W 2216	BR	69550	Black		£60-75	❑
W 2216a	BR	69496	Black		£400-500	❑
W 2217	LNER	9522	Green		£50-75	❑
W 2217a	LNER	2690	Black		£250-300	❑
W 2280	GWR	8230	Green		£300-400	❑
W 2292	SR	2752	Dark Green		£750-1,000	❑
W 2292	SR	2752	Light Green		£750-1,000	❑

Freight Locomotives, '8F' Class (2-8-0)

W 2224	BR	48073	Black		£80-100	❑
W 2224a	BR	48290	Black		£250-300	❑
W 2225	LMS	8042	Black		£80-100	❑
W 2225a	LMS	8233	Black		£200-250	❑
W 2240	LNER	3144	Black		£150-200	❑
W 2272	LMS	8016	Maroon		£300-350	❑
W 2281	WD	302	Grey		£350-400	❑
W 2308	BR	48290	Green		£500-600	❑
W 2409	BR	48102	Black		£375-450	❑

Tank Locomotives, '4MT' Class (2-6-4)

W 2218	BR	80033	Black		£80-100	❏
W 2218	BR	80054	Black		£200-250	❏
W 2218a	BR	80064	Black		£200-250	❏
W 2218a	BR	80079	Black		£200-250	❏
W 2219	LMS	2679	Maroon		£100-150	❏
W 2220	GWR	8230	Green		£125-175	❏
W 2245	SR	1927	Green		£175-225	❏
W 2246	CR	2085	Blue		£300-350	❏
W 2270	BR	80135	Green		£190-220	❏
W 2271	LNER	9025	Green		£300-400	❏
W 2279	BR	80151	Black	(5-pole)	£200-250	❏
W 2307	BR	80079	Black	(unlined)	£300-400	❏
W 2406	BR	80120	Black		£325-375	❏

Diesel-Electric Locomotives, 'BO-BO' Class 20 (4-4)

W 2230	BR	D8017	Green		£50-70	❏
W 2230a	BR	20-008	Blue		£75-100	❏
W 2230b	BR	8003	Blue		£50-70	❏
W 2230bnp	BR	D8015	Blue	(non-powered)	£250-300	❏
W 2230np	BR	D8010	Green	(non-powered)	£250-300	❏
W 2230rf	BR	20-132	Grey	'RAILFREIGHT'	£250-300	❏

Diesel-Electric Shunters, '08' Class (0-6-0)

W 2231	BR	D3763	Green		£60-70	❏
W 2231np	BR	D3768	Green	(non-powered)	£400-500	❏
W 2232	BR	D3464	Blue		£60-70	❏
W 2232np	BR	D3523	Blue	(non-powered)	£400-500	❏
W 2232a	BR	08 762	Blue		£200-250	❏
W 2233	LMS	7124	Black		£70-85	❏
W 2234		72	Red	'NCB'	£70-85	❏
W 2243	LMS		Yellow	'DUNLOP'	£70-85	❏

'Brighton Belle' Two-Car Sets

W 3004/5	BR	Blue/Grey		£200-250	❏
W 3004/5a	BR	Blue/Grey	'150 Years'	£275-350	❏
W 3306/7	Pullman	Brown/Cream (Set 3051, 1988-89)		£250-300	❏
W 3006/7	Pullman	Brown/Cream (Set 3052, 1990-91)		£220-260	❏
W 3006/7a	Pullman	Brown/Cream '150 Years' (1990-91)		£500-600	❏

Wrenn Train Sets

001	'BR' Goods Set	0-6-0 Locomotive, Two Wagons, Guards Van, track oval	£200-250	❏
002	'BR' Freight Set	2-6-4 Locomotive, three Wagons, Guards Van, track oval	£250-300	❏
003	'BR' Pullman Set	West Country Locomotive, two Pullman cars, track oval	£400-500	❏

Passenger Coaches

Ref.	Type	Livery	Name, notes	Market Price Range

Passenger Coaches – Pullman Cars, 1968-1992

'Super Detail' bodies in high impact polystyrene, with die-cast bogies for stability, fitted with metal-tyred wheels and pin-point axles for extra smooth and friction-free running. Interior fitted with seats, tables and lamps.
N.B. This description has been extracted from the first and second edition Wrenn catalogues (1973-74).

Ref.	Type	Livery	Name, notes	Market Price Range	
W 6000	Brake/2nd	Brown/Cream	'Car No77'	£25-30	❑
W 6000a	Brake/2nd	Brown/Cream	'Car No79'	£25-30	❑
W 6001	2nd class	Brown/Cream	'Car No73'	£25-30	❑
W 6001	2nd class	Brown/Cream	'Car No74'	£35-40	❑
W 6001a	Parlour car	Brown/Cream	'Car No87'	£25-30	❑
W 6001b	Parlour car	Brown/Cream	'Car No86'	£25-30	❑
W 6001ag	1st class	Brown/Cream	'AGATHA'	£30-35	❑
W 6001s	1st class	Brown/Cream	'SHEILA'	£40-50	❑
W 6001u	1st class	Brown/Cream	'URSULA'	£30-35	❑
W 6002	1st class	Brown/Cream	'ARIES'	£30-35	❑
W 6002a	1st class	Brown/Cream	'AUDREY'	£30-35	❑
W 6002b	1st class	Brown/Cream	'BELINDA'	£35-40	❑
W 6002v		Brown/Cream	'VERA'	£30-35	❑
W 6002d	1st class	Brown/Cream	'DORIS'	£35-40	❑
W 6002h	1st class	Brown/Cream	'HAZEL'	£30-35	❑
W 6002c	1st class	Brown/Cream	'CARINA'	£40-50	❑
W 6003	Brake/2nd	Blue/Grey (BR)	'S 308 S', (BR logo on some)	£25-35	❑
W 6004	2nd class	Blue/Grey (BR)	'S 302 S', (BR logo on some)	£30-35	❑
W 6004a	Parlour car	Blue/Grey (BR)	'S 287 S', ('Brighton Belle')	£30-35	❑
W 6005	1st class	Blue/Grey (BR)	'S 301 S', ('Golden Arrow')	£30-35	❑
W 6005a	1st class	Blue/Grey (BR)	'S 284 S', ('Brighton Belle')	£30-35	❑
W 6005a	1st class	Blue/Grey (BR)	'S 280 S', ('Brighton Belle')	£30-35	❑
W 6006	Brake/2nd	Green (SR)	'1708'	£25-30	❑
W 6007	2nd class	Green (SR)	'2523'	£25-30	❑
W 6008	1st class	Green (SR)	'1245'	£25-30	❑
W 6009	Brake/2nd	Red (LMS)	'2370'	£25-30	❑
W 6010	2nd class	Red (LMS)	'3459'	£25-30	❑
W 6011	1st class	Red (LMS)	'1046'	£25-30	❑
W 6012	1st class	Brown/Cream	'PEGASUS', ('Golden Arrow')	£30-35	❑
W 6012a	1st class	Brown/Cream	'CECILIA', ('Golden Arrow')	£35-40	❑
W 6012b	1st class	Brown/Cream	'ARIES', ('Golden Arrow')	£35-40	❑
W 6012c	1st class	Brown/Cream	'CYGNUS', ('Golden Arrow')	£40-50	❑
W 6101c	Parlour car	Brown/Cream	'83', (limited edition)	£70-80	❑
W 6102e	1st class	Brown/Cream	'EVADNE', (limited edition)	£70-80	❑

Pullman Cars

Super detail bodies in high impact polystyrene, die cast metal bogies for stability, fitted with metal tyred wheels and pin point axles for extra smooth and friction free running. Interior fitted with seats, tables and lamps.
These Superb Pullmans can be used with most passenger trains as they ran as through coaches. Pulled by a West Country Class Locomotive the famous 'Bournemouth Belle' can be made up.

W6002 Pullman Car 1st. Class

W6000 Pullman Car Brake/2nd.

W6001 Pullman Car 2nd. Class

Vans and Wagons

Private Owner and Standard Wagons, 1968-1992

A fine and very extensive range of 'OO/HO' smooth running wagons each with extremely colourful private-owner markings. The bodies are of high-impact polystyrene, some have opening doors, and with the exception of the all-plastic models have detailed die-cast under frames. Tri-ang couplings are fitted and Hornby-Dublo conversion kits are available. Colours of some wagons may be subject to change without notice. N.B. This information has been extracted from the description provided in the first and second edition Wrenn catalogues (1973-74).

Wheels were initially made entirely of plastic; metal wheels were introduced in 1972. Various shades of grey predominate as the roof colour of a vehicle which has one; the few exceptions are shown below. Note that large shade differences exist in body colours as well, and colour of lettering also varies in shade and intensity. These differences are the result of normal mass-production techniques and do not affect the collectability or price of the model wagons.

Manufacturers name shown on boxes: 'Wrenn OO/HO' (1968-1969), 'Tri-ang Wrenn' (1970-1972), 'Wrenn Railways' (1973-1992).

Ref.	Description	Number	Colour	Notes	Price
W 4300p	Fish Van 'FINDUS FOODS'	E87231	White	Red/Blue	£10-15 ❑
W 4301p	Banana Van 'FYFFES'	B881867	Brown	Blue/White	£10-15 ❑
W 4301p	Banana Van 'FYFFES'	B881867	Green	Blue/White	£10-15 ❑
W 4305p	Long Fruit 'D' Van 'BABYCHAM'	W2910	Maroon	Red/Black/Yellow	£10-15 ❑
W 4305x	Long Fruit 'D' Van/Passenger	W2910	Maroon		£10-15 ❑
W 4310	Brake/Goods Van, 'BR' (ER)	B950350	Brown (matt or gloss)		£10-15 ❑
W 4311p	Guards Van, LMS	M730973	Brown		£10-15 ❑
W 4311x	Guards Van, 'BR' (MR)	M730973	Brown		£10-15 ❑
W 4312	Guards Van, 'BR' (WR)	(Dublo mould faulty, not issued)			NPP
W 4313	Gunpowder Van, 'BR'	B887002	Brown		£10-15 ❑
W 4313p	Gunpowder Van, 'STANDARD FIREWORKS'	B887002	Brown	Red/White	£20-25 ❑
W 4313p	Gunpowder Van, 'STANDARD FIREWORKS'	B887002	Green	Red/White	£20-25 ❑
W 4315p	Horse Box, 'FOXHUNTER CHAMPIONSHIPS'	E96435	Green	Red/Bright Yellow	£20-25 ❑
W 4315p	Horse Box, 'Royden Stables Brighton Oct 6-11'	E96435	Green	Red/Pale yellow	£10-15 ❑
W 4315p	Horse Box, 'Royden Stables Brighton Oct 6-11'	E96435	Green	Red/Green	£40-50 ❑
W 4315p	Horse Box, 'Royden Stables' (no date/place)	E96435	Green	Red/Bright Yellow	£25-30 ❑
W 4315x	Horse Box, 'Royden Stables' (no date/place)	E96435	Green	Red/Bright Yellow	£25-30 ❑
W 4316	Horse Box, 'BR'	E96435	Maroon		£20-25 ❑
W 4317	Ventilated Van 'WALLS'	DE545523	Bright Red	Dull Yellow	£10-15 ❑
W 4318p	Ventilated Van 'PEEK FREANS'	DE545523	Brown	White	£10-15 ❑
W 4318p	Ventilated Van 'PEEK FREANS'	B757051	Brown	Pale White	£10-15 ❑
W 4318p	Ventilated Van 'WALLS'	DE545523	Dull Red	Bright Yellow	£10-15 ❑
W 4318pa	Ventilated Van 'PEEK FREANS'	DE545523	Dark Grey	White	£10-15 ❑
W 4318x	Ventilated Van 'BR'	B757051	Dark Brown		£10-15 ❑
W 4318x	Ventilated Van 'BR'	DE545523	Bright Red		£10-15 ❑
W 4320p	Refrigerator Van 'ESKIMO FOODS'	W59850	Off-White	Red/Black	£10-15 ❑
W 4320x	Refrigerator Van 'BR'	W59850	Off-White		£10-15 ❑
W 4323	Utility Van 'BR'	S 2380 S	Green		£10-15 ❑
W 4323	Utility Van 'SOUTHERN'	S 2380 S	Green	Yellow	£10-15 ❑
W 4324	Utility Van 'BR'	S 2380 S	Bright Blue		£10-15 ❑
W 4325	Ventilated Van 'OXO'	DE545523	White	Light Red	£10-15 ❑
W 4325	Ventilated Van 'OXO'	DE545523	White	Red	£10-15 ❑
W 4600	Ore Wagon with load 'CLAY CROSS'		Light Grey	White/Red	£10-15 ❑
W 4625	20-ton Bulk Grain Wagon 'BR'	B885040	Light Grey		£10-15 ❑
W 4626p	Cement Wagon 'BLUE CIRLE'		Dark Grey	Yellow/Blue	£10-15 ❑
W 4627p	Salt Wagon 'CEREBOS'		Grey	Blue	£10-15 ❑
W 4630	8-ton Cattle Wagon 'BR'	B893344	Brown		£10-15 ❑
W 4630a	8-ton Cattle Wagon 'GW'	103240	Mid-Grey		£10-15 ❑
W 4635p	12-ton Coal Wagon 'HIGGS LONDON'	85	Brown	Red/White	£10-15 ❑
W 4635p	12-ton Coal Wagon 'HIGGS LONDON'	85	Orange	Red/White	£10-15 ❑
W 4635p	12-ton Coal Wagon 'HIGGS LONDON'	85	Dark Green	Red/White	£25-30 ❑
W 4635p	12-ton Coal Wagon 'HIGGS LONDON'	85	Grey	Red/White	£10-15 ❑
W 4640	Goods Wagon, Steel-type	B466865	Brown		£10-15 ❑

Wrenn vans and wagons

W 4640	Goods Wagon, Steel-type	B466865	Buff		£10-15 ❏
W 4644	Hopper Wagon with load	B414029	Grey		£10-15 ❏
W 4644	Hopper Wagon, no load	B414029	Grey		£10-15 ❏
W 4652	Machine Wagon 'LOWMAC', 'BR'	B904631	Gloss or matt Brown		£10-15 ❏
W 4652	Machine Wagon 'LORIOT', 'GW'	43260	Dark Grey		£10-15 ❏
W 4652p	Lowmac Wagon 'AUTO DISTRIBUTORS'		Brown	Turquoise/White/Black	£70-80 ❏
	(with Minix model Ford Anglia and Caravan, colours vary)				
W 4655	16-ton Mineral Wagon 'BR'	B54884	Grey		£10-15 ❏
W 4655a	16-ton Mineral Wagon 'BR'	B550200	Dark Brown		£10-15 ❏
W 4655L	16-ton Mineral Wagon with load 'BR'	B54884	Grey		£10-15 ❏
W 4657	Milk Tanker (6 wheels) 'UNITED DAIRIES'		White	Yellow/Black	£10-15 ❏
W 4658	Prestwin Wagon 'FISONS'	B873000	Red-Brown	White/Black	£10-15 ❏
W 4658x	Silo Wagon 'PRESTWIN', 'BR'	B873000	Red-Brown	White	£10-15 ❏
W 4660p	Open Wagon 'TWININGS'	95	Brown	White/Black	£10-15 ❏
W 4660p	Open Wagon 'TWININGS'	95	Orange	White/Black	£10-15 ❏
W 4665	Salt Wagon 'SAXA'	248	Primrose	Red/Black	£10-15 ❏
W 4665p	Salt Wagon 'SAXA'	248	Yellow	Red/Black	£10-15 ❏
W 4665p	Salt Wagon 'SAXA'	248	Orange	Red/Black	£10-15 ❏
W 4666	Salt Wagon 'SIFTA'	125	Bright Blue	Silver/Pink/Black	£10-15 ❏
W 5000	Coal Wagon 'BLY & Co'		Dark Green	Yellow/White/Black	£10-15 ❏
W 5001	Blue Spot Fish Van 'ROSS FISHERIES'	E87231	White	Red/Blue/White	£10-15 ❏
W 5001x	Blue Spot Fish Van 'BR'	E87231	White		£10-15 ❏
W 5001x	Blue Spot Fish Van 'ROSS FISHERIES'	E87231	Cream		£10-15 ❏
W 5002	Horsebox 'SELSDON STABLES'	E96435	Maroon	Yellow	£15-20 ❏
W 5003	Tank Wagon (6-wheels) 'GUINNESS'		Silver	Red/White/Yellow	£20-25 ❏
W 5004	Ventilated Van 'DUNLOP'	B757051	Yellow	Red/White/Black	£10-15 ❏
W 5004	Ventilated Van 'DUNLOP'	DE545543	Yellow	Red/White/Black	£10-15 ❏
W 5004	Ventilated Van 'DUNLOP' (slogan reversed)	DE545543	Yellow	Red/White/Black	£10-15 ❏
W 5005	Cement Wagon 'TUNNEL'		Grey	Red/Whitre	£10-15 ❏
W 5005	Cement Wagon 'TUNNEL'		Red	Red/White	£10-15 ❏
W 5005x	Cement Wagon		Mid-Grey		£10-15 ❏
W 5006	Ore Wagon with load 'SOUTHDOWN'	17	Grey	Black/Green/Red/White	£10-15 ❏
W 5006	Ore Wagon with load 'SOUTHDOWN'	17	Blue	Black/Green/Red/White	£10-15 ❏
W 5007	Banana Van 'GEEST'	B881867	Brown	Yellow/Blue/White	£10-15 ❏
W 5007a	Banana Van 'GEEST'	B881902	Grey	Yellow/Blue/White	£10-15 ❏
W 5007x	Banana Van 'BR' (no Yellow spot)	B881902	Brown		£10-15 ❏
W 5007x	Banana Van 'BR' (with Yellow spot)	B881902	Brown		£10-15 ❏
W 5008	Open Wagon 'HARRIS'	14	Black	White	£10-15 ❏
W 5009	Gunpowder Van 'BSA'	B887002	Brown	Red/Black/Yellow	£10-15 ❏
W 5010	Ventilated Van 'ROBERTSONS'	B757051	Grey (White roof)	Blue/Yellow/Red/Black	£10-15 ❏
W 5010	Ventilated Van 'ROBERTSONS'	DE545533	Grey	Blue/Yellow/Red/Black	£10-15 ❏
W 5010	Ventilated Van 'ROBERTSONS'	57	Brown Grey	Blue/Yellow/Red/Black	£10-15 ❏
W 5011	Ventilated Van 'WATNEYS'	B757051	Red	White	£10-15 ❏
W 5011x	Ventilated Van 'BR'	DE545553	Red		£10-15 ❏
W 5012	Express Parcels Van 'BR'	E87003	'BR' Blue/Grey		£10-15 ❏
W 5013	Tanker Wagon 'ST IVEL'		White (terra-cotta top)	Blue/White	£15-20 ❏
W 5013a	Tanker Wagon 'ST IVEL GOLD'		White	Blue/White/Red	£50-60 ❏
W 5014	Six-wheel Passenger/Brake 'STOVE'	Not manufactured due to tinprinting required			NPP
W 5015	Ore Wagon with load 'HINCHLEY'	14	Blue	Blue/Black/Yellow	£10-15 ❏
W 5015	Ore Wagon with load 'HINCHLEY'	14	Grey	Blue/Black/Yellow	£10-15 ❏
W 5016	Cement Wagon 'BLUE CIRCLE'		Grey	Blue/Yellow	£10-15 ❏
W 5016	Cement Wagon 'BLUE CIRCLE'		Yellow	Blue/Yellow	£10-15 ❏
W 5017	Ore Wagon with load 'PYCROFT'		Pale Green	Red/Grey	£10-15 ❏
W 5017	Ore Wagon with load 'PYCROFT'		Black	Red/Grey	£10-15 ❏
W 5017	Ore Wagon with load 'PYCROFT'		Grey	Red/Grey	£10-15 ❏
W 5018	Salt Wagon 'STAR SALT'	105(white)	Red	Yellow/White/Black	£10-15 ❏
W 5018	Salt Wagon 'STAR SALT'	105(blue)	Red	Yellow/White/Black	£10-15 ❏
W 5019	Refrigerator Van 'GW'	59828	White	Red	£10-15 ❏
W 5019	Refrigerator Van 'BR'	W59850	White		£10-15 ❏
W 5020	Bulk Grain Wagon 'KELLOGGS'	B885040	Grey	White/Red/Yellow	£10-15 ❏
W 5021	Salt Wagon 'CEREBOS'		Red	Blue/White/Yellow	£10-15 ❏

Cat. No.	Description	Number	Body Colour	Lettering/Detail	Price	
W 5022	Banana Van 'FYFFES'	B881867	Yellow	Blue/White	£10-15	❏
W 5023	Tanker Wagon 'Milk Marketing Board'		Bright Blue	White	£20-25	❏
W 5024	Salt Wagon 'COLMANS' (no 'Liverpool')	15	Yellow	Black/White/Yellow	£10-15	❏
W 5024	Salt Wagon 'COLMANS'	15	Yellow	Black/White/Yellow	£10-15	❏
W 5024	Salt Wagon 'COLMANS'	15	Light Grey	Black/White/Yellow	£10-15	❏
W 5024	Salt Wagon 'COLMANS'	15	Light Grey	White/Black/Yellow	£10-15	❏
W 5025	Ore Wagon with load 'CARTER'	7	Black	Red/White/Black	£10-15	❏
W 5026	Mineral Wagon 'PARK WARD'	7	Brown	White/Black	£10-15	❏
W 5027	Refrigerator Van 'CARR & Co'	W59850	Pale Green	Red/White/Black	£10-15	❏
W 5027	Refrigerator Van (no name)	W59850	All Pale Green		£10-15	❏
W 5028	Banana Van 'NE'	159611	Grey	White	£10-15	❏
W 5029	Steel Open Wagon 'GW'	110265	Dark Grey	White	£10-15	❏
W 5029	Steel Open Wagon with load 'GW'	110265	Dark Grey	White	£10-15	❏
W 5030	Ventilated Van 'LMS'	59673	Red	White	£10-15	❏
W 5031	Goods Guards Van 'NE'	128105	Lt. Grey (White roof)	White	£10-15	❏
W 5032	Plank Wagon with load 'LMS'	24361	Red (White load)	White	£10-15	❏
W 5032	Plank Wagon with load 'LMS'	24361	Red (Black load)	White	£10-15	❏
W 5033	Ventilated Van 'SR'	41596	Brown	White	£10-15	❏
W 5034	Steel Wagon with load 'NTG'	B486863	Yellow	Red/Yellow/Black	£10-15	❏
W 5034	Steel Wagon (no load) 'NTG'	B486863	Buff	Red/White/Black	£10-15	❏
W 5035	Hopper Wagon with load 'NCB'	128	Dark Green	White	£10-15	❏
W 5036	Hopper Wagon with load 'HOVERINGHAM'	230	Terra-cotta	White	£10-15	❏
W 5036	Hopper Wagon (no load) 'HOVERINGHAM'	230	Terra-cotta	White	£10-15	❏
W 5037	Goods Guards Van 'GW'	Dublo mould faulty - not issued			NPP	
W 5038	Goods Guards Van 'SR'	32831	Dark Brown	White	£10-15	❏
W 5039	Petrol Tank Wagon 'ESSO'		Silver	Red/White/Blue	£10-15	❏
W 5040	Petrol Tank Wagon 'SHELL'		Yellow	Red and Black only	£10-15	❏
W 5040	Petrol Tank Wagon 'SHELL'		Yellow	Red/Black/White	£10-15	❏
W 5041	Petrol Tank Wagon 'MOBIL'		Dark Red	Red/White/Blue	£10-15	❏
W 5042	Petrol Tank Wagon 'ESSO'	3300	Dark Turquoise	Red/White/Yellow	£10-15	❏
W 5043	Coal Wagon 'AYR CO-OP'	67	Black	Red/White	£10-15	❏
W 5044	6w Tanker Wagon 'DOUBLE DIAMOND'		Terra-cotta	Red/White/Yellow	£20-25	❏
W 5045	Grain Wagon 'QUAKER OATS'		Terra-cotta	Blue/Red/White/Yellow	£10-15	❏
W 5046	Ventilated Van 'WALLS'	57	Brown	Red/Orange	£10-15	❏
W 5046	Ventilated Van 'WALLS'	B757051	Brown	Red/Yellow	£10-15	❏
W 5046	Ventilated Van 'WALLS'	DE545523	Red	Yellow	£10-15	❏
W 5047	Ventilated Van 'BISTO'	25	Stone (White roof)	Red/Black/Green/White	£10-15	❏
W 5048	Coal Wagon with load 'CRAMSTON'	347	Terra-Cotta	White/Black	£10-15	❏
W 5049	Long Fruit Van 'GW'	27614	Dark Brown	Pale Yellow or White	£10-15	❏
W 5050	Fish Van 'NORTH SEA FISH'	E67840	'BR' Blue/Grey	White/Red	£10-15	❏
W 5051	Mineral Wagon (open) 'SHELL'		Silver	Red/White/Yellow	£15-20	❏
W 5051a	Mineral Wagon (open) 'ESSO'		Silver	Red/White/Blue	£20-25	❏
W 5052	Refrigerator Van 'YOUNGS'	78	White	Red	£10-15	❏
W 5053	Utility Van 'BR'	E37232	Brown		£10-15	❏
W 5054	Ventilated Van 'DECCA'	DE545543	Yellow Grey	Blue/White	£10-15	❏
W 5054	Ventilated Van (no name)	DE545543	Yellow Yellow		£10-15	❏
W 5055	Long Fruit Van 'BR'	W28720	'BR' Blue		£10-15	❏
W 5056	Hopper Wagon with load 'TARMAC'	M82	Stone	White/Black	£10-15	❏
W 5057	Gunpowder Van GPV 'BR'	W105780	Black/Black	Red/White	£10-15	❏
W 5058	Fruit Van 'GW'	38200	Grey/White	White	£10-15	❏
W 5059	Flat Wagon with large tyres 'AUTO SPARES'	115	Terra-cotta	Cream	£20-25	❏
W 5060	Low-sided Wagon	B459325	Grey		£10-15	❏
W 5061	Petrol Tank Wagon 'SHELL-BP'		Stone	Red/Yellow/Black/White	£10-15	❏
W 5062	Petrol Tank Wagon 'ROYAL DAYLIGHT'		Black	White	£10-15	❏
W 5063	Banana Van 'TROPICAL FRUIT'	M40	Light Grey	Yellow/Light Blue	£10-15	❏
W 5064	Fish Van 'BRT'	E67840	Stone/White	White/Red/Black	£10-15	❏
W 5065	Insulated Van 'BIRDS-EYE'	312	'BR' Blue/White	Red/White	£10-15	❏
W 5066	6w Tanker Wagon 'SKOL BEER'		Terra-cotta	Red/Black/Yellow/White	£20-25	❏
W 5067	Plank Wagon with load 'AMOS BENBOW'	3	Grey and Black	White/Black	£10-15	❏
W 5068	Hopper Wagon 'CHARRINGTONS'	B421818	Grey	Black	£10-15	❏
W 5069	Plank Wagon with load 'BRITISH SODA'	14	Terra-cotta	White	£10-15	❏
W 5069	Plank Wagon with load (no name)		Terra-cotta		£10-15	❏

W 5070	Salt Wagon 'DISTILLERS Co'	87	Light Grey	White/Black	**£10-15** ❏
W 5071	Bulk Grain Wagon 'BASS CHARRINGTON'	24	Maroon	White	**£10-15** ❏
W 5072	Bulk Cement Wagon 'BLUE CIRCLE'		Grey	Blue/White/Yellow	**£10-15** ❏
W 5073	Steel Wagon 'BRITISH ANTHRACITE'	4253	Terra-cotta	White/Green	**£10-15** ❏
W 5074	Coal Wagon with load 'BASSETTS'	77	Grey	White	**£10-15** ❏
W 5075	Coal Wagon with load 'TWININGS'	95	Brown	White (or Black/White)	**£10-15** ❏
W 5076	Petrol Tank Wagon 'POWER ETHYL'		Green	White/Red/Black	**£10-15** ❏
W 5077	Tank Wagon 'UNITED MOLASSES'	18	Maroon	White	**£10-15** ❏
W 5078	Hopper wagon 'WILTON QUARRIES'	Not manufactured			
W 5079	Hopper Wagon 'NE'	174369	Dark Grey	White	**£10-15** ❏
W 5079	Hopper Wagon 'NE'	174369	Light Grey	White	**£10-15** ❏
W 5080	Bulk Cement Wagon 'RUGBY CEMENT'	17	Grey	Black/White/Orange	**£15-20** ❏
W 5081	Bulk Cement Wagon 'PRESFLOW', 'BR'	72	Chocolate	White	**£10-15** ❏
W 5082	Hopper Wagon with load 'SYKES'	7	Light Grey	Red/White	**£10-15** ❏
W 5083	Fruit Van 'BR'	B872181	Brown		**£10-15** ❏
W 5084	Bulk Cement Wagon 'BULK CEMENT', 'BR'	52	Terra-cotta	Black	**£10-15** ❏
W 5085	Utility Van 'LMS'	M527071	Maroon		**£25-30** ❏
W 5086	6w Tanker Wagon 'CO-OP MILK'	172	White	Pale Blue	**£40-50** ❏
W 5087	Parcels Van 'RED STAR'	E87003	'BR' Blue/Grey	Red/White	**£15-20** ❏
W 5088	Hopper Wagon 'BRITISH GAS'	142	Dark	White	**£15-20** ❏
W 5089	Refrigerator Van 'INSUL-MEAT'	105721	Grey	White	**£15-20** ❏
W 5090	Goods Brake Van 'BR' (MR)	B950127	Grey		**£15-20** ❏
W 5090	Goods Brake Van 'BR' (MR)	M730012	Grey		**£15-20** ❏
W 5091	6w Tanker Wagon 'UNIGATE'	220	White	Blue/White/Red	**£50-60** ❏
W 5092	Bulk Cement Wagon 'READYMIX'	68	Mid-Grey	Black/Orange	**£25-30** ❏
W 5093	Tank Wagon 'ICI CHLORINE'	163	Black	White	**£15-20** ❏
W 5094	Ventilated Van 'GW'	W145207	Light Grey	White	**£15-20** ❏
W 5095	6w Tanker Wagon 'EXPRESS DAIRIES'	50	Bright Blue	White	**£25-30** ❏
W 5096	5-plank Wagon 'A BRAMLEY'	6	Brown	Black/White	**£25-30** ❏
W 5097	5-plank Wagon 'WEBSTER'	47	Dark Green	Red/White	**£25-30** ❏
W 5098	Hopper Wagon 'BRITISH STEEL'	28	Brown	White	**£25-30** ❏
W 5099	Goods Brake Van (short wheel-base) 'BR'	B950231	Brown		**£25-30** ❏
W 5099a	Goods Brake Van (short wheel-base) 'BR'	B932103	Grey		**£25-30** ❏
W 5100	Ventilated Van 'WRENN RAILWAYS'	W145207	Grey	White/Black/Yellow	**£20-25** ❏
W 5100a	Ventilated Van 'WRENN RAILWAYS'	W145207	Brown	White/Black/Yellow	**£30-35** ❏
W 5101	Salt Wagon 'ICI BULK SALT'	25	Light Grey	White	**£30-35** ❏
W 5102	Gunpowder Wagon 'BR'	B887002	Brown		**£30-35** ❏
W 5103	Lowmac Wagon with load	B904631	Brown	(Brown or 'Stone' load)	**£30-40** ❏
W 5103	Lowmac Wagon 'CEMENT', with load	B904631	Brown	Black	**£50-60** ❏
W 5104	Tank Wagon 'BULK FLOUR', 'BR'	20	White	Black	**£50-60** ❏
W 5105	Banana Van 'JAFFA'	B881902	Grey	Green/Yellow	**£50-60** ❏
W 5106	High-sided Wagon 'HUGHES'	29	Grey	White/Black	**£30-40** ❏
W 5107	5-plank Wagon 'CONSOLIDATED FISH'	76	Grey	White/Black	**£30-40** ❏
W 5108	Long Fruit Van 'BR'	B517112	Light Grey		**£30-40** ❏
W 5109	5-plank Wagon 'BARNSLEY COLLIERIES'	350	Terra-cotta	White	**£50-60** ❏
W 5110	Tank Wagon 'BRITISH SUGAR'	23	Dark Red	White	**£50-60** ❏
W 5111	Hopper Wagon 'WEAVER TRANSPORT'	152	Chocolate	White	**£50-60** ❏
W 5112	Ore Wagon with load 'CLAY CROSS'		Black	Red/White/Black	**£50-60** ❏
W 5113	Cattle wagon 'MANOR FARM'	50	Brown	White	**£50-60** ❏

Note: Items W5109 to W5113 inclusive are the over-run of these Limited Edition Wagons:

Limited Edition Wagons with numbered certificates

(W5500-5502 - only 500 of each W5503-5504 - only 350 of each)

W 5500	5-plank Wagon 'BARNSLEY COLLIERIES'	350	Terra-cotta	White	**£50-60** ❏
W 5501	Tank Wagon 'BRITISH SUGAR'	23	Dark Red	White	**£50-60** ❏
W 5502	Hopper Wagon 'WEAVER TRANSPORT'	152	Chocolate	White	**£50-60** ❏
W 5503	Ore Wagon with load 'CLAY CROSS'		Black	Red/White/Black	**£50-60** ❏
W 5504	Cattle Wagon 'MANOR FARM'	50	Brown	White	**£50-60** ❏

'OO' and 'HO' Gauge Auction Results

See also Reference 'OO' Gauge Auction Results on pages 104 – 112.

Bonhams

BONHAMS CHELSEA, 65-69 LOTS ROAD, LONDON

These descriptions of paintwork are used in Bonhams catalogues:

M	Mint toys apparently never taken out of mint original boxes
E	Excellent toys with no apparent paint shipping or defects
G	Good toys with minimum scratches to the paint
F	Fair toys with an acceptable amount of paint damage
P	Poor toys probably suitable for repainting or restoration
Sd	Some damage
Fatigue	Potentially unstable cracking or expansion of metal

These descriptions of boxes are used in Bonhams catalogue:

E	Excellent original box with no damage, complete with all interior fittings
G	Good box with normal use wear only, but fittings not necessarily complete
F	Fair box, possibly slightly torn or split, but with label intact
P	Poor box, likely to be split or torn, and in need of repair

N.B. Bonhams reserve the right to restrict handling of items described as mint.

A HORNBY R357 'DUKE OF SUTHERLAND LOCOMOTIVE AND TENDER, English, 1980s. The boxed LMS 4—6-0 Patriot locomotive and tender, with instructions, in a red window box with colour card insert (E-M, box G).....................................**£20**

TWO HORNBY '00' GAUGE CLASS SP5F LOCOMOTIVES AND TENDERS, English, 1980s. The boxed R 061 LMS 4-6-0 locomotives and tenders, in red window boxes with black and white card insert (E-M, boxes G), contain sticker and instructions, one box end tab torn... **£40**

TWO HORNBY R855 'FLYING SCOTSMAN LOCOMOTIVES, English, 1980s. The two boxed LNER Class A3 locomotives and tenders with instructions and card inserts, in red window boxes (E-M, boxes G)..**£60**

A HORNBY R309 'MALLARD LOCOMOTIVES, English, 1970s—1980s. The boxed BR Class A4 Pacific locomotive and tender, with plastic figures, instructions and colour card inserts, in brown and orange window box (E-M, box G)..........................**£35**

A HORNBY R859 'BLACK FIVE' CLASS LOCOMOTIVE, English, 1970s. The boxed BR 4-6-0 locomotive and tender with instruction sheet and plastic sprue, in pictorial lidded box (E-M, box G), tape marks to lid.................**£20**

A HORNBY R552 'OLIVER CROMWELL' LOCOMOTIVE, English, 1970s. The boxed BR 4-6—2 locomotive and tender, with instructions in a pictorial lidded box (G-E, box G), damage to rear of tender. £30

FIVE HORNBY 0-4-0 LOCOMOTIVES. English, 1970s—1980s. The boxed models comprising an R376 LMS 4P loco; an R378 LNER Class D49/1 loco 'Cheshire'; an R380 SR Schools Class V loco 'Stowe'; an R350 SR Li loco and an R450 LMS Class 2P Fowler loco (E-M, boxes G).. **£140**

A TRI-ANG HORNBY R8695 WINSTON CHURCHILL LOCO AND TENDER. English, 1970s. The boxed model finished in SR green, No. 21C151 (E—M, box G), cellophane torn with instructions, decal sheet and glue **£20**

A TRI-ANG HORNBY R871 CORONATION LOCOMOTIVE. English, 1970s. The boxed 4-6-2 locomotive and tender finished in LMS maroon, No. 6244, with instructions and sticker sheet (E, box G), cellophane torn, lacks nameplate sticker on left side.............U/S

TWO TRI-ANG HORNBY R861 'EVENING STAR'. English, 1970s. The two boxed locomotives and tenders finished in BR green No, 92220, in pictorial lidded boxes with instructions (E-M, boxes G) **£70**

A TRI-ANG HORNBY R259NS 'BRITANNIA' LOCOMOTIVE. English, 1970s. The boxed 4-6-2 locomotive and tender finished in BR green, in a window box with sticker sheet, decal, instructions and glue (E-M, box G)..**£15**

3 TRI-ANG HORNBY 'ALBERT HALL' LOCOMOTIVES. English, 1970s. One boxed R759A locomotive and tender; together with two boxed R759 locomotives, with separately boxed R760N tenders, all finished in GWR green, No. 4983 (E-M, boxes)........**£45**

THREE MAINLINE TANK LOCOMOTIVES. 1970s. Boxed models comprising three 0-6-OT J72 Class tank locos one in LNER green livery, the others in black BR livery (E-M, boxes C) **£30**

SEVEN MAINLINE LOCOMOTIVES WITH TENDERS. English, 1980s. The boxed models comprising two 4-6-0 Jubilee Class 5XP locomotives, one in LMS crimson, the other in BR green,; two 4—6-0 Standard Class 4 locomotives, one in BR green, the other BR black; two 0-6-0 2251 Class Collett locomotives, one in BR green, the other in BR black; and a type 4 iCO—COl diesel locomotive in BR green (E-M, boxes G), green Jubilee Class lacks outer window box .. **£200**

NINE LIMA 'HO' GAUGE LOCOMOTIVES. English, 1970s - 1980s. The boxed models including two 5103W 'King George V' locomotives and tenders a 205119 maroon locomotive and tender; a 205120 BR black locomotive and tender; four 5102 MW tank locos and a 5110MWG 2-6-2 tank loco (E-M, boxes F-C)..................**£140**

TWELVE LIMA 'HO' GAUGE COACHES. English, 1970s. The boxed rolling stock including LMS maroon and GWR brown and cream liveries (E, boxes C) **£10**

SEVENTEEN GRAHAM FARISH '00' GAUGE PASSENGER COACHES. English, 1980s. The boxed coaches in LMS dark maroon and crimson, in clear plastic boxes (E-M, boxes C) **£140**

A COLLECTION OF BOXED TRI-ANG HORNBY '00' GAUGE VANS AND WAGONS. English, 1970s. Including an R402 operating mail coach set; a Freightliner train wagon; plate wagons; a car transporter; brake vans; coke wagons; mineral wagons and more (E-M, boxes C). (approx 40) **£85**

A LARGE COLLECTION OF HORNBY '00' GAUGE COACHES. English, 1970s - 1980s. Including LNER, GWR, SR, BR, LMS and Pullman coaches, all in window boxes E-M, boxes C). (approx 90) **£420**

A LARGE COLLECTION OF TRI-ANG HORNBY '00' GAUGE COACHES. English, 1970s. The boxed models including coaches in GWR, Pullman, SR, BR, LNER and LMS liveries (E-M, boxes C). (approx 60) **£370**

'OO' and 'HO' Gauge Auction Results

A TRI-ANG RAILWAYS TRAIN SET R3 VX. English, circa 1965. The set containing two diesel engines, a baggage car and a passenger coach, all in blue and yellow livery, with track (C, box F), box torn in places ....U/S

A WRENN RAILWAYS W.2230 BO-BO DIESEL ELECTRIC LOCOMOTIVE. English, 1980s. The boxed model finished in BR green, No. D8017 (C, box G), box taped **£18**

A WRENN RAILWAYS W.2231 0-6-0 DIESEL ELECTRIC LOCOMOTIVE. English, 1970s. The boxed model finished in BR green, No. D3763, with instruction sheet (E, box G), tape tear to box lid side **£30**

A WRENN RAILWAYS W.2209 4-6-2 CLASS A4 'GOLDEN EAGLE. English, 1980s. The boxed locomotive and tender finished in LNER green, No. 4482, with instruction booklet and coupling converter (E, box G), box lid taped **£50**

A TRI-ANG WRENN W.2236 'DORCHESTER LOCOMOTIVE English, 1970s. The boxed locomotive and tender finished in BR green, No. 34042, with instruction booklet (E, box G), box lid taped **£70**

A TRI-ANG WRENN W.2236 'DORCHESTER LOCOMOTIVE English, 1970s. The boxed locomotive and tender finished in BR green, No. 34042, with instruction booklet (E, box C) **£60**

TEN WRENN RAILWAYS PULLMAN CARS. English, 1980s. The boxed coaches including 1st Class, 2nd Class and brake 2nd, all in window boxes (E - M, boxes F - C), one box torn **£150**

A TRI-ANG WRENN W.222 'DEVIZES CASTLE LOCOMOTIVE. English, 1980s. The boxed model finished in BR green, No. 4075, with instruction booklet (E, box G), tape and price sticker marks to lid **£40**

TRI-ANG WRENN W.227 'CITY OF STOKE' LOCOMOTIVE AND TENDER. English, 1970s. The boxed model finished in LMS black, No. 6254, with instruction booklet (E, box C) **£45**

A TRIX TWIN DIESEL FIVE-CAR UNIT. English, 1970s. The electric diecast American style locomotive and carriages finished in blue and cream livery, No. 2782 on engine side (G - E) **£180**

TWO WRENN TANK ENGINES. English, 1970s. A W.2246 2-6-4 engine No. 2085 in CR blue livery; and a W.2217 0-6-2 engine No. 9522 in green LNER livery (G-E, boxes C) **£120**

TWO WRENN 7P CLASS LOCOMOTIVES. English, 1970s. A W.2265 'Winston Churchill' locomotive No.34051 and tender in green BR livery; and a 4 - 6-2 'Lyme - Regis' locomotive No.21C109 in Southern green livery (C-E, boxes C) **£260**

TWELVE TRIX TWIN COACHES. English, 1970s. Tin coaches include three BR coaches, two brown and cream livery, one maroon; together with nine various plastic coaches (C - E) **£60**

A TRIX TWIN BOXED SET. English, 1940s - 1950s. The red hinged lid box containing a black '4762' 0-4-0 loco with cow catcher and tender; a green '46258' 0-4-0 loco; a black BR '85' 0-4-0 tank loco; two green Pullman coaches '2531' and '9106'; a baggage coach, '1241'; a red 'Shell' tanker and a controller (C, box F-C); together with a boxed Trix whistling signal box and a Dublo three-piece footbridge **£300**

Lacy Scott & Knight

THE AUCTION CENTRE
10 RISBYGATE STREET, BURY ST. EDMUNDS, SUFFOLK

Condition grading used in Lacy Scott & Knight's catalogues:

B BOXED – in the manufacturers original box or container, in appropriate condition
D DAMAGED – refers to box only
M MINT – in perfect or near perfect condition
G GOOD – in good general condition with some chips or scratches of a minor nature
F FAIR – in fair condition with an average proportion of chips and marks for age
P POOR – in only moderate condition, perhaps incomplete
R REPAINTED – has in whole or in part been repainted or has had some touching in.

SATURDAY 16TH MARCH 1996

A **Hornby 0-4-0 dock shunter**, red livery (R253) (BDG) **£60**

12 Dublo various 2R goods wagons (G-F) **£40**

A **Trix Twin Railway Set** in set box with 0-4-0 tank loco, 5 goods wagons, track and controller (BDF)...**£50**

A **Trix Set Box with 0-4-0 loco (black 7890) and tender**, LMS with 4 goods wagons, track and controller (BDF)................................**£20**

A **Tri-ang TT station set** (T31) with some additional items (BF)**£15**

9 Tri-ang TT bogie coaches (4 WR, 2 maroon suburban, 3 blue/grey, 2 restaurant cars) **£50**

8 Tri-ang TT maroon bogie coaches incl. 2 restaurant cars and sleeping car (2 BG, 6 F)..**£35**

5 Tri-ang TT maroon bogie coaches (incl. 2 restaurant and 1 sleeping car), Pullman car 'Snipe' and passenger luggage van, maroon (G-F) **£28**

27 various Tri-ang TT goods vehicles (6 BG, G-F) **£58**

A **Tri-ang TT tank loco** (T90) (BG), 0-6-0 diesel shunter and Co Co diesel (F) **£20**

A **Trix 3R 0-4-0 tank loco** (No. 42), 4 wheel tender, quantity of station accessories in TV suppressor set box and switch boxes, some Dublo (F) **£18**

4 Trix yard lamps (761) (BM) and American observation car (BG) **£35**

A **Trix crane on base** (715) (BG), Weltrol wagon with transformer (BF) and ditto with boiler (BF) **£18**

A **Trix Meteor 3 coach 3R diesel express** (377) with direction control (BDF)..**£80**

Lacy Scott & Knight (continued)

SATURDAY 5TH JULY 1997

A **Dublo 3R boxed set EDG7** comprising 0-6-2 LMS loco, 3 goods wagons, LMS controller and track (BDG)......................**£40**

A **Dublo 3R boxed EDG7 Tank Goods Set**: LMS 0-6-2 loco and 3 LMS goods wagons, track and controller (BDG-F).....................**£55**

A **Dublo 3R boxed set EDP1** comprising 4-6-2 loco and tender (7) 'Sir Nigel Gresley', 2 teak coaches, controller and track (BDF) ..**£55**

A **Dublo 3R boxed set EDP12** comprising 4-6-2 loco and tender 'Duchess of Montrose', 2 R and C coaches, controller and track (BDF).......................**£40**

An **Ever Ready 3 car 3R underground set** with track and battery control box.......................**£40**

A **Dublo 3R Passenger Set EDP2** comprising 4-6-2 loco and tender 'Duchess of Atholl', 2 coaches, track, controller and oil bottle (BG) **£60**

A **Dublo 3R 0-6-2 tank loco EDL7** LMS 6917 (BG) **£48**

2 Dublo 3R oil tanks DI Royal Daylight, DI LMS meat van (BG), DI BR brake van and mineral wagon (wrong box) (BF) **£30**

A **Dublo 3R 4-6-2 loco and tender** 'Silver King' with 4 coaches (F) (2 R/C, 2ER) in Set Box (P).......................**£38**

A **very large quantity** of 3R Dublo track, hand points, 5 electric points and Marshall II controller (F).......................**£32**

9 x 3R Dublo goods wagons and 2 bogie coaches (F-P)..............**£22**

2 Dublo Pullman cars Nos. 74 and 79 (dirty) (F).......................**£22**

A **Dublo 3R SR electric driving motor coach** (roof cracked, 3 side frames missing) and chassis for 0-6-0 shunter (F).......................**£68**

A **Trix Set Box** containing 3R 0-4-0 tank loco (84), 0-4-0 loco and tender (31820), 2 maroon suburban bogie coaches, controller, 2 Trix Year Books 54155 and post war manual (BF) **£30**

3 Dublo S/D maroon composite coaches (2 x 1st, 1 x 2nd) (F)..**£30**

A **Dublo 3R The Flying Scotsman** passenger train set comprising -6-2 loco and tender 'Mallard', 2 coaches and track (P15) BDG **£170**

A **Dublo 3R passenger train 'Royal Scot' Set** (EDP22) comprising 4-6-2 loco and tender 'Duchess of Montrose', 2 coaches and track, with 'Rail Layouts' book (BDG).......................**£90**

A **Dublo D1 girder bridge** (BM) and island platform lit (5030) (BF) **£48**

A **Dublo breakdown crane** (4620) (BM) **£40**

A **Dublo 3R SR Surburban electric driving coach** only (2250) (F) **£115**

12 Dublo railway station personnel, platelayers hut (F), loading gauge and horsebox with horse BR (4315) (BG) **£42**
2 Mainline diesels, Type 4 Co Co BR green 'Sherwood Forester'

(37041) and Type 4 BB hydraulic BR green (High Flier) (37-064) with 2 Mainline goods wagons (BM)...**£45**

A **Dublo 3R tank goods train set** BR (EDG17) comprising 0-6-2 tank loco with 4 goods wagons and track and controller (BG) **£90**

A **Dublo 3R passenger train set** (EDP2) comprising 4-6-2 loco and tender 'Duchess of Atholl' with 2 LMS coaches, track and controller with oil bottle and spanner and additional transformer and controller (BDG).......................**£175**

A **Dublo Suburban coach** brake/2nd BR, maroon (4084) (BG)..**£24**

A **Dublo packing van** (F), UGB sand wagon (4660) and 6 ton refrigerator van (WR) (4320) (BG)...**£22**

A **Hornby wooden through station** **£50**

Barry Potter Auctions

13 YEW TREE LANE, SPRATTON, NORTHAMPTON

GRAHAM FARISH RAILWAYS

This Collection includes almost every item produced by Graham Farish between 1948 and 1960. All locomotives have correct original mechanisms, complete with gearing to tender where appropriate.

Merchant Navy 4-6-2 Loco and Tender Southern Green No. 21C90 'Sir Eustace Missenden' rare version without golden arrow, with instructions, Near Mint Boxed **£320**

Merchant Navy 4-6-2 Loco and Tender Southern Green No. 21C25 'Brocklebank Line', with instructions, Excellent Plus Boxed.....**£360**

Merchant Navy 4-6-2 Loco and Tender Southern Green No. 21C90 'Sir Eustace Missenden' with Flags to front and Golden Arrows to sides, with instructions (Cabside numbers removed on one side), Excellent Boxed.......................**£180**

Merchant Navy 4-6-2 Loco and Tender Southern Green No. 21C103 'Plymouth', Excellent Plus Boxed...............................**£200**

Merchant Navy 4-6-2 Loco and Tender BR Blue No. 35017 'Belgian Marine', with original Receipt dated 1951, Excellent Plus Boxed.......................**£340**

Merchant Navy 4-6-2 Loco and Tender BR Blue No. 35017 'Belgian Marine, with Tested Board from Factory, Excellent Plus Boxed.......................**£260**

Merchant Navy 4-6-2 Loco and Tender BR Blue No. 35017 'Belgian Marine', cabside numbers worn, Tender is Excellent, Loco is Good Boxed.......................**£160**

Merchant Navy 4-6-2 Loco and Tender BR blue No. 34101 'Exeter', Excellent Boxed..**£190**

Merchant Navy 4-6-2 Loco and Tender BR blue 'Port Line', cabside numbers worn, Excellent Boxed **£220**

Merchant Navy 4-6-2 Loco and Tender Southern Green No. 21C103 'Plymouth', chassis damaged, lacking front bogie, Fair Boxed **£60**

New York Hudson 4-6-4 Loco and Tender 'New York Central' Black No. 5403, original Wooden Box, Excellent Plus Boxed **£280**

King Class 4-6-0 Loco and Tender BR Blue 'King George V', version without bell to front, with instructions, Near Mint Boxed **£160**

King Class 4-6-0 Loco and Tender BR blue 'King Charles I', Excellent Boxed...**£210**

King Class 4-6-0 Loco and Tender BR blue 'King Henry V', Excellent Boxed...**£180**

King Class 4-6-0 Loco and Tender BR blue 'King John', incorrect box, good repair to rear of tender, Good Plus Boxed **£190**

King Class 4-6-0 Loco and Tender GWR Green 'King John', Factory Tested Label still attached, Near Mint Boxed **£210**

King Class 4-6-0 Loco and Tender GWR Green 'King Henry V', Near Mint Boxed **£200**

King Class 4-6-0 Loco and Tender GWR Green 'King George V', with Bell to front, slight box damage, Loco is Mint, Boxed **£150**

King Class 4-6-0 Loco and Tender GWR Green 'King Charles I', box is worn, Loco is Excellent Plus, Boxed **£100**

King Class 4-6-0 Loco and Tender GWR Green 'King George V', version without bell to front, box is worn, Loco is Excellent Plus, Boxed **£130**

Boxed Freight Set, with 4-6-0 BR Black Loco and Tender, 6 Wagons and Track, separately boxed within the set, very colourful box, Excellent Boxed...**£170**

Formo Train Set, with 0-6-0 BR Black Loco and Tender, 4 Wagons, Track and Wire, with all inserts, Attractive early set, Near Mint Boxed **£200**

LMS Suburban Bogie Coaches - All 3rd, All 1st 1st/3rd, Brake/3rd, All Mint Boxed...**£95**

BR Maroon Suburban Bogie Coaches - all 3rd, All 1st, 1st/3rd, brake/3rd, All Mint Boxed..**£110**

Southern Suburban Bogie Coaches - All 3rd, All 1st, 1st/3rd, Brake/3rd, All Excellent Plus Boxed...**£180**

Pullmans, 1st series - 'Lydia', 'TC 94', 'Minerva', 'Iolanthe', 'Phyllis', 'Pauline', Very attractive, 2 are Excellent Plus Boxed, 4 are Mint Boxed...**£210**

'New York Central' Coach, No. 3029, Silver, slightly bowed but runs fine, Mint Boxed **£80**

Golden Arrow Pullman, 'Phyllis', Blue 'Wagon Lits' Dining Car, both with slight bowing to ends, Both Near Mint Boxed **£80**

2-6-2 Prairie Tanks, 1st series, BR black, Good Boxed, GWR Green (Slight warping to chassis front), Excellent Boxed....................**£140**

Formo 0-6-0 Loco and Tender BR Black (Loco is in black prairie tank box, tender is in correct box), 10 Wagons (Opens, Closed Vans and Brake), Bakelite Controller, all in coloured Formo boxes, All Near Mint Boxed **£75**

Suburban Bogie Coaches, 1st series, BR All 1st, BR All 3rd, both Mint Boxed. BR All 3rd, Southern All 3rd, both Excellent Plus ...**£50**

Pair of 4-wheeled BR Suburban Coaches, All 1st and Brake/3rd (Lacking 1 buffer), Both Excellent Plus, 2 repainted 4-wheeled Suburbans **£85**

Pullmans, 2nd series, 'Phyllis' and 'Minerva', lacking some wheels, slight distortion to ends, in 'Wagons Lits' boxes, Both Excellent Plus Boxed...**£20**

Coach Kits - 4 Suburban Coach Kits, 2 Mainline Coach Kits, all complete and unused. All Mint Boxed..**U/S**

Coach Kits - 9 Suburban Kit boxes containing parts for 15 Coaches, all part completed, (9 boxes) **£30**

Pullmans, later series (Yellow/Blue boxes), 2 Diners, 2 Composite, all with unused Name Transfers, All Mint Boxed.........................**£70**

2-6-2 GWR Green Prairie Tank (Later series), Grafar - 0-6-0 BR Black Tank No. 9410, GWR Coach, Southern Coach, LMS Coach, 8 Wagons, All Mint Boxed **£80**

Damaged and incomplete Locos etc. Merchant Navy 'Exeter', 3 King Class, 2 Prairie Tanks, Early Pullman, 8 Early Wagons, a useful lot for spares...**£100**

4-6-0 Black 5 Loco and Tender, 1st series with painted cabside numbers, Excellent Plus Boxed..**£80**

4-6-0 Black 5 Loco and Tender, 2nd series without cabside numbers, Excellent Plus Boxed..**£55**

4-6-0 Black 5 Loco and Tender, 1st series with painted cabside numbers, Excellent Plus. Another Black 5, superbly repainted LMS Black, Mint. Empty Wooden Box for NYC Hudson Loco **£110**

0-6-0 Tank BR Black No. 9410, Excellent Boxed. 0-6-0 Tank GWR Green No. 9410, Excellent. 9 Wagons, Lilliput Wagon, All Mint Boxed. Trix 4-6-0 Loco and Tender BR Black No. 73000, Good Plus **£65**

Phillips

PHILLIPS INTERNATIONAL AUCTIONEERS & VALUERS
10 SALEM ROAD, BAYSWATER, LONDON

These descriptions of condition are used in Phillips catalogues:

E	Excellent	G	Good	F	Fair
P	Poor	SD	Some Damage	AF	As Found

Hornby Dublo. A rare **EDG3 CANADIAN PACIFIC FREIGHT SET** (E, box G, but one card insert has been reproduced) **£800**

Hornby Dublo **3221 'LUDLOW CASTLE'** (G, box G-F) **£240**

Wrenn **W2267 4-6-2 BR Merchant Navy Class** 'LAMPORT & HOLT' 35026 and tender (E, box G) £260

Hornby Dublo **3235 4-6-2 SR 'DORCHESTER'** 34042 and tender (G, box G- F) £130

Hornby Dublo **3218 2-6-4T BR locomotive** 80059 (G-F, box G-F) **£70**

Trix Express Set (Made in Germany) consisting of 0-4-0 locomotive 20-053 and tender (F) 'JAMAICA BANANA BREMEN' wagon (G) bogie baggage van (G) tank wagons 'STANDARD' and 'LEUNA' (both G-F) 'V.S.N.' tarpaulin wagon (G) various other wagons and track (box F) £320

Hornby Dublo **2250 Electric motor coach** brake/3rd SR S65326 (E, box G, some tears), **4250 (Export) Electric driving trailer coach** SR S77511 (E, box G, some graffiti) £280

Hornby Dublo **2050 Suburban Electric train set** (E, box G)....£260

Hornby Dublo **EDP1 'SIR NIGEL GRESLEY' set** with two LNER 3rd coaches. Label on box: 'please Note - this Set contains two Third Class Coaches instead of one Brake/Third Coach and one First/Third Coach, which are now not available' (G, box G-F, torn) £360

Hornby Dublo **EDL7 0-6-2T 'SOUTHERN' locomotive** 2594 (G-E, box G) £320

EDP2 'DUCHESS OF ATHOLL' set (G, box G) £120

Hornby Dublo **EDP1 'SIR NIGEL GRESLEY' set** (G-F, some corrosion, box G) £120

Wrenn **W2237 4-6-2 Southern 'LYME-REGIS'** 21C109 and tender (E, box G- E), **W2228 4-6-2 BR 'CITY OF BIRMINGHAM'** 46235 and tender (E, box G-E), **W2206 BR 0-6-0T locomotive** 31340 (E, box G-E) £180

Wrenn 2 car set **'THE BRIGHTON BELLE'** consisting of W 3004/5 BR blue/grey and W3006/7 Pullman brown/cream (both E, box G-F, some tears)..£160

Wrenn **W2236 4-6-2 BR 'DORCHESTER'** 34042, **W2235 4-6-2 BR 'BARNSTABLE'** (both E, boxes G)...................................£170

Wrenn **W2236 4-6-2 West Country class 'PLYMOUTH'** 21C103 (G, box G), **W2207 0-6-0T Tank Loco** SR 1127 (E box G) £110

Hornby Dublo **5083 Terminal station** composite kit (E, box G) **£130**

Wallis and Wallis

WEST STREET AUCTION GALLERIES
LEWES, EAST SUSSEX

Condition grading system used in Wallis and Wallis catalogues:

Mint	Virtually original state
VGC	Very Good Condition – a fine item
GC	Good Condition – a sound item
QGC	Quite Good Condition – some wear and/or damage
FC	Fair Condition – much wear and/or damage, or parts missing
POOR	Items seldom catalogued in this state unless rarity or historical value makes them nevertheless worthy of collection
AF	At Fault or As Found
WO	Working Order – is used to describe functioning items in conjunction with grades of condition, e.g. VGWO&C (Very Good Working Order and Condition), GWO&QGC (Good Working Order and Quite Good Condition), etc.

MONDAY 6TH JANUARY 1997

A scarce **Hornby Dublo 3 rail 4-6-0 Ludlow Castle loco and tender**, in green BR livery, running number 5002. In original box with packing, paperwork and testers label. VGC to Mint...........**£340**

A scarce **Tri-ang Railways OO gauge Giraffe car set** (R348), containing yellow and black plastic bogie giraffe car TR937, Giraffe. In original box with insert and paperwork. VGC **£65**

A **Trix Twin OO railway set** comprising 0-4-0 locomotive and tender in black BR livery RN 48427; 6 wagons, bogie brick, low side, standard wagn, high side wagon, Shell tanker, and double ended brake van. In original box with insert and packing and instruction book, VGC **£70**

A desirable **Hornby Dublo 3 rail passenger train set** EDP1 Sir Nigel Gresley, comprising 4-6-2 streamline loco and tender in LNER mid blue livery RN7, 2 bogie LNER teak coaches white roofs, RN42759 and 45402. In original box. GC to VGC.....................**£240**

Hornby Dublo EDG7 LMS goods set, contents include LMS 0-6-2 locomotive running number 6917, three wagons, oval of track and controller, all in very condition. Box has inner packing piece missing but lid is the rare version with Royal Scot label. Loco is contained in repair box. GC to VGC...**£65**

A rare **Tri-ang railways OO Defender (RS50) train set**, comprising 0-6-0 diesel shunter, multi rocket firing wagon, searchlight wagon, and a Warhead exploding car bogie wagon. In original box with all inserts. VGC **£200**

A rare **Tri-ang railways OO gauge set RS38**, comprising 0-4-0 diesel shunter in red, American style bogie snow plough green/black, bogie NATO helicopter wagon complete, and an ambulance coach RAMC and red crosses to sides and roof, roof x detached but present, complete with brown sleepered track. In original box with all inserts. VGC (a few small parts AF, box some wear), Est.£150..............**£200**

'OO' and 'HO' Gauge Auction Results

6 Lima OO gauge British outline model locomotives Warships (2) Bo Bo diesel electric one maroon Rapid D838 one blue Dragon D814, Co Co Deltic type The Fife and Forfar Yeomanry, 2-6-4 class 45 in GWR green 4589, 0-6-0T in LNER green 8920, all in original boxes together with unboxed class 73 Stewarts Lane in light./dark grey livery with Arrow logo. QGC to GC **£60**

Quantity of **Trix Twin Graham Farish railway items**: 6 pre war LMS short bogie coaches, 2 post war maroon short bogie coaches, 1 maroon suburban coach, a quantity of pre and post war wagons including pre war Hinchliffes, LMS open wagon in grey, LMS 7401 4 wheels short brake, a number of metal figures, pre war telegraph pole, electric signal and buffer stop. Crescent footbridge and 9 Graham Farish metal goods wagons including guards van, ventilated wagon, steel sided wagon (grey and brown) and coal wagon. QGC to GC (signs of age wear on some items) **£140**

Quantity of **Tri-ang TT railway items**: 06-0 Jinty in original box, 4-6-2 Clan line and tender, 46-0 Windsor Castle and tender, 0-6-0 Jinty, WR Restaurant car, Suburban brake 2nd (2), bogie well wagon, various coaches and wagons. Some items are boxed. QGC to GC **£60**

Quantity of **OO Tri-ang/Hornby model railway items:** R376 LMS class 4P 4-4-0 compound, R088 LMS class 4P 2-6-4T, Hornby LMS coaches R452, R453, track underlay (3), track and lineside accessories. All items boxed. VGC.................................**£110**

Quantity of **OO Tri-ang/Hornby Model Railway items,** R355 MR 4-4-0 compound running number 1000, R450 LMS 4-4-0 class 2P Fowler, 2 Pullmans, Anne and Ruth, various lineside accessories including Merit and H and M controllers, all in original boxes. GC to VGC...**£75**

4 scarce Tri-ang 1960s US outline Transcontinental coaches, coach No. 70831, diner, baggage car and end observation coach No. 91119. In green, dark green with yellow lining and lettering with grey roofs. VGC minor wear **£70**

2 Tri-ang/Hornby locomotives and other misc Tri-ang items, R258 LMS 4-6-2 locomotive and tender Princess Elizabeth in maroon (gloss finish), running number 6201 to cabside and LMS to tender. Model includes smoke and exhaust steam sound, in original box with instructions. A BR Evening Star 2-10-0 locomotive and tender in green (gloss finish) in original box but instructions and inner packing missing. Early plunger pick up Princess Elizabeth, Lord of the Isles, 3 Tri-Ang Pullman cars and other wagons and coaches. AF to VGC **£100**

2 Tri-ang OO locomotives R258 4-6-2 The Princess Royal, in maroon livery contained in original box, 4-6-2 Britannia in BR green running no 60022. Princess box is age worn, models are QGC to GC **£45**

Tri-ang OO TC series railway items Bo Bo diesel electric in blue yellow with TR logo to cab side, 4 coaches in blue/yellow, baggage, observation, diner and saloon, track, river bridge and engine shed. Plus DC Trix 4-4-0 Pychley and 0-6-0 shunter. (Some parts may be missing) QGC to GC **£45**

3 Hornby Railways OO gauge locomotives, R053 4-6-0 LNER class B17 locomotive Manchester United in original box, R357 4-6-0 Duke of Sutherland in LMS maroon (associated box), R859 4-6-0 in LMS maroon running number 4657 plus Airfix 4-6-0 Royal Scots Fusiliers in LMS black. QGC to GC..**£70**

Hornby Dublo EDP1 Sir Nigel Gresley passenger train set, containing early horseshoe magnet motor locomotive (some "whiting" to paintwork), tender has unpainted bogies, two LNER teak coaches, composite and brake third, track packing parts spanner nd oil bottle, (controller is missing). Box lid has been repaired. fine example of this set only marred by the paintwork on locomotive and box lid. Recommend buyer inspects. QGC to VGC **£120**

A **Trix OO 4-6-2 streamlined Mallard** in LNER blue RN 4468. In original box with inner packing, minor damage to packing. VGC to Mint **£45**

A Quantity of **Tri-ang OO gauge railway** R357 Co Co diesel electric locomotive RN D5572 BR green; 16 various wagons including R242 Thestol, R247 bogie tanker, R349 bogie chlorine tanker, R139 picklecar, 4 tank wagons, container wagon Tri-ang/Pedigree, 2 open wagons, 3 closed wagons, flat cable car, brake van (all boxed) and a flat car with 3 crate load; 3 platform packs, ticket office, and a large quantity of track sections. Series 4, points motors, lever frames etc. Many items boxed, minor wear. GC to VGC (minor wear) **£82**

A scarce **Tri-ang OO gauge 4-2-2 Lord of the Isles locomotive and tender,** in dark green and maroon Great Western livery No. 3046 complete with 2 coaches in cream and dark brown; plus a track cleaning car, boxed and a 2 rail 0-6-0 diesel electric shunting locomotive, D3302 in green BR livery, boxed, and a brass track cleaning brush. GC to VGC (Minor wear) **£60**

8 Tri-ang TC series OO gauge items: 4-6-2 Pacific locomotive and tender Hiawatha in black (R54S & R32), RNTR 2335, Caboose (R115), oil tank bogie wagon (R117), stock car (R126), oil tank bogie wagon (R129), box car (R136), pulp wood car (R235), together with RT297 wheel cleaning brush, R298 home maintenance set. All boxed, very minor wear. VGC (minor wear)......................................**£115**

4 Tri-ang Railways TC series OO gauge R159 double ended diesel locomotive BoB in mid blue with deep yellow flashes, cab ends and roof line, (R132) Vista dome, R133 observation car, and R325 Diner coaches all in mid blue and yellow. All boxed, minor wear but some sellotape applied to seal end flaps. VGC (minor wear).................**£30**

A **Tri-ang-Hornby OO 4-6-2 Flying Scotsman and tender** in LNER gloss green, RN4472 (R855N). In original box with slip over case, minor wear. VGC (minor wear)...................................**£30**

Hornby Dublo accessories, inc. good quantity of 3 rail track, approx 90 long straights, 35 long curves, 15 short straights, 20 short curves, small quantity of halves and quarters, 3 crossovers, 17 point, buffers, footbridge, signal box, level crossing, through stations, island platforms, signal etc. some boxed. QGC to GC (some age wear overall)...**£110**

2 Hornby Dublo locomotives and tenders, Duchess of Montrose 4-6-2 RN 8-46232; and Britol Castle 4-6-0 RN 7013 both in BR green livery, 3 rail running, and 4 Western Region bogie coaches 1st/3rd composite corridor, restaurant car, and 2 brake end. QGC to GC (Some age wear overall, minor rusting to some coaches) **£70**

2 Hornby Dublo tank locomotives, Prairie 2-6-4 RN 80054 3 rail and 0-6-2 RN 69567 both BR black liveries; together with 5 wagons bogie brick, Mobil oil, meat box van, bolster wagon, flat car and brake van, all 3 rail running. GC to GC (some age wear overall)..........**£55**

Wallis and Wallis (continued)

2 Hornby Dublo 4-6-2 Pacific Sir Nigel Gresley, RN7 in blue, and a City of London 4-6-2 RN 46245 in BR maroon livery, together with 2 LNER teak coaches full printed tinplate bodies and LMS Maroon with acrylic windows suburban brake, all 3 rail running. QGC to GC (age wear overall to most) **£100**

2 Hornby Dublo locomotives and tenders, 2-8-0 freight RN 8F 48158 BR black, and 0-6-2 tank LMS RN 6917 in black (post war version body), together with 5 wagons, bogie brick, power petrol, box van, open wagon, and LMS brake van, all for 3 rail running. QGC to GC (some age wear overall) **£65**

2 Hornby Dublo 4-6-2 Duchess class and tenders, Atholl in maroon LMS livery, RN6231, and Montrose in BR matt green RN 8-46232; together with 4 maroon and cream coaches, 2 1st/3rd and 2 brake ends, all 3 rail versions. QGC to GC (some overall age wear)......**£55**

A Trix Twin OO gauge mainline railway, comprising 4-4-0 locomotive and six wheel tender Pytchley name on central splasher, RN 62750 BR green body and tender, together with 2 bogie coaches 1st class and 2nd brake end in maroon with pierced acetate glazed windows, tender and coaches tinplate bodies; 3 rail fibre base track including uncoupler and power connecting rails, and train controller with whistle. In original box with outer sleeve, near mint. VGC to Mint (controller box minor distortion)..**£100**

A Wrenn OO gauge No. 2235 Barnstable locomotive, 4-6-2 and tender in BR green livery, RN 34005. In original box, minor wear. VGC (minor wear)..**£82**

A Hornby Dublo No. 3211 Mallard locomotive and tender BR green livery 4-6-2 RN 60022 for 3 rail running. In early all blue 2 piece box and instructions, ends to lid taped. GC to VGC. (Minor wear) **£115**

A Hornby Dublo No. 3221 Ludlow Castle locomotive and tender in BR green livery, RN 5002 for 3 rail running, 4-6-0, nickel plate wheels. In original 2 part box (top corners split and some taping) with paperwork and test label. VGC minor wear)..............................**£280**

A Hornby Dublo No. 3235 Dorchester locomotive and tender in BR green livery RN 34042 for 3 rail running 4-6-2 with nickel plate wheels, In original 2 part box, minor wear with paperwork and test label. VGC (minor wear) **£155**

Scarce Bing table top railway, comprising 2-4-0 tank locomotive in Great Western green livery, electric motored and a 4 wheel first class coach GW brown and cream, 2-4-0 clockwork tank locomotive in LMS maroon, 3 4 wheel LMS coaches, 2 1st class 3rd brake end, LMS open truck and closed van and 4 wheel tender, station with platform ramp ends good period advertisements, signal box all in printed tinplate, 12 curved and 3 straight lengths 3 rail track, 2 junction, 1 double and 3 single signal posts, a telegraph pole, single line tunnel, level crossing gate and bag of various parts. GC to VGC for age. (some wear to several items, station chimney replaced) **£180**

MONDAY 18TH AUGUST 1997

4 Mainline OO locomotives and tenders: 3 4-6-0 patriot in LMS black, Sir Frank Ree RN 5530 (No. 37065); similar in BR apple green Sir Robert Turnbull RN 45540 (No. 37075) and Royal Scot LMS Crimson RN 6100 with steam sound (No. 37090) together with Mogul in GW green RN 5322 (No. 37090). All in original boxes, minor wear. Ex shop stock. VGC to Mint **£75**

3 Mainline OO locomotives and tenders all 4-6-0, Royal Scot BR green RN 46100 (No. 37057), Collett GWR green RN 3205 (No. 37058), Erlestoke Manor BR black RN 7812 (No. 37079), Jubilee Class "Leander" RN 45690 (BR green) (No. 37089). All in original boxes and packing, minor wear. Ex shop stock. VGC to Mint **£75**

3 Lima OO locomotives: 2 class 33 Bo Bo BR blue livery with yellow cabs "Earl Mountbatten of Burma" RN 33027 and RN 33025, together with a Diesel overall maroon warship class Rapid, RN D838. All boxed ex shop stock. VGC to Mint **£50**

3 Lima OO locomotives: electric Bo Bo in BR blue yellow cab ends, single pantograph to roof "City of London" RN 87005, 2 diesel electric Co Co BR blue with yellow cab end Eagle RN 50043 and Western Pioneer in BR green overall RND 1003. All boxed, ex shop stock. VGC to Mint **£45**

3 Lima OO locomotives: 2 class 87 Bo Bo electric both BR blue and single pantograph to roof, one yellow cab "Cock O the North" RN 87022, and a yellow cab end City of London, RN 87005, with a class 33 Bo Bo BR blue with yellow and black cabs RN 33025. All boxed, ex shop stock. VGC to Mint **£40**

3 Lima OO locomotives Co Co diesel electric class 10 Western series, Gladiator in overall maroon RN D1016; Enterprise overall beige RN D1023 and Renown overall blue with yellow cab ends RN D1071. All boxed, ex shop stock. VGC to Mint..........................**£45**

3 Lima OO locomotives electric Bo Bo BR light and dark grey livery, yellow cab ends, single pantograph City of Birmingham, RN 87009, and 2 diesel Bo Bo overall blue BR livery Dragon RN 814 and overall green BR livery Sharpshooter RN D 843. All boxed, ex shop stock. VGC to Mint (1 cellophane damaged) **£35**

3 Lima OO locomotives 2 King class 4-6-0 and tender King George V in GW green livery RN 6000, and a 0-6-0 diesel shunter LMS black RN 7120. All boxed ex shop stock. VGC to Mint (minor box wear) **£40**

A Wrenn OO 4-6-2 Mallard (W2211) in BR green livery RN 60022. In original box with paperwork. Ex shop stock. VGC to Mint (minor box rubs)..**£140**

A Wrenn OO 4-6-2 City of London (W2226) in maroon with BR logo to tender RN 46245. In original box with paperwork. Ex shop stock. VGC to Mint (minor box rubs) **£120**

Barry Potter Auctions

13 YEW TREE LANE, SPRATTON, NORTHAMPTON

SATURDAY 25th JANUARY 1997

WRENN LOCOMOTIVES

4-6-2 loco and tender LMS red No. 2644 streamlined 'King George VI', with instructions, Near mint boxed **£420**

4-6-2 loco and tender LMS blue No. 6621 streamlined 'Queen Elizabeth', with instructions, Near Mint Boxed **£360**

4-6-2 loco and tender BR black No. 46251 'City of Nottingham', limited edition complete with stand, certificate and instructions, MINT BOXED **£480**

4-6-2 loco and tender LNER green No. 4464 'Bittern', limited edition complete with stand, certificate and instructions, MINT BOXED **£520**

2-8-0 loco and tender BR black No. 48102, limited edition complete with stand, certificate and instructions, MINT BOXED **£250**

4-6-2 loco and tender BR green NO. 34090 'Sir Eustace Missenden', limited edition complete with stand, certificate and instructions, MINT BOXED **£310**

4-6-0 loco and tender LMS black No. 6146 'The Rifle Brigade', limited edition complete with stand, certificate and instructions, MINT BOXED **£280**

4-6-2 loco and tender BR green No. 34052 'Lord Dowding', limited edition complete with stand, certificate and instructions, MINT BOXED **£290**

4-6-2 loco and tender BR blue No. 35003 'Royal Mail', limited edition complete with stand, certificate and instructions, MINT BOXED **£460**

4-6-0 loco and tender BR green No. 5034 'Corfe Castle', limited edition complete with stand, certificate and instructions, MINT BOXED **£310**

2-6-4 Tank BR black No. 80120, limited edition complete with stand, certificate and instructions, MINT BOXED **£280**

4-6-2 loco and tender LMS maroon No. 6223 'Princess Alice', limited edition complete with stand, certificate and instructions, MINT BOXED **£290**

4-6-2 loco and tender Southern green No. 21C111 'Tavistock', limited edition complete with stand, certificate and instructions, MINT BOXED **£320**

4-6-2 loco and tender BR green No. 46231 'Duchess of Atholl', limited edition complete with stand, certificate and instructions, MINT BOXED **£280**

4-6-2 loco and tender BR green No. 34057 'Biggin Hill', limited edition complete with stand, certificate and instructions, MINT BOXED **£470**

4-6-2 loco and tender LNER blue No. 4468 'Mallard', limited edition complete with stand certificate and instructions, MINT BOXED **£360**

4-6-0 loco and tender BR green No. 7007 'Great Western', limited edition complete with stand, certificate and instructions, MINT BOXED **£290**

4-6-0 loco and tender BR green No. 7007 'Great Western'. limited edition complete with stand, certificate and instructions, MINT BOXED **£320**

2-6-4 Tank BR black No. 80120, limited edition complete with stand, certificate and instructions, MINT BOXED **£330**

4-6-0 loco and tender BR green NO. 4075 'Ludlow Castle'. A very rare locomotive with Cardiff Castle number and box, only 50 are believed to have been produced. With instructions, MINT BOXED **£660**

4-6-0 loco and tender BR blue No. 46159 'The Royal Air Force', with instructions, MINT BOXED **£350**

4-6-2 loco and tender Southern Green No. 21C155 'Fighter Pilot', with golden arrows to sides and flags to front, with instructions, MINT BOXED **£310**

4-6-2 loco and tender BR green No. 34053 'Sir Keith Park', with golden arrows to smoke deflectors and flags to front, with instructions, MINT BOXED **£310**

4-6-0 loco and tender LMS black No. 6102 'Black Watch', with instructions, NEAR MINT BOXED **£130**

4-6-2 loco and tender BR green No. 34065 'Hurricane', with instructions, NEAR MINT BOXED **£270**

0-6-0 Tank SE&CR green No. 69, with instructions, MINT BOXED **£90**

4-6-0 loco and tender LMS maroon No. 6100 'Royal Scot', with instructions, NEAR MINT BOXED **£130**

4-6-2 loco and tender Southern green No. 21C103 'Plymouth', with instructions, MINT BOXED **£240**

4-6-2 loco and tender Southern black No. 21C5 'Canadian Pacific', with instructions, MINT BOXED **£610**

4-6-2 loco and tender BR green No. 34092 'City of Wells', with golden arrows to sides and flags to front, with instructions, MINT BOXED **£325**

2-6-4 Tank Southern green No. 1927, instructions, NEAR MINT BOXED **£160**

4-6-2 loco and tender BR green No. 34036 'Westward Ho', with instructions, MINT BOXED **£300**

4-6-2 loco and tender LMS grey No. 6234 'Duchess of Abercorn', with instructions, MINT BOXED **£370**

4-6-2 loco and tender BR green No. 34042 'Dorchester', NEAR MINT BOXED **£150**

4-6-2 loco and tender LMS black No. 6229 'Duchess of Hamilton', with instructions, NEAR MINT BOXED **£230**

4-6-0 loco and tender BR light green No. 5023 'Brecon Castle', with instructions, MINT BOXED **£150**

4-6-0 loco and tender BR blue No. 4082 'Windsor Castle', with instructions, MINT BOXED **£150**

4-6-0 loco and tender BR blue No. 4082 'Windsor Castle', with instructions, MINT BOXED **£120**

4-6-0 loco and tender GWR green No. 7002 'Devizes Castle', with instructions, MINT BOXED **£110**

4-6-0 loco and tender GWR green No. 7002 'Devizes Castle', with instructions, MINT BOXED **£110**

4-6-2 loco and tender BR green No. 34092 'City of Wells', with instructions, MINT BOXED **£260**

4-6-2 loco and tender Southern green No. 21C155 'Fighter Pilot', with instructions, MINT BOXED **£330**

4-6-2 loco and tender BR green No. 34042 'Dorchester', MINT BOXED **£130**

2-8-0 loco and tender BR black No. 48290, with instructions, MINT BOXED **£160**

4-6-2 loco and tender BR blue No.46242 'City of Glasgow', MINT BOXED **£110**

The Brighton Belle 2 Car Blue and Grey Pullman Set, with instructions, also 2nd Class Blue and Grey Pullman Coach, BOTH MINT BOXED. (2)..**£305**

4-6-0 loco and tender LMS maroon No. 6100 'Royal Scot', with instructions, NEAR MINT BOXED **£110**

4-6-0 loco and tender GWR green No. 7029 'Clun Castle', with instructions, NEAR MINT BOXED **£100**

2-6-4 Tank BR green No. 80135, with instructions, MINT BOXED **£240**

4-6-2 loco and tender BR green No. 34021 'Dartmoor', EXCELLENT PLUS BOXED **£300**

4-6-2 loco and tender BR green No. 34066 'Spitfire', EXCELLENT PLUS BOXED..**£310**

4-6-2 loco and tender BR green No. 34036 'Westward Ho', with instructions, EXCELLENT PLUS BOXED..**£250**

4-6-2 loco and tender BR green No. 34065 'Hurricane', with instructions, EXCELLENT PLUS BOXED..**£240**

4-6-2 loco and tender BR green No. 35010 'Blue Star', EXCELLENT PLUS BOXED **£380**

4-6-2 loco and tender BR green No. 34028 'Eddystone', with instructions, MINT BOXED **£180**

The Brighton Belle 2 Car Pullman Set, with brown and cream 'Car No. 90' and 'Car No. 91', NEAR MINT BOXED..**£110**

2-6-4 Tank BR green No. 80135, with instructions, MINT BOXED **£230**

4-6-2 loco and tender Southern Green No. 21C155 'Fighter Pilot', with flags to front and golden arrows to sides, with instructions, NEAR MINT BOXED **£330**

4-6-2 loco and tender BR blue NO. 35026 'Lamport and Holt Line', with instructions, MINT BOXED **£290**

WRENN ROLLING STOCK AND CATALOGUES

Tankers. 12 'Guinness' Tankers, 6 'Double Diamond' Tankers, 'Milk Marketing', 'Shell', silver 'Esso', 'Mobil', Co-Op Milk. A nice rake, ALL MINT BOXED **£360**

Catalogues. A complete set - 1st edition, 2nd, 3rd, 4th, 5th, 6th, 7th, ALL MINT **£210**

BARRY POTTER AUCTIONS
SATURDAY 29TH JUNE 1996

'OO' AND 'N' GAUGE TRAINS

PRICES SHOWN REPRESENT BARRY POTTER'S PRE-SALE ESTIMATES

Bachmann 4-6-0 Loco and Tender LMS Black No. 5552 'Silver Jubilee', Limited Edition complete with certificate and wooden presentation case, some silver plate missing from dome, Near Mint Boxed **£150-250**

Bachmann 4-6-0 Loco and Tender LMS Maroon No. 6100 'Royal Scot', Limited Edition complete with certificate and wooden presentation case, nameplates, crew and deflectors still packeted and unapplied, Mint Boxed..**£130-170**

Bachmann 4-6-0 Loco and Tender Southern Green No. 850 'Lord Nelson', Limited Edition complete with certificate and wooden presentation case, Mint Boxed..**£130-170**

Bachmann 4-6-2 Loco and Tender LNER Blue No. 4489 'Dominion of Canada', Limited Edition complete with certificate and wooden presentation case, nameplates and crew still packeted and unapplied, Mint Boxed..**£80-120**

Lima BR Diesels - Blue 73002, Grey and Yellow No.33065, Maroon 'Rapid', Blue No. 27102, Green 'Sir Edward Elgar', two-tone Green No. D1842, Blue No. 26027, All Mint Boxed..**£100-140**

Lima BR Diesels - Blue No. 40052, Blue 'Pride in Huddersfield' (box worn), two-tone green No. 1761, Blue No. 26003, Blue 'Broadlands', Railfreight No. 26004, 0-6-0 Shunter LMS Black No. 7120, All Mint Boxed **£100-140**

Lima Diesels. 10 BR Diesels including 'Windsor Castle', Western Pioneer', 'Eagle' etc. **7 Hornby Diesels** including Railfreight No. 58001, All Excellent - Mint. 5 mainly Lima repainted Diesels **£160-220**

Romsey Auction Rooms

86 THE HUNDRED, ROMSEY, HAMPSHIRE SO51 8BX.

ROMSEY AUCTION ROOMS, SEPTEMBER 1997 AUCTION

Price range shown represents Auctioneers pre-sale estimates Model and Box condition. Each lot is individually described as per the following listings.

Hornby **R055 LMS Class 4p 2-6-4T** in maroon lined livery. Good condition, box fair/good..............................**£15-£20**

Hornby **R055 LMS Class 4p 2-6-4T** in maroon, good boxed, plus **R052 0-6-0T** in fair boxed condition (wired for Zero 1) ......**£20-£30**

Hornby **R084 LMS No. 6201 'Princess Elizabeth.** Good boxed ....**£20-£30**

Hornby **R1150 LNER B12/3** in unlined black. Mint boxed. **£25-£30**

Hornby **R154 S.R. King Arthur class 'Sir Dinadian'.** Fair/good condition, box fair/good...............................**£20-£25**

Hornby **R157 B.R. Diesel Railcar,** power coach and trailer. Mint condition, box good ....**£20-£25**

Hornby **R186 BR 0-6-0ST** Class J52 in black lined livery. Good condition, in good R053 box...............................**£15-£20**

Hornby **R261 Southern Class E2 0-6-0T.** Mint boxed........**£15-£20**

Hornby **R302 BR 0-6-0T.** Mint condition, box good, and **R062 BR 2-6-4T,** mint condition, no box outer...........................**£30-£45**

Hornby **R307 B.R. Class 47 'County of Norfolk'** and **R780 class 08 diesel shunter.** Both good condition, no box outers.............**£15-£20**

Hornby **R307 BR Class 47 'County of Norfolk'** and **R084 class 29 diesel** - both blue. Both good condition, boxes poor.............**£20-£25**

Hornby **R311 LMS Patriot class 'Duke of Sutherland'** and **R376 Class 4p Compound.** Both maroon, good/mint condition, boxes poor/fair...**£25-£35**

Hornby **R314 B.R. 4-6-0,** black 5, No. 44932. Good boxed..**£25-£30**

Hornby **R315 LBSC 0-6-0T.** Mint condition, box good ......**£15-£20**

Hornby **R316 Class 47 diesel 'Lady Diana Spencer'** and **R084 Class 29 diesel,** both blue. Good condition, boxes poor ....**£25-£30**

Hornby **R319 GWR 'Hagley Hall'** and **R392 'County of Bedford'.** Both mint condition. Boxes poor ....**£30-£40**

Hornby **R319 Class 47 diesel 'The Queen Mother'.** Good/mint boxed ....**£25-£30**

Hornby **R319 Class 47 diesel 'The Queen Mother'.** Good boxed ....**£20-£25**

Hornby **R326 BR 'Skipper' class 142 Twin Railbus.** Mint boxed ....**£25-£30**

Hornby **R332 BR Co-Co diesel** class 58. Good/mint boxed.**£25-£30**

Hornby **R333 B.R. Bo-Bo** Class 86 - Intercity.Good boxed ..**£20-£25**

Hornby **R335 B.R. Bo-Bo** electric class 86 'Halleys Comet'. Mint condition, box good ....**£20-£30**

Hornby **R347 Limited Edition B.R. Class 5** in green lined livery, No.44932. Mint condition, box fair/good..............................**£30-£40**

Hornby **R355 Midland Railway 4-4-0 Compound** No.1000 and **R301 LMS 0-6-0T,** both maroon lined livery. Both mint, boxes good ....**£25-£30**

Hornby **R360 B.R. Class 86/2 electric 'Phoenix'** and **R084 class 29 diesel.** Both blue, good condition, boxes poor/fair...............**£20-£25**

Hornby **R372 LNER Class A4 'Seagull'.** Mint condition, box good ....**£45-£50**

Hornby **R374 Southern 'Battle of Britain' class 'Spitfire',** plus **R261 Southern class E2 0-6-0T.** Both mint condition, boxes fair .... **£40-£50**

Hornby **R376 LMS Class 4p 4-4-0 Compound** in maroon lined livery. Mint boxed...**£25-£30**

Hornby **R376 LMS Class 4p 4-4-0 Compound** in lined maroon livery. Mint boxed...**£25-£30**

Hornby **R378 LNER Class D49/1 'Cheshire'.** Mint boxed..**£35-£45**

Hornby **R378 LNER Class D49/1 'Cheshire'.** Mint boxed..**£35-£45**

Hornby **R378 LNER Class D49/1 'Cheshire'.** Mint condition, box good..**£30-£40**

R380 Southern Schools Class 'Stowe'. Mint boxed...........**£40-£50**

Hornby **R380 Southern Schools Class 'Stowe'.** Mint condition, box fair ....**£30-£40**

Hornby **R392 GWR 'County of Bedford'.** Mint condition, box fair/good...**£25-£35**

R532 GWR 2-8-0 loco & tender No. 2859. Mint boxed......**£30-£40**

Hornby **R533 S.R. Schools class 'St. Lawrence'.** Limited Edition with certificate. Good condition, box fair/good ....**£30-£40**

Hornby **R589 BR Bo-Bo** electric class 86 'Post Haste'. Mint boxed ....**£25-£30**

Hornby **R683 Southern Schools Class 'Repton'.** Mint condition (one smoke deflector bent), box good ....**£30-£40**

Hornby **R687 3 car DMU unit pack** - good boxed..............**£25-£30**

Hornby **R761 GWR 'Kneller Hall'** and **R392 'County of Bedford'.** Both mint condition. Boxes poor...........................**£30-£40**

Hornby **R761 GWR 'Kneller Hall', R059 class 2721 0-6-0T** and **R300 class 57xx Pannier Tank.** All mint, boxes poor ....**£30-£40**

Hornby **R778 B.R. Class 52 'Western Harrier'** (blue) and **R080 class 29** in green. Both good/mint, boxes fair/good..............**£25-£35**

Hornby **R863 Brush type 4 diesel electric loco**. Good condition, box fair ....**£12-£15**

Hornby **R066 LMS Coronation Class 7p 'Duchess of Sutherland'** and four LMS coaches. All good condition, unboxed ....**£25-£30**

Tri-ang **RS1 train set with 'Princess Victoria' loco**, and two coaches. Good condition, box poor/fair ....**£20-£25**

Tri-ang **R537 Set 'Davy Crockett' 2-6-0 loco** & tender with two coaches (no track in box). Good condition, box fair ....**£35-£40**

Tri-ang **R52S 0-6-0T loco with Synchro-Smoke** (chassis only) plus 4-4-0 chassis. Both good condition ....**£20-£30**

Tri-ang **R59 B.R. 2-6-2T**, lined green (minus decals) and **R357 A-1-A diesel**, gloss green. Both fair/good, unboxed....................**£20-£25**

Tri-ang **'OO' TC Series**. R25 Vista Dome, R125 Observation Car (both silver/red), R117 Oil Tank, R129 Refrigerator Car and R249 Exploding Car. All good to mint, boxes fair/good.................**£30-£40**

Tri-ang Railways - **Assortment circa 1957** - R54 4-6-2 Pacific TC loco and tender, 3 SR and one B.R. coach, 3 wagons. Various accessories including platforms, track and points mostly boxed. All good condition..**£30-£50**

Tri-ang - **Coaches and Trucks**, all early period plus boxed set. A quantity in mixed unboxed condition....................................**£20-£30**

Tri-ang/Hornby **RS51 'The Freight Master' boxed set**. Good/mint condition..**£30-£40**

Tri-ang/Hornby **R552 'Blue' Pullman train set**. Fair/good boxed plus a made up Kitmaster set of 3 Blue Pullmans.................**£30-£45**

Tri-ang/Hornby **R354 GWR 'Lord of the Isles'** (gloss finish). Good condition, sleeved box good...**£20-£25**

Tri-ang/Hornby **R251 0-6-0 loco with R33 tender**, in maroon lined livery. Good boxed ....**£18-£20**

Tri-ang/Hornby **R855 LNER 'Flying Scotsman with Special Corridor Tender**. Good condition (slight added detail). Box fair/good ....**£15-£20**

Wrenn **W2265 BR(S) 4-6-2 'Winston Churchill'**. Mint boxed **£220**

Wrenn **W2265/A Golden Arrow S.R. 'Fighter Pilot'**. Mint boxed **£285**

Wrenn **W2265 AX SR 4-6-2. 'Fighter Pilot'**. Mint boxed........**£460**

Wrenn **W2266 SR 4-6-2 'Plymouth'**. Mint boxed....................**£245**

Wrenn **W2266AX BR(S) 4-6-2 'City of Wells'**. Mint boxed **£250**

Wrenn **2267 Merchant Navy Class BR Blue No. 35026 'Lamport and Holt'** Line. Mint boxed...**£300**

Wrenn **W2268 BR(S) 4-6-2 'Yeovil'**. Mint boxed...................**£285**

Wrenn **W2269X BR(S) 4-6-2 'Sir Keith Park'**. Mint boxed **£335**

Wrenn **W2270 2-6-4T in BR green**. Mint boxed......................**£180**

Wrenn **W2276X SR 4-6-2 'Exeter'**, 5 pole motor. Mint boxed..**£610**

Wrenn **W2277 BR(S) 4-6-2 'Spitfire'**. Mint boxed...................**£360**

Wrenn **W2278 SR 4-6-2 'Blue Funnel Line'**, black livery. Mint condition, box good **£440**

Wrenn **W2281 2-8-0 Freight War Dept** grey. Mint boxed........**£300**

Wrenn **W2301 Coronation LMS Blue 'Queen Elizabeth'**. Mint boxed **£510**

Wrenn **W2401 'Princess Alice'**, Limited Edition. Mint boxed...**£290**

Wrenn **W3004/5 'Brighton Belle'**, 2 car set in blue/grey. Mint boxed **£125**

Wrenn **W2227 LMS 4-6-2 'City of Stoke-On-Trent'**, black livery. Mint boxed..**£65**

Wrenn **W2229 B.R. 4-6-2 'City of Glasgow'**, blue livery. Mint boxed..**£110**

Wrenn **W2236 'Dorchester', rebuilt**, West Country green livery. Mint boxed...**£130**

Wrenn **W2237 Southern 4-6-2, 'Lyme Regis'**. Mint boxed......**£120**

Wrenn **W2238 4-6-2 'Clan Line Merchant Navy'** in B.R. green livery. Mint boxed..**£185**

Wrenn **W2296 'Dartmoor'**. Rebuilt West Country B.R. green livery. Mint boxed..**£440**

Wrenn **W2235 B.R. 4-6-2 'Barnstable'** (spelt wrong on box). Mint boxed..**£135**

Wrenn **W2267 'Lamport and Holt Line'** in blue B.R. livery. Mint boxed..**£320**

Wrenn **W2275 B.R.(5) 4-6-2 'Hurricane'** 5 pole motor. Near mint, box good/mint **£270**

Wrenn **W2302 Coronation in LMS red 'King George VI'**. Mint condition, box good **£440**

Wrenn **W2402 'Sir Eustace Missenden'**, Limited Edition No. 176 of 250 with certificate. Mint boxed..**£360**

Wrenn **W2219 LMS 2-6-4T**. Mint condition, box good............**£80**

Wrenn **W2221 B.R.(W) 'Cardiff Castle'**. Mint condition, box good **£70**

Wrenn **W2223 B.R.(W) 'Windsor Castle'** (blue livery). Mint condition, box fair/good **£100**

Tri-ang/Wrenn **W2226 B.R.(M) 4-6-2 'City of London'**. Mint condition, box fair/good **£65**

Wrenn **W2227 LMS 4-6-2 'City of Stoke-On-Trent'**, black livery. Mint boxed..**£65**

Wrenn **W2229 B.R. 4-6-2 'City of Glasgow'**, blue livery. Mint boxed **£110**

Wrenn **'00' W2236 'Dorchester'**, rebuilt, West Country green livery. Mint boxed..**£130**

Vectis Model Auctions

FLECK WAY, THORNABY, STOCKTON-on-TEES, TS17 9JZ

Condition grading used in Vectis' catalogues:

A+   As near mint or pristine condition as at time of issue

A   Virtually mint boxed – any faults of a most minor nature

B+   Model is near mint – box has very slight faults

B   Slight model or box faults e.g. Some chips or box rubs but model and box complete

C   More obvious model chips and box faults inc. tears but still complete

D   Same as C but box has one or more end flaps missing and model may have faded paint as well as chips

E   Model and box have considerable faults

R   Repaint

WEDNESDAY 22ND JANUARY 1997

TRI-ANG HORNBY BOXED SETS

RS8 'The Midlander' with 0-6-0 BR maroon 3775 loco & tender with 2 maroon/grey corridor coaches, track etc. all in A to A+ shrink-wrapped 'never run' condition with A picture lid - superb......... **£160**

RS51 Freightmaster Set with 7 vans/wagons (1) BR green D5572 - card inserts, superb A in B+ to A long picture box; (2) BR blue D55R - superb A in plastic tray in B+ box - lovely pair **£210**

RS62 The Blue Pullman - superb A in B+ box with card inserts, plus R555C Pullman train, grey/blue/yellow ends-A (no box sleeve)...**£90**

RS62 Car-A-Belle Set - superb A to A+ inc. 12 Minix cars - box lid is A apart from one split corner **£180**

RS609 Express Passenger Set with 4-6-2 'Princess Elizabeth' LMS maroon 6201 with matching tender and 2 LMS maroon/black/yellow lined coaches, track etc. - all A to A+ shrink wrapped 'never run' condition with B lid...**£130**

RS615 'The Railway Children' Set - condition as last lot apart from tear in perspex by 0-4-0 tank loco - lid is A, very scarce **£150**

R641 'Davy Crocket' 2-6-0 TRR 1863 loco and tender with No 257 Smoking Car - A to A+ in B+ plain red box - very scarce **£100**

Rovex Richmond Production rare early (c.1952) BR/LMS Passenger Train with models in individual picture boxes within red cut-out compartments. 4-6-2 Princess Elizabeth - black 4620/with plunger pick-ups with matching Tender (BR LION motif) with 2 maroon/grey LMS coaches - (1) 1st, (2) 3rd - full box of track - plus black plastic battery box, all superb A apart from some warping to plastic coaches - box lid is B to B+, picture is A...**£160**

RS3 4-6-2 'Britannia' BR Green 70000 with matching Tender and Pullman set, 'Jane', 'Ruth', 'Car 79' - brown/cream/white roofs - superb A with track, oil etc. all literature inc. 7th edition (1961) 32 page catalogue - A...**£150**

RS21 4-6-2 'Princess Victoria' - BR black 46205 with matching tender passenger set with 2 maroon/cream/grey coaches, track etc. inc two figures - superb A in B+ to A box - scarce (c.1962) set **£180**

RS30 Breakdown Train Set - superb A in B+ to A box - plus Tri-ang/Hornby R739 Breakdown Crane Set - superb A **£130**

LOCOMOTIVES AND COACHES

RS63 4-2-4 Caledonian Loco & Tender - blue with three R427 1st/3rd composite coaches - all A to A+ WB (some slight box faults) plus R59 2-6-2 Tank Loco, BR green 82004 - A in B card box and 3521 Canadian Railway Diesel rail car, silver/black with dummy end and 1111 brown hopper wagon 'CN' - all A to A+ in perspex bubble packaging..**£150**

R350 4-4-0 BR green 31767 loco & tender; R251 0-6-0 maroon loco and 3775 tender and R26 GWR 1st/3rd coaches (3) - plus R743 (4) and R744 GWR composite and 3rd class seating - all A to A+ in B or B+ WB **£150**

ROLLING STOCK & ACCESSORIES

Large Quantity (approx 30) Vans & Wagons inc. R348 Giraffe car set - A to A+ picture boxed; R342 car transporter with 5 Minix cars; R740 breakdown train unit; R633 Freightliner wagon; R578 Horse box converter wagon, plus R628 BR buffet car, crimson & yellow, and R625 'Wagons Lit' sleeper - a II A to A+ in B to A boxes - good lot. **£210**

HORNBY DUBLO SETS - 3 RAIL

EDG7 Tank Goods Train 'GWR' with 0-6-2 Tank Loco - Dark Green/Black/6699 Black Footsteps/Gold 6699 on buffer ends, three vans/wagons/black controller with instructions and track - B+ to A (loco is superb) with packing ends, instructions, etc. blue box with small picture is C **£320**

EDP10 0-6-0 BR Tank Passenger Train - all in long blue box with large picture and covered with sealed brown paper – contents must be untouched since production...**£460**

SETS - 2 RAIL

'Ready To Run' Electric Train. A to A+ with instructions, box lining, etc. in B+ 'flip top' box and 0-6-0 Tank Goods Set BR Black/three van/wagons - B+ to A - lid is B to C **£300**

0-6-0 Tank Goods Set - (1) BR Green - superb A to A+ with all literature in B+ box apart from small lid fault; (2) as last lot but loco is BR black and lid is C...**£180**

0-6-0 Tank Passenger Set with BR Green Loco and two SR Suburban Coaches, track, etc. - Plus Literature - A to A+ with C box Lid .**£130**

A similar set but BR black loco and two maroon/grey Suburban Coaches, all literature - A to A+ with B to B+ lid.......................**£160**

'The Talisman' Passenger Train with 4-6-2 'Golden Fleece' loco and tender - Plus two maroon/grey Corridor Coaches, all literature - A to A+ with B lid (one corner seam has split)................................. **£160**

2-6-4 Tank Goods Train with BR Black 80033 loco and four vans/wagons inc. flat truck with Dinky Dublo tractor and all literature - A to A+ lid is good C - sold with original receipt dated March 1965 for £4.15s.0d (reduced from £6.7s.6d) **£110**

'The Red Dragon' Passenger Train with 4-6-0 'Cardiff Castle' BR Green 4075 and tender - Plus two WR corridor coaches, literature, etc. A to A+ with B lid...**£210**

Diesel-Electric Goods Train - A to A+ (loco is B+ to A) - slight box compartment faults - lid is C...**£130**

SR Pullman Train with 4-6-2 'Barnstable' BR Green 3400S & tender - Plus three brown & cream Pullman coaches 'Aires' '74' and '79' - literature etc. A to A+ lid is B+ apart from one split corner seam **£270**

Breakdown Train with 0-6-2 BR Black 69550 loco with coal - A to A+ with B lid..**£300**

SR Suburban Electric Train complete and A to A+ with all literature - box lid is B **£220**

ACCESSORIES

Terminal (Through Station Composite Kit) - appears complete - A - box lid is B (picture is A) **£190**

Girder Bridge - A in B (faded one lid end) RW box.................**£160**

LOCOMOTIVES

Group of 3 Limited Edition Class A3 'Pretty Polly' - (1) R059 BR green; (2) R129 BR blue; (3) R375 LNER green-A to A+ **£190**

A Pair of Limited Editions - (1) R099 Class A4 'Herring Gull' (very scarce) (2) R528 'Sir Nigel Gresley' - preserved livery - A to A+ **£180**

Great Western - (1) R141 'Saint Catherine'; (2) R761 'Kneller Hall' - plus R303 'King George II' - BR green, all A to A+ **£130**

Class A4 - (1) R144 'Dominion of Canada'; (2) 'Walker K Whigham' and R765 'Lord Westwood' - A to A+ (R765 box is B) **£110**

The Flying Scotsman Limited Edition LNER green 4472 with coal & water tenders, **plus later R098 and R089 special sets** with 'Flying Scotsman Enterprises' water tender and 3 coaches - A to A+ **£200**

'Lord of the Isles' GWR Classic Limited Edition with 3 Clerestory coaches - A to A+ in special presentation box - **plus R763** ex-Caledonian Presentation Edition - A to A+ in B special box **£180**

'Time for a Change' - 60th Anniversary Limited Edition with 'Regal Power' Royal Doulton Plate 'King Henry VI' - A to A+ in special presentation box **£75**

LONE STAR

'Treble O-lectric' sets 51 Passenger and 52 Goods & Accessories - all A in C picture boxes - now scarce **£130**

SETS

Set 1 Goods 'BR' with 0-6-0 Tank Loco 31337 in black plastic, 4 wagons, track, literature etc **£100**
Set 2 Freight 'LMS' with 2-6-4 tank loco - maroon/2679 plus 4 wagons, track, literature etc **£280**

Set 3 Pullman 'BR' with 4-6-2 'Barnstaple' - green with matching tender and 2 Pullman cars, (1) 'Aries', (2) No 22, plus track and literature...**£240**
No WPG 300 Passenger/Goods Set with 2-6-4 BR black tank loco No 8003, B+; 2 suburban coaches S46291/543381 and 4 wagons, very scarce...**£200**

WHC 400 Electric Horn Control Set with hymek diesel loco R758 (Tri-ang/Hornby) and two-tone horn control, very scarce.............**£95**

TANK LOCOMOTIVES

2207/A 0-6-0 'SR' dark olive green (1) 1127; (2) 1152.............**£240**

W2246 2-6-4 'Caledonian' blue/2085 - very scarce **£170**

A CLASS 4-6-2 W2209 'Golden Eagle' 'LNER' green/4482....**£80**

CASTLE CLASS 4-6-0 W2221B 'Brecon Castle' 'BR' light green/5023 ....**£120**

CITY CLASS 4-8-2 W2241 4-6-2 'Duchess of Hamilton' LMS black 6229 A to A+ in B box **£120**

FREIGHT 8F CLASS 2-8-0 W2240 'LNER' - black/3144 ....**£80**

WEST COUNTRY CLASS 4-8-2 W2235 'Barnstaple' - 'BR' green/34005 ....**£130**

MERCHANT NAVY CLASS 4-6-2 W2265 'Winston Churchill' 'BR' green/30451 ....**£240**

W2266 'Plymouth' 'Southern' green/21C/03 ....**£200**

W2267 'Lamport & Holt' 'BR' blue/35026 - scarce...............**£310**

ROYAL SCOT CLASS 4-6-0 W2260 'Royal Scot' 'LMS' maroon/6100 - smoke deflectors still in packet. **£170**

LIMITED EDITIONS

W2410 0-6-0 Tank 'Southern'- dark green/olive green/I 047, No 52 of 350, very scarce **£450**

W2412 'Seaton' 4-6-2 'BR' green/34020 No 161 of 250...........**£400**

3006/7 'Brighton Belle' two car Pullman set - brown & cream, 'car 90' and 'car 91' **£140**

COACHES
A group of 4 brown and cream Pullman W6000 'Car 77'; W6001 'Car 73'; (2) & W6002 'Aries'...**£120**

Three 'Southern' W606/7 & 8 plus W4315 'Foxhunter' (no date) horse box, and '4323P Southern Utility Van.............................**£120**

VANS & WAGONS
A group of 12 inc 'Guinness' tanker; 'BSA'; 'Fyffes'; 'Dunlop'; 'Geest'; 'Watneys'; 'Higgs', etc...**£110**

A group of 20 inc 'Cerebros'; 'Quaker Oats'; 'Geest'; 'Fyffes'; 'Robertsons'; 'Bly'; 'Harris'; 'Blue Circle' etc. **£120**

Barry Potter Auctions

13 YEW TREE LANE, SPRATTON, NORTHAMPTON

SATURDAY 30TH NOVEMBER 1996

HORNBY DUBLO 3 RAIL LOCOMOTIVES

4-6-2 loco and tender BR maroon No. 46247 City of Liverpool, Near Mint Boxed **£370**
2-6-4 Tank Locomotive BR black No.80059, with instructions, Near Mint Boxed **£330**

4-6-0 loco and tender BR green No. 5002 Ludlow Castle, with instructions, Near mint Boxed......................................**£350**
2-8-0 loco and tender BR black No. 48094, Near Mint Boxed .**£300**

4-6-2 loco and tender BR green No. 34042 Dorchester Excellent Plus Boxed..**£260**
The Bristolian Passenger Set (4-6-0 Bristol Castle loco and tender, 2 coaches, track, oil, instructions etc), box lid corners repaired, Near Mint Boxed **£210**

2-8-0 loco and tender BR black No. 48158, Mint Boxed **£180**
4-6-2 loco and tender BR green No. 60022 Mallard, early version with plain blue box, Near Mint Boxed.................................**£140**

Deltic Diesel Loco St. Paddy, Excellent Plus Boxed **£310**
4-6-2 Tank Southern malachite green No. 2594, Good Plus **£180**

Canadian Pacific Passenger Set - 4-6-2 loco and tender Canadian Pacific black No. 1215, 2 tinplate red and cream coaches, track, instructions, oil, spanner, CPR advertising leaflet, box lid corners repaired. A rare set, Near Mint Boxed **£920**
Canadian Pacific Freight Train Set - 4-6-2 loco and tender Canadian Pacific black No.1215, tube, bolster and caboose wagons, track, instructions, oil, spanner, CPR advertising leaflet. Without loco packing ends (easily obtained - same as British sets), box lid corners repaired. A rare set, Near Mint Boxed **£1,520**

4-6-2 loco and tender BR green No. 34042 Dorchester , with oil and instructions, Excellent Plus Boxed...**£260**
4-6-2 loco and tender BR maroon No. 46247 City of Liverpool Excellent Boxed..**£270**

Bo-Bo Diesel No. D8000, rare Canadian version without buffers, with instructions,light wear to box, Mint Boxed..............................**£860**
4-6-2 loco and tender Canadian Pacific black No.1215, Good .**£180**

2-8-0 loco and tender BR black No. 48094, box damaged, Excellent Plus Boxed..**£270**
2-6-4 Tank BR black No. 80059, Excellent **£230**

0-6-2 Tank GWR green No. 6699 (with horseshoe magnet), and
0-6-2 Tank LNER green No. 9596, Both Excellent Plus (2) **£260**

4-6-0 loco and tender BR green No. 7013 Bristol Castle, with instructions, picture box, Excellent Plus Boxed...........................**£110**
4-6-2 loco and tender BR green No. 60022 Mallard , Excellent Plus Boxed..**£120**

2-8-0 loco and tender BR black No. 48158, with instructions, Near Mint Boxed **£130**

Co-Co Diesel, with instructions, Near Mint Boxed **£140**

Canadian Pacific Tender, in rare dark blue original box, Mint Boxed **£360**
Canadian Pacific Tender, in rare dark blue original box, Mint Boxed **£320**
Canadian Pacific Tender, in rare original brown paper wrapper, Mint **£150**

Canadian Bo-Bo Diesel No. D8000, rare model without buffers, Good..**£320**
4-6-0 loco and tender BR green No. 5002 Ludlow Castle with instructions, slight wear to box, loco is Near Mint Boxed..........**£320**

Electric Motor Coach, box insert faded, Near Mint Boxed. Trailer Coach, Near Mint **£330**

4-6-2 loco and tender BR maroon Duchess of Atholl, with instructions, Near Mint Boxed..**£150**
4-6-2 loco and tender BR gloss green Silver King, with instructions, Near Mint Boxed **£170**

Sir Nigel Gresley Passenger Set (4-6-2 loco and tender, 2 LNER coaches, track and controller), loco has horseshoe magnet Excellent Boxed..**£130**
The Bristolian Passenger Set -4-6-0 loco and tender Bristol Castle loco and tender, 2 coaches, track, instructions (box lid repaired), Excellent Plus Boxed..**£130**

Freight Train Set 2-8-0 loco and tender BR black No. 48158, 5 wagons, track (box lid edges taped), Excellent Boxed **£140**

HORNBY DUBLO 2 RAIL LOCOMOTIVES

Electric pantograph locomotive No. E3002, complete with both instruction and box insert, Mint Boxed.....................................**£500**
2030. Canadian Diesel Electric Goods Train Set - Bo-Bo Diesel No. D8017 (Canadian version without buffers), 5 wagons, track, oil, instructions, a very rare set..**£1,220**

Canadian Bo-Bo Diesel No. D8017, rare non-powered version without buffers, with instructions and oil, Mint Boxed...............**£660**
Canadian Bo-Bo Diesel No. D8017, rare non-powered version without buffers, with instructions and oil. Near Mint Boxed **£580**

4-6-2 loco and tender BR green No. 34005 Barnstable , in rare plain red export box, with instructions and oil, Mint Boxed...............**£230**
Electric pantograph locomotive No. E3002, Near Mint **£210**

Electric Driving Motor Coach and Trailer Car, with instructions, Both Mint Boxed **£280**

Co-Bo Diesel, with card retainers / instructions, Mint Boxed.....**£150**
Co-Bo Diesel, with instructions, Mint Boxed...........................**£140**
Bo-Bo Diesel No. D8017, with instructions, Mint Boxed...........**£90**

4-6-2 loco and tender BR green No. 6003 Golden Fleece, with instructions, Near Mint Boxed..**£130**
4-6-0 loco and tender BR green No. 4075 Cardiff Castle, with instructions, Near Mint Boxed..**£110**

2033. Co-Bo Diesel Goods Set - Co-Bo Diesel, 4 wagons, track, oil, instructions, Near Mint Boxed..**£280**

2207. 0-6-0 Tank Passenger Set -0-6-0 Tank BR green No. 31340, 2 tinplate SR coaches, track, instructions, Mint Boxed **£220**

HORNBY DUBLO ROLLING STOCK

4071. BR Restaurant Car, 4070. WR Restaurant Car, Both Mint Boxed...**£220**
Pullman Coaches - two 2nd Class, 2 Aries (1 lacking a coupling), 2 Brake/2nd, All Mint Boxed **£100**

Super Detail Southern Coaches - four 1st/2nd Corridors (all without bogies), Suburban 2nd Class, All Mint Boxed. Suburban Brake/2nd, Near Mint Boxed.......................................**£160**
BR Super Detail Coaches - 1st Class, 2nd Class, two 1st/2nd Brake/2nd 2 Sleeping Cars, Passenger Brake, All Mint Boxed...**£140**

Six-wheeled Passenger Brake Van, Caustic Liquor Bogie Wagon, SR Horsebox with horse, All Mint Boxed....................**£230**
Super Detail Wagons - 16 including UD Tanker, Brown Brake Van, Chlorine Tanker, Gunpowder, Banana, All Mint Boxed **£120**

Canadian CPR Caboose, Mint Boxed **£310**
Super Detail Wagons - Caustic Liquor Bogie Tanker, United Glass Limited, BR Horsebox with Horse, Packing Van, Tankers - silver Esso, black Esso, Shell, Chlorine, UD, All Mint Boxed.............**£260**

HORNBY DUBLO ACCESSORIES AND CATALOGUES

Canadian Catalogues - 1953/4, 1954/5, 1955/6, 1956/7, 1957, 1958, two 1961, 1962, two 1963, 1964, 6 CPR advertising leaflets (2 different), 2 coloured leaflets, 3 rail layouts, Meccano Products 1963, Generally Excellent Plus **£440**
Signal Cabin with Green Roof, Near Mint Boxed **£170**
Terminal or Through Station Kit, Excellent Plus Boxed **£180**

Vectis Model Auctions

35 CASTLE STREET, EAST COWES, ISLE OF WIGHT

Condition grading used in Vectis' catalogues:

A+ As near mint or pristine condition as at time of issue
A Virtually mint boxed – any faults of a most minor nature
B+ Model is near mint – box has very slight faults
B Slight model or box faults e.g. Some chips or box rubs but model and box complete
C More obvious model chips and box faults inc. tears but still complete
D Same as C but box has one or more end flaps missing and model may have faded paint as well as chips
E Model and box have considerable faults
R Repaint

BOXED LOCOMOTIVES - (Three Rail)

The following six lots were all purchased from the Conduit Street London W.1 Model Railway Shop when the changeover to 2R was announced. They are all 'never run' with DOCUMENTATION and BLUE/WHITE STRIPED PICTURE BOXES TO MATCH

No. 3217 0-6-2 Tank Loco - B.R. Black No. 69567 ....**£360**
No. 3221 4-6-0 'LUDLOW CASTLE' and Tender - B.R. Green No. 5002 - slight lid faults **£450**

No. 3226 4-6-2 'CITY OF LIVERPOOL' and Tender B.R. Maroon No. 46247 - slight lid faults **£600**

3235 4-6-2 'DORCHESTER' and Tender - B.R. Green No. 34042 ....**£310**
L30 Bo-Bo Diesel Electric Loco - B.R. Green/Grey No. D8000 - slight lid faults...**£110**

No. 3218 2-6-4 Tank Loco - B.R. Black No. 80054 - A with Test Tag box shows No. 80059 ....**£170**
LT25 8F 2-8-0 Freight Loco and Tender - B.R. Black No. 45158 - A to A+ with instructions and Test Tag........................**£180**

3231 0-6-0 Diesel-Electric Shunter No. D3302 - A to A+ with Test Tag - box lid is B+...**£190**
EDL 7 0-6-2 Tank 'LNER' Green No. 9596 - 'EDL 7' underneath - lovely A apart from chip to boiler door) in B blue box with cover strip - lid has factory repair no. on each end **£150**
EDLT 20 4-6-0 'BRISTOL CASTLE' - A with instructions in B to B+ box **£100**

LT 25 L.M.R. 8F 2-8-0 Freight Loco and Tender - A with Test Tag in B+ to A box **£100**
No. 3224 L.M.R. 8F 2-8-0 Goods Loco and Tender No. 48094 B.R. Black - B+ to A in B to B+ correct box....................**£440**

No. 3211 4-6-2 'MALLARD' and Tender No. 60022 B.R. Green with Nickel-Silver wheels and plastic bogie and tender wheels - A - Tender is B+ - box is C. NB A similar model in B+ box sold for £180 in our July 1992 auction.................................**£190**
No. 3226 4-6-2 'CITY OF LIVERPOOL' No. 46247 and Tender B.R. Maroon - lovely B+ to A with added footplatemen (2) in B+ box with B lid NB. A similar model sold £440 in our July 1992 auction
....**£500**

No. 3235 4-6-2 S.R. 'DORCHESTER' No. 34032 and Tender - B.R. Green - lovely A with instructions in A box with B lid. NB. A similar model sold for £310 in our July 1992 auction **£310**
No. 3231 0-6-0 Diesel-Electric Shunting Loco. D3763 - A in B box NB. A similar model in slightly better box sold for £140 in our July 1992 auction **£140**

BOXED LOCOMOTIVES - (Two Rail)

No. 2218 2-6-4 Tank No. 80033 B.R. Black - A in B+ box with C lid NB. A slightly better model and box sold for £120 in our July 1992 auction **£110**
No. 2226 'CITY OF LONDON' No. 46245 with Tender - B.R. Maroon - A in B+ to A box **£140**

No. 2235 4-6-2 S.R. 'BARNSTABLE' No. 34005 with Tender - B.R. Green - with instructions in B+ box with C lid **£130**

BOXED SETS (Three Rail)

EDP1 PASSENGER TRAIN 'SIR NIGEL GRESLEY' 4-6-2 No. 7 with Tender - L.N.E.R Blue - Block Magnet Motor - A - tender is B+ with two D1 Corridor Coaches Brake/3rd and 1st - Teak/white - wear to roofs and silvering of windows with 6 curved and 2 straight sections of track - blue printed box compartments all about B - box lid has EDP11 end label partially covered by factory repair number - lid picture is C (no end label)..**£140**
EDP20 Passenger Train 'BRISTOLIAN' with 4-6-0 'BRISTOL CASTLE' N. 7013 and Tender both B.R. Green and two D21 W.R. Corridor Coaches - brown/cream/grey 1st/2nd and Brake/2nd with 8 curved and 2 straight track sections - all A to A+ in 'never run' condition with instructions, EDP20 Leaflet, Guarantee, Rail Layout, Booklet etc. - Yellow box compartments all A to A+ - box lid is B+ - a lovely 'as new' set..**£500**

Tin-plate Trains – Every Home Should Have One

Did you get one in your stocking? A tin train I mean. Between the World Wars and the 1950s no Christmas was complete without one and a conservative guess would be that 80 percent of the families in this country had one at some time or another.

And it wasn't just the lads; many a girl became the surprised recipient from a sonless father. A friend bought his third daughter a train set in desperation before he had two further children, both daughters, and no more trains!

The tin train set was usually the first, cheap, set bought for a young child and only those who showed some affinity progressed further into the world of model railways. I can remember finding my first set on one dark Christmas morning in the very early 1930s. It was in a pillow case - they were usually too big for stockings - tied to the end of the brass and iron bedstead, but I had to wait until the candles were lit to really see the toy train, as my grandparents' Victorian terrace house in the country had only oil lamps downstairs and candles upstairs!

I am told that my reaction was to throw that first little green locomotive across the bed because it wasn't black like one owned by a cousin! Christmas day probably started with a clout!

The first cheap tin trains began soon after their counterparts, the stronger, more detailed toys and models, at the end of the 19th century. The early ones were usually floor trains, they were not made to be run on rails. In the Edwardian period the firms of Bing, Karl Bub and later Fischer, Kraus and others in Germany, produced little tin engines driven by slender clockwork motors, running on tinplate rails.

In order to combat this trade and the products of British rivals in the late 1920s and the 1930s, the well known firm of Hornby developed its own cheap end of the range, the 'M' series. It even introduced its only streamlined train, 'Silver Link' in this series and not in the top range like the 'Princess Elizabeth', as had been expected. The 'M' series (we don't know what the 'M' stood for) started in 1926 and had a completely different range of stations, signal boxes, signals, telegraph poles, bridges, etc. from the standard series in 1933 the passenger set was 5s 9d.

In a further attempt to capture more of the low end of the market, in 1932 Hornby produced the 'British Express'. These sets had different tin printing from the 'M' series, being marketed through chain-stores, they carried no trade marks so as not to upset the normal franchised dealer. The sets are now quite rare.

The bulk of these toy trains sold by Woolworths and small corner shops were manufactured by a number of British firms who produced all sorts of toys in tinplate. In 1914 Brimtoy was established and made little 0-4-0 engines amongst other items, its trademark being Nelson's column and the Brimtoy name.

However, in 1932 Brimtoy was amalgamated with Wells O' London, a firm started by Arthur Wells in 1919 which had been successfully providing cheap trains to Woolworths. The trade mark showed two wells. Both trade marks were in use for many years afterwards; some products were marked Wells Brimtoy and many not marked at all. Manufacture stopped in the late 1960s.

A large range of locomotives, usually brightly coloured and freelance in style. Streamliners were built before and after the last war, based on the LNER A4, carrying proud names like 'Silver Streak', 'The National', 'Golden Eagle' and 'King George'. They were often issued without tenders.

Mettoy was another prolific manufacturer. Started at Northampton in 1933 by a refugee, Philip Ullman of Tipp & Co., the firm continued after the war until it transformed itself in 1954 to a producer of die-cast under the name of Corgi. Products included a blue streamlined 0-4-0 No. 4490 and variants, a small 'schools' class, 'Eton' 4-4-0, a little No. 490 and a 2-4-0 made to look like a truncated streamlined Merchant Navy.

Some boxes carry a Mettoy logo but most of the items are not marked. Numerous pieces of rolling stock and accessories were made, including old and modern designs in stations and signal boxes, carrying the name 'Joy Town'.

In 1932 the massive USA of Marx set up a factory at Dudley, later moving to Swansea and making trains until the 1950s. They were all rather heavy looking 0-4-0s, but there were two attractive streamliners with articulated coaches - 'Silver Jubilee', the LNER A4 in silver and the 'Coronation Scot' an LMS pacific in blue. The locos are good simple representations but the carriages are American in character and carry the usual Marx symbol, MAR over an X in a circle.

Chad Valley, named after the river Chad at Harborne where it was started in 1897 by Joseph Johnson, did not come into the train world until late in its life. Before the last war it took over the firm of Burnett which had made a very simple green 0-4-0 'Royal Scot' with a bobbin style clockwork motor. It had no tender or coaches and Chad Valley re-issued it in red. From 1949 three basic designs were made, a clockwork 0-4-0 in blue No. 10138, a small 0-4-0 in red or green and a streamlined 2-4-0 like an A4, No. 60027 and called 'Merlin'. It was driven by battery or clockwork. This small range was supported by a variety of rolling stock, signals, signal boxes, buffers, etc.

All the products mentioned run on 'O' gauge track - which is 32mm gauge - however, their scale, which should be 7mm to a foot, varies considerably. The vast majority do not pretend to look like real trains but are colourful items to stir the imagination of the child. They certainly look nothing like the stirring prototypical pictures on the boxes!

With some exceptions these little tin jewels are not the province of the railway model enthusiasts, but more that of the tin toy collectors. With prices around £10 for the more common post war locomotives, sets at £25-30 and stations at £5 it is still an inexpensive area of collecting. Collecting the streamliners makes a pleasant theme, but you will have to pay well over £100 for a Hornby one.

This article first appeared in the 'Antiques and Collectables Magazine' in January 1994 (Copyright Roy Chambers).

Dinky Toys Trains

While the models listed below are unlikely to fill the needs of a true railway modelling enthusiast, they are nevertheless products of the Meccano factory and have their rightful place in the history of British toys and models.

Some of the very earliest of these products were made in lead and had 'HORNBY SERIES' cast in. Later versions had 'DINKY TOYS' cast in and Mazak (diecasting zinc alloy) was soon introduced, both materials being in used right up to the first year of the war.

Dinky Toys Trains were originally equipped with lead wheels and since they were designed primarily as toys they had no more need of track than the children who happily pushed them along on the linoleum. Later issues were able to run more freely on their standard Dinky Toys 'smooth' (later 'ridged') diecast hubs fitted with rubber tyres.

This listing is taken from 'British Diecast Model Toys Catalogue', 7th Edition, Volume One.

Ref.	Year(s)	Model name	Colours, features, dimensions	Market Price Range	
16	1936-37	Silver Jubilee Set	Locomotive and two interlocking coaches, 'LNER' and '2590' cast-in, open windows, smooth hubs with White tyres, special box, 300 mm.		
			Silver loco and coaches, Grey, Mid-Blue, Dark Blue, Red or Orange trim	**£200-250**	❑
			Silver loco and coaches with Dark Blue trim	**£200-250**	❑
			Cream loco and coaches with Red trim	**£250-275**	❑
			Blue loco and coaches with Dark Blue trim	**£250-275**	❑
			Green loco and coaches with Dark Green trim	**£250-275**	❑
16	1937-40	Streamlined Train Set	As previous models but with a change of name and box	**£200-250**	❑
16	1946-52	Streamlined Train Set	Blue/Black loco, 'LNER', Brown/Grey coaches, solid windows, Black tyres	**£125-150**	❑
16 (798)	1952-54	Streamlined Train Set	As previous model but with 'BR' crest on tender	**£100-125**	❑
16z	1935-40	Articulated Train	Two-tone Blue, or Gold/Red, or Cream with Red, Blue or Orange. French issue sold in UK	**£200-250**	❑
17	1935-40	Passenger Train Set	Black/Maroon loco 17a, Maroon tender 17b, Maroon/Cream coaches 20a/20b	**£300-400**	❑
			Black/Green loco 17a, Green tender 17b, 2 Green/Cream coaches 20a/20b	**£300-400**	❑
			Lead and Mazak set in 2nd type box with correct colour spot	**£400-500**	❑
17a	1934-40	Locomotive	Black/Maroon or Black/Green, diecast cab/boiler, lead chassis, 82 mm	**£100-125**	❑
17b	1934-40	Tender	Maroon or Green diecast body, 62 mm	**£40-50**	❑
18	1935-40	Tank Goods Train Set	Green/Black loco (21a), and 3 Green/Black open wagons (21b)	**£300-400**	❑
19	1935-40	Mixed Goods Train	Maroon/Black loco (21a), Green/Red open wagon (21b), Red/Blue 'SHELL' tanker wagon (21d), Yellow/Red/Green lumber wagon (21e)	**£400-500**	❑
	rare box version:		Set in 3rd type pictorial landscape box	**£800-1,000**	❑
20	1935-40	Tank Passenger Set	Green/Black loco (21a), 2 Brown/Green coaches (20a), Guard's van (20b)	**£300-400**	❑
20a	1935-40	Coach	Brown/Cream or Green/White roof, diecast body, lead chassis, 81 mm	**£40-60**	❑
20b	1935-40	Guard's Van	Brown/Cream or Green/White roof, diecast body, lead chassis, 81 mm	**£40-60**	❑
21	1933-35	Modelled Miniatures Train Set	Blue/Red loco (21a), Green open wagon (21b), Green/Blue crane wagon (21c), Red/Blue 'SHELL' tank wagon (21d), Yellow/Red/Green lumber wagon (21e)	**£500-600**	❑
21a	1932-34	Tank Locomotive	Red/Blue 0-6-0 tank loco, 'HORNBY SERIES' cast into lead body, 82 mm	**£50-75**	❑
	1934-41		Maroon/Black or Green/Black, 'DINKY TOYS' cast into lead body, 82 mm	**£50-75**	❑
21b	1932-34	Open Wagon	Green/Red, Green/Blue, Green/Black, Maroon/Black, 'HORNBY SERIES' cast into lead body	**£40-50**	❑
	1934-41		Colours as previous model, 'DINKY TOYS' cast into lead body, 58 mm	**£40-50**	❑
21c	1932-34	Crane Wagon	Green body, Blue chassis, 'HORNBY SERIES' cast-in, lead, 62 mm	NGPP	❑
21d	1932-34	Tanker Wagon	Red tank, Blue or Black chassis, 'HORNBY SERIES' cast-in, lead, 58 mm	**£35-45**	❑
	1934-41		Red tank, Blue or Black chassis, 'DINKY TOYS' cast-in, lead, 58 mm	**£35-45**	❑
21e	1932-34	Lumber Wagon	Brown/Blue, Yellow/Red or Yellow/Black, 'HORNBY SERIES' in lead	**£35-45**	❑
	1934-41		Brown/Blue, Yellow/Red or Yellow/Black, 'DINKY TOYS', lead, 58 mm	**£35-45**	❑
26	1934-40	G.W.R. Rail Car	Early issues are lead, later issues are mazak, plastic rollers, 106 mm.		
			Cream roof, Brown, Green, Yellow or Red body	**£100-125**	❑
			Green body with Red roof	**£125-150**	❑
26z	1937-40	Diesel Road Car	Cream roof, Red, Green, Orange, Yellow or Blue body, 99 mm. (French)	**£100-125**	❑
784	1972-74	Dinky Goods Train Set	Blue loco 'GER', one Red Truck, one Yellow Truck	**£30-40**	❑
798 (16)	1954-59	Express Passenger Train Set	Green/Black loco, BR crest, Cream coaches (Grey roofs), Black hubs/tyres	**£100-125**	❑
			Green/Black loco, BR crest, Cream coaches/roofs/hubs, Black tyres	**£80-100**	❑
			Green/Black loco, BR crest, Cream coaches/roofs, Red hubs, White tyres	**£100-125**	❑

LONE STAR

TREBLE·O·LECTRIC

RAILWAYS

PRICE 2d

D.5900 Loco hauling passenger coaches and D.5000 Loco with mixed goods train.

MADE IN ENGLAND BY:—
LONE STAR PRODUCTS (Treble-O-Lectric Division)
152 GREEN LANES · PALMERS GREEN · LONDON N.13

Lone Star Railways

Robert Newson has provided this information and listing of Lone Star's miniature railway items.

The series was launched in 1957 as a push-along railway system called 'Lone Star Locos'. All items were to '000' scale and the track gauge was 8.25 mm, exactly half of '00' gauge. The rolling stock and track were made entirely of diecast metal, and were reasonably accurate models, giving a range which today is quite collectable.

In 1960 an electric system called 'Treble-O-Lectric' was introduced. This used many of the same basic models as the Lone Star Locos (which continued in production) but modified for electric operation. The track gauge was the international standard N gauge (9 mm) and the rolling stock had Tri-ang type couplings in place of the hook and eye couplings of the Lone Star Locos. Also plastic wheels were fitted so as not to short-circuit the track! New diesel locomotives were introduced since the push-along locomotives were too small to accommodate a motor.

In 1962 the range of American rolling stock in the Treble-O-Lectric series was expanded with several new liveries. Also in that year the Lone Star Locos were issued in new blister packs numbered from 50 to 84.

A range of buildings called 'Gulliver County' was introduced in 1963 to complement the various railway models. These were one-piece vinyl mouldings. Also new was a set of five diecast road vehicles. In 1964 rolling stock in Canadian liveries was introduced.

In 1966 the push-along range was re-launched as 'Treble-O-Trains'. The rolling stock was now the same as Treble-O-Lectric (but non-motorised) i.e. with Tri-ang type couplings and plastic wheels. The track was moulded in grey plastic rather than the diecast track of the Lone Star Locos. The Treble-O-Lectric range continued unchanged for several more years and was still available in 1970 but was discontinued fairly soon thereafter.

The various series have overlapping number ranges and many items appear in more than one series. For example the signal box in the different types of packaging was numbered 33, 80, EL.152 or 92, yet the model stayed the same throughout!

Market Price Range - Lone Star Railway models are not highly collectable and therefore models may still be obtained at a fairly low cost.

Lone Star Locos

1	0-6-0 Class 3F Tank Loco ☐	12	U.S. Diesel Loco ☐	23	Re-railer track (3) ☐
2	2-6-2 Class 3 Tank Loco ☐	13	Brake Van ☐	24	Station and platform ☐
3	Open Goods Wagon (2) ☐	14	Cattle Wagon ☐	25	Flat Wagon (3) ☐
4	Midland Region Coach ☐	15	'U.D.' Tank Wagon ☐	26	U.S. Passenger Coach ☐
5	Straight track ☐	16	'B.P.' Tank Wagon ☐	27	Girder Bridge with Piers ☐
6	Curved track ☐	17	'Shell' Tank Wagon ☐	28	Incline piers (6) ☐
7	0-6-0 Diesel Shunting Loco ☐	18	Goods Van (2) ☐	29	Plastic Trees (3) ☐
8	4-6-2 Class A4 Gresley Loco ☐	19	B.R. Mk.I Composite Coach ☐	30	Telegraph Poles (plastic) ☐
9	Tender for no.8 ☐	20	Points (1 LH, 1 RH) ☐	31	Fences and Gates (plastic) ☐
10	4-6-2 Class 8P Loco Princess Royal ☐	21	Crossovers (2) ☐	32	Semaphore signals (2) ☐
11	Tender for no.10 ☐	22	Sleeper built buffer (3) ☐	33	Signal box ☐

Lone Star Locos – blister-packed

50	0-6-0 Class 3F Tank Loco with track ☐		Open Goods Wagon ☐	74	Points (1 LH, 1 RH) and track (2) ☐
51	2-6-2 Class 3 Tank Loco with track ☐	61	'U.D.' Tanker with straight track ☐	75	Re-railer track (4) ☐
52	0-6-0 Diesel Shunting Loco with track ☐	62	'B.P.' Tanker and Flat Wagon ☐	76	Crossover (1), Buffer (2) and track (2) ☐
53	4-6-2 Class A4 Gresley Loco ☐	63	'Shell' Tanker with re-railer track ☐	77	Level crossing and re-railer track ☐
54	4-6-2- Class 8P Loco Princess Royal ☐	64	Goods Van and Open Goods Wagon ☐	78	Girder Bridge with Piers ☐
55	Tender for no. 53 with 2 straight tracks ☐	65	100 ton Breakdown Crane Wagon ☐	79	Incline Piers (6) ☐
56	Tender for no. 54 with 2 straight tracks ☐	66	U.S. Diesel Loco ☐	80	Signal box and Signal ☐
57	Midland Region Coach with track ☐	67	U.S. Passenger Coach ☐	81	Signals (3) ☐
58	B.R. MkI Composite Coach ☐	68	Bogie Flat Wagon with track ☐	82	Plastic trees (5) ☐
59	Brake Van and Flat Wagon ☐	69	Bogie Tank Wagon ☐	83	Telegraph Poles, Fences and Gates ☐
60	Cattle Wagon and	70	U.S. Caboose ☐	84	Station and Platform ☐
		71	U.S. Box Car ☐		
		72	Straight track (5) ☐		
		73	Curved track (5) ☐		

Gulliver County Buildings

1320	Inn ☐	1324	Shop and Car Park ☐	1328	Thatched Cottage ☐
1321	Church ☐	1325	Garage Service Station ☐	1340	Twin Falls Station ☐
1322	Fire Station ☐	1326	Pair of Shops ☐		Scenic Village Set ☐
1323	Ranch Style Bungalow ☐	1327	Two Storey House with Garage ☐		

Lone Star

Treble-O-Trains – blister-packed

74 U.S. Diesel Loco 'Union Pacific' .... ❑
75 D5900 Diesel Loco .... ❑
76 U.S. Baldwin 0-8-0 Steam Loco
    (without tender) .... ❑
77 B.R. Mk.I Composite Coach .... ❑
78 U.S. Passenger Coach .... ❑
79 U.S. Box Car 'New Haven' .... ❑
80 Bogie Tank Wagon 'Shell' .... ❑

81 Bogie Flat Wagon with
    Citroen DS19 and Land Rover .... ❑
82 100 ton Breakdown Crane Wagon ...... ❑
83 U.S. Caboose 'New Haven' .... ❑
84 Cattle Wagon and Brake Van .... ❑
85 Curved track (6) .... ❑
86 Straight track (6) .... ❑
87 Trees (6) .... ❑

88 Level crossing with
    Barriers and track .... ❑
89 Figures, Telegraph Poles,
    Fences and Gates .... ❑
90 Footbridge .... ❑
91 0-6-0 Tank Loco and
    Open Goods Wagon .... ❑
92 Signal Box and
    Colour Light Signals (2) .... ❑

Treble-O-Lectric

Note: In order to concentrate on the more collectable items, track and spare parts have not been listed.

EL.50   Standard Goods Set .... ❑
EL.51   Standard Passenger Set .... ❑
EL.52   Goods Set with Accessories .... ❑
EL.53   Passenger Set with Accessories . ❑
EL.54   Transcontinental Passenger Set .. ❑
EL.55   Transcontinental Goods Set .... ❑
EL.56   B.R. De Luxe Scenic Set .... ❑
EL.60   D5000 Diesel Loco .... ❑
EL.60A D5000 Diesel Loco
        (non-motorised) .... ❑
EL.61   D5900 Diesel Loco .... ❑
EL.61A D5900 Diesel Loco
        (non-motorised) .... ❑
EL.62   U.S. F.7 Diesel Loco
        'Union Pacific' .... ❑
EL.62A U.S. F.7 Diesel Loco 'Union
        Pacific' (non-motorised) .... ❑
EL.63   U.S. F.7 Diesel Loco
        'New Haven' .... ❑
EL.64   U.S. F.7 Diesel Loco
        'Chesapeake & Ohio' .... ❑
EL.65   U.S. F.7 Diesel Loco
        'Kansas City Southern' .... ❑
EL.66   U.S. 0-8-0 Baldwin Steam Loco
        and Tender 'Union Pacific' .... ❑
EL.67   F.7 Diesel Loco
        'Canadian Pacific' .... ❑
EL.68   F.7 Diesel Loco
        'Canadian National' .... ❑
EL.70   Mk.I Composite Coach,
        maroon .... ❑
EL.71   Mk.I Brake End Coach,
        maroon .... ❑
EL.72   U.S. Coach 'Union Pacific' .... ❑

EL.73   U.S. Vista Dome Coach
        'Union Pacific' .... ❑
EL.74   Mk.I Composite Coach - green . ❑
EL.75   Mk.I Brake End Coach - green . ❑
EL.76   U.S. Coach 'New Haven' .... ❑
EL.77   U.S. Vista Dome Coach
        'New Haven' .... ❑
EL.78   U.S. Coach 'Pullman' .... ❑
EL.79   U.S. Vista Dome Coach
        'Pullman' .... ❑
EL.80   Brake Van .... ❑
EL.81   'Shell' Tank Wagon .... ❑
EL.82   'B.P.' Tank Wagon .... ❑
EL.83   'U.D.' Tank Wagon .... ❑
EL.84   Cattle Wagon .... ❑
EL.85   Open Goods Wagon .... ❑
EL.86   Goods Van .... ❑
EL.87   U.S. Box Car 'Union Pacific' .... ❑
EL.88   100 ton Breakdown
        Crane Wagon .... ❑
EL.89   Bogie Flat Wagon with Citroen
        DS19 and Land Rover .... ❑
EL.90   Bogie Tank Wagon 'Mobilgas' .. ❑
EL.91   U.S. Caboose 'Union Pacific' .... ❑
EL.92   U.S. Box Car 'Boston & Maine' ❑
EL.93   U.S. Box Car 'New Haven' .... ❑
EL.94   U.S. Box Car 'Santa Fe' .... ❑
EL.95   Bogie Tank Wagon 'Texaco' ...... ❑
EL.96   Bogie Flat Wagon with
        Austin Articulated Lorry .... ❑
EL.97   U.S. Caboose 'New Haven' .... ❑
EL.98   U.S. Caboose
        'Chesapeake & Ohio' .... ❑
EL.99   U.S. Caboose
        'Kansas City Southern' .... ❑
EL.130 'Canadian Pacific' Coach .... ❑
EL.131 'Canadian Pacific'
        Vista Dome Coach .... ❑

EL.132 'Canadian National' Coach .... ❑
EL.133 'Canadian National'
        Vista Dome Coach .... ❑
EL.140 Box Car 'Canadian Pacific' .... ❑
EL.141 Caboose 'Canadian Pacific' .... ❑
EL.142 Refrigerated Box Car
        'Canadian National' .... ❑
EL.143 Caboose 'Canadian National' .... ❑
EL.150 Station and Platform .... ❑
EL.151 Platform Extension with
        Lamp Standards .... ❑
EL.152 Signal Box .... ❑
EL.153 Semaphore Signal - Home (2) ... ❑
EL.154 Semaphore Signal - Distant (2) . ❑
EL.155 Rail built buffer (3) .... ❑
EL.156 Girder Bridger and Piers .... ❑
EL.157 Incline Piers (6) .... ❑
EL.158S Incline tray - straight .... ❑
EL.158C Incline tray - curved .... ❑
EL.159 Telegraph Poles (28) .... ❑
EL.160 Fences (24) and Gates (4) .... ❑
EL.161 Trees (plastic) (3) .... ❑
EL.162 Tunnel .... ❑
EL.163 Footbridge .... ❑
EL.164 Level crossing with Barriers ...... ❑
EL.165 Loading gauge (3) .... ❑
EL.166 Colour Light Signals (3) .... ❑
EL.167 Set of 12 plastic figures
        (unpainted) .... ❑
EL.168 Set of five road vehicles:
        Citroen DS19, Land Rover,
        Dennis Fire Engine, Austin
        Articulated Flat Lorry, AEC
        Regal IV Single Deck Bus. .... ❑
EL.169A Bridge Girder .... ❑
EL.169B Bridge Pier .... ❑
EL.177 Scenic Baseboard .... ❑

Master Models

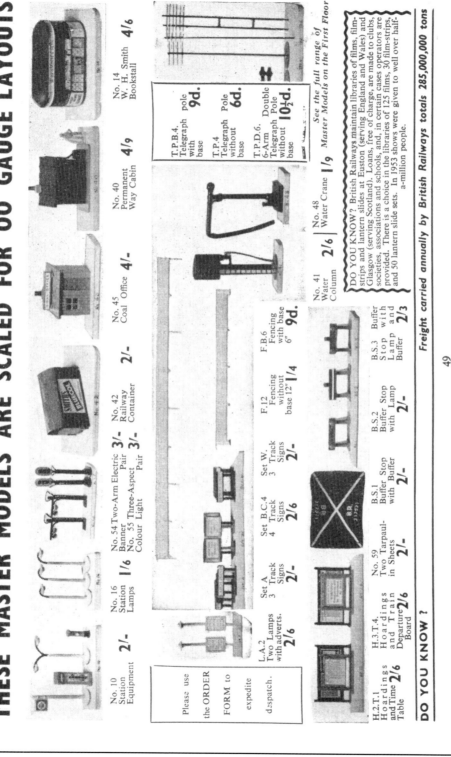

THESE MASTER MODELS ARE SCALED FOR OO GAUGE LAYOUTS

No. 14 W. H. Smith Bookstall **4/6**

No. 40 Permanent Way Cabin **4/9**

No. 45 Coal Office **4/-**

No. 42 Railway Container **2/-**

No. 54 Two-Arm Electric Banner Pair **3/-**
No. 55 Three-Aspect Colour Light Pair **3/-**

No. 16 Station Lamps **1/6**

No. 10 Station Equipment **2/-**

T.P.B.4. Telegraph pole with base **9d.**
T.P.4. Telegraph Pole without base **6d.**
T.P.D.6. Double 6-Arm Telegraph Pole without base **10½d.**

See the full range of Master Models on the First Floor

No. 48 Water Crane **1/9**

No. 41 Water Column **2/6**

Please use the ORDER FORM to expedite dispatch.

L.A.2 Two Lamps with adverts. **2/6**

Set A 3 Track Signs **2/-**

Set B.C.4 4 Track Signs **2/6**

Set W. 3 Track Signs **2/-**

F.12 Fencing without base 12" **1/4**

F.B.6 Fencing with base 6" **9d.**

B.S.3 Buffer Stop with Lamp and Buffer **2/3**

B.S.2 Buffer Stop with Lamp **2/-**

B.S.1 Buffer Stop with Buffer **2/-**

No. 59 Two Tarpaulin Sheets **2/-**

H.3.T.4. Hoardings and Train Departure Board **2/6**

H.2.T.1 Hoardings and Time Table **2/6**

DO YOU KNOW?

DO YOU KNOW? British Railways maintain libraries of films, film-strips and lantern slides at Euston (serving England and Wales) and Glasgow (serving Scotland). Loans, free of charge, are made to clubs, societies, associations and schools, and, in certain cases operators are provided. There is a choice in the libraries of 125 films, 30 film-strips, and 50 lantern slide sets. In 1953 shows were given to well over half-a-million people.

Freight carried annually by British Railways totals 285,000,000 tons

49

A FULL RANGE OF 'MASTER MODELS' THAT WILL

No. 25 Placards **1/3**

No. 19 Tar Barrels **1/-**

No. 20 Oil Barrels **1/-**

No. 8 Milk Churns **1/6**

No. 18 Cable Drums Unlagged **2/-**

No. 67 Street Personnel **2/-**

No. 12 Electric Trolley and Trailer **2/6**

No. 5 Seated Figures **2/-** (*Seat not included*)

No. 1 Railway Staff **2/-**

No. 4 Seated Figures (*No seat*) **2/-**
No. 75. With Seat **2/6**

No. 23 Track Repair Party **2/-**

No. 3 Assorted Figures **2/-**

No. 2 Railway Passengers **2/-**

No. 57 Crew Unloading Trucks **2/6**

No. 65 Charringtons Coal Bunkers, Scale and Coalman **4/-**

No. 39 Station Name and Seat **2/-**

No. 69 Belisha Set Crossing **1/6**

No. 78 Sitting Army Figures (*No seat*) **2/-**

No. 79 Sitting Naval Figures (*No Seat*) **2/-**

No. 73 Pit Workers **2/-**

No. 74 6in. Fence **6d.**

No. 72 Gent's Toilet **4/6**

No. 70 Bus Shelter **2/6**

No. 64 Wicket Gates **2/6**

No. 76 Level Crossing Gates, Double Track **3/9**

No. 9 Level Crossing Gates, Single Track **3/-**

No. 68 Girder Bridge for Single Track **12/9**

No. 77 Girder Bridge for Double Track **10/6**

Model Dept. First Floor

● *All goods deliver- ed free in our own extensive van area.*

NEW MODELS

GAMAGES, HOLBORN, LONDON, E.C.I.   HOLborn 8484

Nearest Railway Stations — Chancery Lane and Farringdon

50

PUT THE 'FINISHING TOUCH' TO YOUR LAYOUT

No. 15 Two Telephone Kiosks **2/-**	No. 66 Two Station Clocks **1/6**	No. 31 Enquiry Kiosks **2/-**
No. 32 Lagged Cable Drums **2/-**	No. 24 Police Boxes **2/-**	No. 34 Watchman's Hut and Workman **2/6**
No. 33 6 Esso Oil Drums **2/-**	No. 22 Station Platform Garden (2) **1/3**	No. 21 Island Platform Garden (2) **1/3**
No. 44 Esso Petrol Pumps **2/-**	No. 30 Corrugated Sheet Iron **1/-**	No. 29 Glass Crates **1/-**
No. 56 Aspect Searchlight Signals (2) **2/9**	H.1/T.3 Small Hoarding, Large Time **2/6**	No. 53 Two 4 Aspect Searchlight Junction Signals **3/6**
No. 52 Disc Shunting Signals **3/6**	No. 50 A.A. Box and Patrolman **2/6**	No. 7 Platform Accessories **2/-**
No. 26 Sleeper Buffer **2/-**	No. 27 Scale, Weights, Light Luggage **1/-**	No. 43 Cycle Rack, 4 Cycles **2/-**
No. 62 Police Box and Patrolman **2/-**	No. 63 Two Oval Pillar Boxes **1/6**	No. 38 Sand Bin and Fire Buckets **2/-**
No. 35 Cable Laying Party **2/6**		

Save Money on Postage—See Post Details on Page 118

DO YOU KNOW? *British Railways own 51,000 Houses and Flats and numerous other properties*

51

Mettoy Railways

The Mettoy Company of Harlestone Road, Northampton issued affordable tinplate train sets.
The following listing represents those items listed in the Mettoy Playthings Catalogue of 1951.
Boxed sets sell for £50 – £75.
The Editor would welcome any further information.

'Inexpensive' Train Sets

5336/1 **Passenger Train Set**, clockwork. Fully detailed. Locomotive fitted with connecting rods and cylinders, tender, one Pullman coach, 4 curved rails. Attractively boxed.

5337/1 **Passenger Train Set**, clockwork. Fully detailed. Locomotive with connecting rods and cylinders, tender 2 Pullman coaches, 4 curved rails.

5353/3 **Passenger Train Set**, clockwork. Locomotive with brake operating from rail, connecting rods and cylinders, tender, 2 Pullman coaches, 5 curved and one brake rail.

Passenger Train Sets

5362 **Passenger Train Set**, clockwork. Semi-streamline loco. with brake, connecting rods and cylinders, tender, 3 coaches, 6 curved rails.

5364/1 **Passenger Train Set**, clockwork. Semi-streamline loco. with reversing mechanism, brake operating from track. Tender, 3 Pullman coaches, 6 curved rails, one straight and one brake rail.

5452/1 **Passenger Train Set**. Locomotive with bogie, connecting rods and smoke deflectors, reversing clockwork. Brake operating from track, tender, 2 Pullman coaches, 6 curved, 1 straight and brake rail.

Goods Train Sets

5398/1 **Goods Train Set**. Fully detailed clockwork locomotive with connecting rods and cylinders. Tender, open truck, 4 curved rails.

5402/2 **Goods Train Set**. Clockwork Locomotive with brake, connecting rods and cylinders, tender, closed truck, 1 open truck, 6 curved rails.

5404/2 **Goods Train Set**. Clockwork locomotive with brake operating from track, connecting rods, cylinders, 1 open, 1 closed and stanchion truck, 1 oil tank wagon, 6 curved rails, 1 straight and brake rail.

Combination Train Sets

5552 **Combination Train Set**. Clockwork Locomotive, 1 tender, 1 coach, tunnel, signal, signal box and 4 curved rails

5555/2 **Combination Train Set**. Modern clockwork locomotive with brake operating from track. Tender, 1 coach, station, tunnel, signal, 5 curved and 1 brake rail.

5561/2 **Combination Goods Train Set**. Clockwork Locomotive with brake operating from track, connecting rods, cylinders, tender, open truck, closed truck, station, tunnel, signal, 5 curved and 1 brake rail.

5562/2 **Combination Train Set**. Clockwork Locomotive with brake operating from track. Connecting rods, smoke deflectors, tender, 2 coaches, signal box, station, signal bridge, tunnel, 6 curved and 1 brake rail.

5565/1 **Combination Goods Train Set**. Clockwork locomotive with brake operating from track, connecting rods and cylinders. Tender, open wagon, closed wagon. Detachable container on stanchion truck, tunnel, station, signal, signal box, bridge, 6 curved and 1 brake rail.

5563/1 **Combination Passenger and Goods Train Set**. Clockwork loco, brake operating from track, connecting rods and smoke deflectors. Tender, 2 coaches, 1 open truck, 1 closed truck, 1 detachable container van on stanchion truck, signal cabin, tunnel, station, signal, 6 curved, 1 straight and 1 brake rail.

Miniature Train Sets

5703 **Miniature Train Set**. Clockwork streamline locomotive with brake, tender, 3 coaches, 8 curved rails.

5702 **Miniature Passenger Train Set**. Clockwork streamline locomotive with brake, tender, 2 coaches, 8 curved rails.

5724 **Miniature Goods Train Set**. Clockwork locomotive with brake, tender, open truck, closed truck, tank wagon, stanchion truck, 8 curved rails.

5722 **Miniature Goods Train Set**. Clockwork locomotive with brake, tender, open truck, closed truck, 8 curved rails

5730 **Passenger or Freight Train Set**. Clockwork loco with brake, tender, 2 coaches, 1 open truck, 1 closed truck, 1 tank wagon, 1 double arm signal, 8 curved rails, 2 straight rails, 'OO' gauge.

5710 **'Banjo' Train Set**. Clockwork Streamline locomotive operating on track with automatic turntables.

Playcraft Railways

Playcraft formed part of the Mettoy Group which manufactured Corgi Toys. Train sets were issued circa 1956 with either plastic-bodied electric or clockwork locomotives. The electric locomotives would operate from batteries or any 12v DC mains operated power unit. Coaches had removable roofs and bogies, plus detailed interiors which included compartments with seats, tables, lamps, beds, washbasins, etc.

The following listings have been extracted from a 3rd edition Playcraft Railways catalogue. It is not known whether all the items listed were actually issued.

Boxed sets in good complete condition sell for £35–£45.

The Editor would welcome any further information.

Electric Locomotives

P. 837 B.R. D6100 Diesel Locomotive, Eight wheel drive for maximum traction
P. 831 Tank Locomotive, four wheel drive
P. 838 B.R. Diesel Shunter
P. 836 4-6-2 Locomotive S.N.C.F. Pacific type 23C and tender, six wheel drive

B. R. Main Line Coaches

B.R. 2nd Class Open Coach
P. 456 Standard Livery
P. 346 Western Region Livery
P. 336 Southern Livery

B.R. Restaurant/Kitchen Car
P. 345 Western Region Livery
P. 335 Southern Region Livery
P. 455 Standard Livery

B.R. 1st/2nd Class Composite Coach
P. 337 Southern Region Livery
P. 457 Standard Livery
P. 347 Western Region Livery

B.R. 2nd Class/Brake Corridor Coach
P. 458 Standard Livery
P. 348 Western Region Livery
P. 338 Southern Region Livery

Clockwork Train Sets

P. 1001 'BISHOPSGATE' Goods Train Set contains:
P. 535 Clockwork Tank Locomotive: P. 631 Open Goods Wagon; P. 630 B.R. Brake Van; 8 P. 4700 Curved Rails.

P. 1100 'SUBURBAN' Passenger Train Set contains:
P. 535 Clockwork Tank Locomotive; 1 Suburban Passenger Coach; 8 P. 4700 Curved Rails.

P. 105 'CREWE' Goods Train Set contains:
P. 535 Clockwork Tank Locomotive; P. 631 Open Goods Wagon; P. 646 Dropside Goods Wagon; P. 654 Transporter with 6 Cars; P. 630 B.R. Brake Van; 8 P. 4700 Curved Rails; 4 P. 4750 Straight Rails.

P. 1150 'LIVERPOOL STREET' Passenger Train Set contains:
P. 535 Clockwork Tank Locomotive; P. 457 B.R. 1st/2nd Class Composite Coach; P. 458 B.R. 2nd Class/Brake Coach; 8 P. 4700 Curved Rails; 4 P. 4750 Straight Rails.

Electric Train Sets

P. 1305 'CLAPHAM' Goods Train Set contains:
P.838 Electric 0-4-0 Diesel Shunter; P. 631 Open Goods Wagon; P.635 Goods Van with sliding doors; P. 630 B.R. Brake Van; 7 P. 4700 Curved Rails; 1 P. 470 Reversing Contact Curved Rail.

P. 1410 'SWINDON' Passenger Train Set contains:
P. 831 Electric Tank Locomotive; P. 347 1st/2nd Composite Coach; P. 348 2nd Brake Coach; 8 P. 4700 Curved Rails; 2 P. 4750 Straight Rails; P. 88 Power Connector.

P. 1320 'SNOW HILL' Goods Train Set contains:
P. 831 Electric Tank Locomotive; P. 631 Open Goods Wagon; P. 644 Dropside Wagon with tubes; P. 642 Bulk Cement Wagon; P. 630 B.R. Brake Van; 8 P. 4700 Curved Rails; 2 P. 4750 Straight Rails; P. 88 Power Connector. 2 Containers.

P. 1450 'EUSTON' Passenger Train Set contains:
P. 837 D.6100 Diesel Locomotive (8 wheel drive); P. 456 B.R. 2nd Class Open Coach; P. 457 BR 1st/2nd Class Composite Coach; P. 458 B.R. 2nd Class/Brake Corridor Coach; 8 P. 4700 Curved Rails; P. 4750 Straight Rail; 2 P. 4755 Straight Rail; P. 881 Power Connector.

P. 350 'STRATFORD' Goods Train Set contains:
P. 837 D.6100 Diesel Locomotive (8 wheel drive); P. 654 Bogie Car Transporter with 6 cars; P. 651 Bogie Tanker - Shell; P. 650 Bogie Goods Wagon - Straight Connector Rail; 8 P.4700 Curved Rails; P. 881 Power Connector.

P. 460 'LONDON/PARIS' NIGHT FERRY Passenger Train Set contains: P. 836 Pacific Locomotive and tender; 3 P. 863 Channel Ferry Sleeping Car; 8 P. 4700 Curved Rails; 4 P. 4755 Straight Rails; P. 88 Power Connector.

Goods Wagons

P. 630 B.R. Brake Van	P. 653 Bogie Goods Van with
P. 633 Open Mineral Wagon	sliding doors
P. 635 Goods Van	P. 654 Bogie Car Transporter
P. 640 Tank Wagon (Shell/BP)	with six cars
P. 642 Bulk Cement Wagon	P. 655 Bogie Bolster Wagon
P. 643 Barrel Wagon	with legs
P. 644 with tubes	P. 656 Bogie Refrigerator Van
P. 645 with containers	P. 657 Bogie Hopper Wagon
P. 646 Dropside Wagon	P. 658 Bogie Well Wagon
P. 650 Bogie Goods Wagon,	with transformer
(Deep)	P. 659 Bogie Bolster Wagon
P. 651 Bogie Tank Wagon, Shell	with three cars
P. 652 Bogie Goods Wagon,	
Dropside	

"Trix Twin" Railway

Gauge 'OO' (16mm), radius 13½ inches, for AC / DC Mains or Accumulators

The Trix Twin Railway system enables two model trains to operate on the same track under separate control. Originally a German model train manufacturer, Trix linked up with Bassett-Lowke in 1936 to introduce Trix Twin Railway into Britain (see page 37). Eventually a British Trix company was formed and the models were made in Britain.

The pre-war range of models is listed in the following reprinted pre-war catalogue pages. Post-war listings have been taken from the Trix 1955, 1964 and 1968 Catalogues. Consult the auction results section for guidance on market price levels. The Editor welcomes any additional information.

Pre-war address: TRIX LTD, St. John's House, Clerkenwell Road, London E.C.1

Post-war address: BRITISH TRIX LIMITED, (part of Courtaulds Group) Industrial Estate, Wrexham Denbighshire.

Address as shown in 1960s advertisements: TRIX TWIN RAILWAYS, 308 Summer Lane, Birmingham

Trix Twin, 1955

1/540	Scale Model 4-6-2 Pacific. Remote controlled uncoupling anywhere on the track ❑	
2/536	Scale model of a famous type used on B.R. Midland Region 4-4-0 compound ❑	
20/56	Scale model of a Continental 2-4-2 Tank loco with remote control uncoupling at both ends, two front and two rear lamps ❑	
1/515	B.R. Goods Tank Loco, 0-4-0 ❑	
1/510	B.R. Passenger Tank loco, 0-4-0 ❑	
1/520	B.R. 0-4-0 Passenger loco and tender ❑	
1/525	B.R. 0-4-0 Goods loco and tender ❑	
9/525	American type switcher loco with slope back tender, dummy marker and back-up lights, operating headlight ❑	

9/520   American type Passenger loco and tender with operating headlight ❑

20/58   The Diesel Flyer. Scale model high-speed train with white head and red rear lamps which automatically change on reversing. 17" overall ❑

1/323   B.R. Goods Train with 0-4-0 Loco and tender. 5 Wagons, without Controller. Rails extra ❑

9/320   American Freight Train with loco and tender, gondola car, box car and caboose without controller. Rails extra ❑

1/336   B.R. Express Passenger Train with 4-4-0 loco and tender, 3 coaches, without controller. Rails extra ❑

9/330   American Passenger Train, loco and tender, 3 passenger cars, without controller. Rails extra ❑

ROLLING STOCK

600	Three Plank ❑
606	Coal, high ❑
607	Private Owner ❑
608	Coal wagon, low ❑
609	Ballast wagon ❑
612	Container Wagon ❑
615	Crane Truck Set, with detachable working crane and match truck ❑
627	Cattle wagon ❑
640	Tank wagon, Esso ❑
643	Tank wagon, Shell ❑
650	Goods Brake ❑
660	Tarpaulin wagon ❑
677	Weltrol wagon without load ❑
678	Weltrol wagon with marine boiler ❑

680	Weltrol wagon with Callender cable drum ❑
681	Flat car ❑
682	Lumber car, empty ❑
683	Lumber car, loaded ❑
684	American Gondola car ❑
685	Box car ❑
686	Refrigerator car ❑
687	Fruit car ❑
688	Union Oil Tank car ❑
689	Texaco Oil Tank car ❑
690	American Caboose ❑
715	Crane only mounted on base ❑
1/560	Bogie Coach, 1st ❑
1/570	Bogie Coach, Brake 3rd ❑
1/580	Bogie Coach, Dining Car ❑
9/565	American Pullman car ❑

9/575	Baggage car ❑
9/585	American Observation car ❑

PASSENGER COACHES

1/568	1st Class Corridor Coach w/lights ❑
599	Pullman Saloon with lights ❑
1/578	Third Class Brake Corridor Coach with lights ❑
1/588	Dining Car Corridor Coach with lights ❑
653	Standard B.R. Goods Brake with red tail and white window light ❑
767	Coach lighting unit ❑
57	Station lighting unit ❑

Trix Twin, 1964 and 1968

LOCOMOTIVES 2 RAIL

1102	0-6-2 tank loco - Black ❑
1106	0-6-2 tank loco - Green ❑
1108	0-6-0 tank loco - Black ❑
1111	4-6-2 Britannia loco - Green ❑
1114	4-6-0 Class V loco - Black ❑
1117	4-6-0 Class V loco - Green ❑
1120	Warship Diesel loco - Green ❑
1123	Bo-Bo overhead electric loco - Black ❑
1126	Bo-Bo overhead electric loco - Green ❑

1128	E.3000 Class AEI loco - Blue ❑
1139	Adler Set ❑
1141	Class E.10 Bo-Bo loco - Blue ❑
1142	BLS overhead electric locomotive - Green ❑
1143	Class E.50 overhead electric Co-Co loco - Green ❑
1144	Class E.40 overhead electric locomotive - Green ❑
1146	BLS overhead electric locomotive - Brown ❑
1147	4-6-2 steam loco - Black ❑
1148	4-6-2 Bavarian steam loco - Black ❑

1150	4-6-0 Steam loco P.8 - Black ❑
1151	4-6-0 Steam loco P.8 - Green ❑
1152	4-6-4 Tank loco - Black ❑
1153	4-6-0 Steam loco - Black ❑
1154	Electric loco Co-Co - Green ❑
1155	Electric freight loco - Green ❑
1163	Western Class Diesel - Blue ❑
1165	0-4-0 tank loco - Black ❑
1167	Diesel loco Enterprise - Green ❑
1170	Diesel V.200 loco - Red ❑
1175	U.S. Diesel unit - Silver ❑
1176	U.S. Diesel Unit - Black ❑
1177	Bo-Bo Diesel - Red/White ❑
1180	The 'Flying Scotsman' ❑

Trix Twin, 1964 and 1968 (continued)

1183 4-6-2 'Pacific' type - Black............❏
1184 Dutch Electric 2 car set - Green.....❏
1195 Diesel 2 car set - Red ....❏

SETS

1255 Complete Starter set ....❏

LOCOMOTIVES 3 RAIL

1100 0-6-2 tank loco - Black ....❏
1104 0-6-2 tank loco - Green ....❏
1107 0-6-0 tank loco - Black ....❏
1109 4-6-2 Britannia loco - Green ....❏
1112 4-6-0 Class V loco - Black ....❏
1115 4-6-0 Class V loco - Green ....❏
1118 Warship Diesel loco - Green ....❏
1121 Bo-Bo overhead electric loco -
Black...❏
1124 Bo-Bo overhead electric loco -
Green ....❏
1127 E.3000 Class AEI loco - Blue ....❏
1130 Adler Set...................................❏
1131 Class E.10 Bo-Bo loco - Blue ....❏
1132 BLS overhead electric loco
- Green......................................❏
1133 Class E.50 overhead electric
Co-Co loco - Green ....❏
1134 Class E.40 overhead electric
loco - Green ....❏
1136 BLS overhead electric loco -
Brown.......................................❏
1137 4-6-2 steam loco - Black ....❏
1138 4-6-2 Bavarian steam loco -
Black...❏
1160 Diesel V.200 loco - Red................❏
1166 0-4-0 tank loco - Black ....❏
1168 Diesel loco Enterprise - Green......❏
1172 Brush type 4 diesel - green or blue❏
1181 Flying Scotsman ....❏

ACCESSORIES

1401 Catenary mast..............................❏
1402 Catenary terminal mast ....❏
1403 Set catenary wires 1 doz. ....❏
1404 Set catenary mast track clips,
1 doz. 3 rail..............................❏
1405 Set extension girders for
catenary 1 doz. ....❏
1406 Set catenary wire joining clips.......❏
1408 Set catenary mast track clips,
1 doz. 2 rail..............................❏
1418 Permanent switch - Red.................❏
1437 Centre rail connector ....❏
1438 Two way switch - Yellow ....❏
1439 Isolating check switch ....❏
1449 Double impulse switch - Black ......❏
1454 Colour light signal.......................❏

1471 Coil of Wire - Red.......................❏
1472 Coil of Wire - Green......................❏
1473 Coil of Wire - White......................❏
1474 Coil of Wire - Black......................❏
1475 Coil of Wire - Yellow....................❏

WAGONS

1601 Open wagon - Red........................❏
1602 Open Wagon - Grey........................❏
1603 Open Wagon Trestle and steel
plate - Grey...............................❏
1604 Pig iron - Red ....❏
1605 Pig iron - Grey.............................❏
1606 Mineral - Grey.............................❏
1607 Mineral - Red ....❏
1608 Wagon with coal - Grey ....❏
1609 Wagon with iron ore - Grey ....❏
1610 Crane with truck...........................❏
1611 Wagon with ballast - Red ....❏
1612 Wagon with coal - Red...................❏
1613 Covered van - Red ....❏
1614 Covered van - Grey........................❏
1616 Con. flat A unloaded - Red ....❏
1617 Con. flat A.B.R. container - Red....❏
1618 Con. flat A.B.R. Insulated
cont. - White ....❏
1619 Con. flat. 2 Birds Eye cont............❏
1620 Shunters truck - Grey ....❏
1621 Goods Brake - Grey ....❏
1622 Goods Brake - Red ....❏
1623 Speedfreight container wagon........❏
1624 Freight wagon with cab. - Brown...❏
1626 Small livestock wagon - Brown ......❏
1630 Cattle wagon French - Brown ....❏
1631 Interfrigo UIC - White ....❏
1632 Livestock wagon - Brown ....❏
1633 Open wagon UIC - Brown ....❏
1634 Ore carrier with flaps - Brown ....❏
1635 Closed van UIC - Brown.................❏
1636 Van Italian - Silver or Brown ....❏
1637 Heavy duty flat carrier - Black.......❏
1638 Large capacity carrier -
Silver or Blue ....❏
1639 Tank wagon B.P. - Green................❏
1640 Tank wagon Gasoline - Red ....❏
1641 Tank wagon Shell - Red ....❏
1644 Tank wagon Shell - Silver ....❏
1646 Tank wagon Esso - Silver...............❏
1648 Hopper wagon - Brown ....❏
1651 Low sided wagon - Brown ....❏
1652 Track cleaning wagon -
various colours ....❏
1653 Goods van - Brown........................❏
1654 Continental brake van - Green ....❏
1655 Dump wagon - Brown.....................❏
1656 Seven Plank Wagon - Black ....❏
1657 Triple container wagon open -
Grey ....❏
1658 Triple container wagon closed -
Grey..❏

1660 Mineral wagon with tarpaulin -
Grey ....❏
1663 Car transporter - Brown ....❏
1677 Weltrol wagon - Black ....❏
1678 Weltrol wagon with marine
boiler - Black ....❏
1679 Weltrol wagon with
transformer - Black ....❏
1680 Weltrol wagon with cable drum -
Black...❏
1683 Bulk carrier - Dark Brown ....❏
1687 Ore bogie wagon - Brown ....❏
1691 American freight car -
various colours ....❏
1698 Low gondola - Brown.....................❏
1699 Rail transporter bogie wagon
- Black ....❏

COACHES

1901 Composite coach B.R. - Maroon....❏
1902 Composite brake B.R. - Maroon ....❏
1903 Buffet B.R. - Maroon ....❏
1911 Composite coach W.R.
- Brown/Cream ....❏
1912 Composite brake W.R.
- Brown/Cream ....❏
1913 Buffet - Brown/Cream ....❏
1921 Composite coach S.R. - Green ....❏
1922 Composite brake S.R. - Green ....❏
1923 Buffet S.R. - Green ....❏
1931 Pullman.......................................❏
1951 Coach light set for 1901-1931
series ....❏
1953 Buffet - Blue/Grey B.R. ....❏
1960 Express coach OBB - Green ....❏
1961 Dining car ISC - BLue ....❏
1962 Dining car ISC - Brown ....❏
1963 Sleeping car ISC - Blue ....❏
1964 Sleeping car ISC - Brown ....❏
1965 Parcel Coach - Green ....❏
1966 Express coach Old Timer -
Green ....❏
1967 Pcl. coach with cab,
Old Timer - Green ....❏
1968 Compartment coach,
Old Timer - Green ....❏
1969 Compartment coach with cab,
Old Timer - Green ....❏
1970 4 wheel passenger coach - Green...❏
1971 4 wheel parcel coach - Green.........❏
1980 Touropa express coach - Blue ....❏
1982 Passenger coach - Green ....❏
1983 Sleeping car DSG - Red.................❏
1984 Dining car DSG - Red....................❏
1986 Express coach - Green ....❏
1987 Express luggage coach ....❏
1996 Diesel V.200 centre car - Red........❏
1997 Dutch centre car - Green ....❏
1998 Express parcel Swiss - Green.........❏
1999 Express coach Swiss - Green ....❏

SCALE MODELS
DESIGNED BY BASSETT-LOWKE

TWO TRAINS ON THE SAME TRACK UNDER SEPARATE CONTROL ——— IDEAL SIZE FOR MODERN ROOMS

L.N.E.R. 4472
"FLYING SCOTSMAN"

LOCOMOTIVE History in Great Britain was made in 1922 with the coming on the then Great Northern Railway of Sir Nigel Gresley's first "Pacific" locomotive—the most reliable and capable express class the country has yet seen. In speed, too, they excel, as witness the "Flying Scotsman's" test run in November 1934, attaining 100 m.p.h. Our model faithfully reproduces the leading external features.

SPECIFICATION.

Movement. The latest T.T.R. six-coupled electric mechanism—precision-made—all parts interchangeable—main axle bearing with continuous lubrication—working from 14 volts A.C and 12 volts D.C.

Control. Remote control reversing. Fitted with auto-uncoupling device in the tender by means of which the loco can be detached from its train anywhere on the track without the need for a ramp rail. The uncoupling device is operated with either the Standard or the Super Controller.

Wheels. Standard pattern—die-cast.

Body. Pressure die-cast from steel mould, ensuring accurate detail.

Valve Gear. Walschaert's, as illustration.

Tender. Eight-wheeled, fitted with automatic-uncoupling device.

Finish. The whole locomotive and tender hand painted in correct L.N.E.R. colours, with lettering and lining, according to the latest practice.

No. 4 540. L.N.E.R. 4-6-2. **£4.7.6**

"THE GREATEST LITTLE TRAIN IN THE WORLD"

6

Picture taken from the 1938/39 "Trix Twin" Railway catalogue

SCALE MODELS
DESIGNED BY BASSETT-LOWKE

THE NEW GAUGE 00 SCALE MODEL COACHES

This range of passenger rolling stock has been specially designed to suit the new 4-6-2 "Pacific" type locomotives already described.

They are made throughout of best steel plate, accurately pressed from precision dies, and have windows glazed with transparent "Celastoid." The bogies are of the latest type, fitted with insulated bakelite wheels. Axle boxes to scale are fitted under the main frames, and each vehicle is fitted for automatic coupling and remote control uncoupling, see page 14. Finish, lettering and lining are in the latest correct style.

Scale model L.M.S Brake Third Coach, all-steel type.
Length overall 8¾".

No. 2 577. **7/6**

Scale model L.M.S. Dining Car, all-steel type.
Length overall 8¾".

No. 2 587. **7/6**

Scale model L.M.S 1st Class Corridor Coach, all-steel type.
Length overall 8¾".

No. 2/567. **7/6**

Also in L.N.E.R. colours :
No. 4 577. Scale model L.N.E.R. Brake Third Coach. **7/6**

No. 4 587. Restaurant Car in L.N.E.R. colours : **7/6**

No. 4/567. Scale model L.N.E.R. 1st Class. **7/6**

LIGHTING UNITS

The realism of these model Coaches reaches its highest when they are electrically illuminated from the interior. The Lighting Units can be fitted to any of the scale model Coaches.   No. 767. **2/6**

Picture taken from the 1938/39 "Trix Twin" Railway catalogue

"TRIX TWIN" RAILWAY

SEPARATE LOCOMOTIVES

AMERICAN MODELS, with operating headlights. Passenger Engine and Tender with cow catcher free lance model **£4.15.6**

Freight or Switcher Engine with characteristic slope back tender 9/520. **£4.15.6**

PASSENGER LOCO and TENDER 0-4-0, B.R. Livery Green and Orange 1/520. **72/-**

GOODS LOCO and TENDER 0-4-0, B.R. Black with Emblem & Numbers 1/525. **72/-**

MIXED TRAFFIC TANK LOCO. Black with correct lining and lettering. 1/510. **63/-**

GOODS TANK LOCO. Black with correct emblem and number 1/515. **63/-**

4-4-0 Locos and Tenders finished in correct colours, lining and emblems. Compound Class Scale Model —Midland Region 2/536. **£6.6.**

or Hunt Class Scale Model Eastern Region 4/536. **£6.6.**

FLYING SCOTSMAN. Scale Model Loco & Tender correct in all details—traverses standard TRIX curves. Fitted with remote uncoupling in tender operating anywhere on track 1/540. **£10**

SPARE PARTS

31/ 2	Piston Rods	set	2,3
31/ 3	Reduction Gear		2,6
31/ 5	Control Shaft		2,6
31/ 10	Reversing Arm		3,3
31/ 25	Clamps and Screws	set	3,9
31/ 27	Carbon Brushes	,,	2,6
31/ 30	Side Frame		3,3
31/ 36	Wheels on Axles	set	3,3
31/ 40	Shoes for 0-4-0		3,6
57/ 40	Shoes for 4-6-2—4-4-0	,,	3,6
74/ 40	Shoes for Whistlg. Van	,,	3,3
31/ 50	Plugs - 6	,,	2,3
31/ 53	Shoes for 653	,,	3,-
31/ 72	Sockets for 31,74		4½d.
31/ 74	14-Volt Bulbs		1/2
31/ 77	Lamp for 439		1/-
31/ 78	TRIX Oil		9d.
31/ 85	Wire Coil		1/-
31/ 94	Shoes for Lighting	set	2/6
31/ 99	Instruction Book		1/6
31/200	Track Manual		3/6
31/285	Table Top Plan		1/6
31/303	Year Book with Catalogue		2/6
31/ 17	Uncoupler coupling not for conversions		6d.

London's Headquarters for 'Trix Twin'

GAMAGES, HOLBORN, LONDON, E.C.I. HOLborn 8484

38

Picture taken from the 1959 Gamages catalogue.

ACCESSORIES

Yard Lamps for Goods Yards and Stations, 14 volt-0.075 amps. 761	6/6
Station Notices—New Set of 6 No. 176	6/-
Trackside Notice—New Set of 6 No. 178	6/-
Signals—Hand-operated	
Home 701	2/9
Distant 705	2/9
Telegraph Pole 771	1/11
Derelict Coach Huts 551	9/-
Crane on Base 715	15/6

Model Crane Truck Set with detachable working Crane and match Truck.
615 .. .. .. Set 26/6

"TRIX TWIN" RAILWAY

PASSENGER ROLLING STOCK

Accurately stamped with precision dies from best steel plate, these models of modern all-steel stock are finished in correct approved livery.

SUBURBAN COMPARTMENT COACH

NEW—correct dimensions, 7 in. long. 1/553		11/6
Bogie Parcels Van to attach to all trains NEW—1/557		11/6

EXPRESS BOGIE COACHES

Correct B.R. colours, 7 in. long.

1/560	1st Class	11/6
1/570	Brake third	11/6
1/580	Dining Car	11/6

AMERICAN PASSENGER STOCK

9/565	Pullman Coach	22/6
9/585	Observation Car	22/6
9/575	Baggage Car	22/6

SCALE MODEL COACHES WITH LIGHTS

Each fitted with 2-lamp lighting unit 8¾ in. long.

1/578	Brake Third with red tail light in addition to inside light	21/6
1/568	1st Class with lights	21/6
1/588	Dining Car with lights	21/6

LIGHTING UNITS for SCALE MODEL

Coaches only—2 bulbs—767 .. .. 8/-

599 Pullman Saloon with lights .. 25/9

DO YOU KNOW? *British Railways' Steepest Main Line Gradient—Lickey Incline (1 in 37.7)*

39

"TRIX TWIN" RAILWAY

LIGHTED
Goods Brake, 653 **19/9**
Scale Model, Red Tail and White Window Light. New Light Alloy, Die Cast Shell on fully detailed underframe casting, makes any Goods Train complete.

OPERATING
Dump Wagon, 666 **20/-** Ingenious Action, Super detail die cast hopper body on die cast chassis. A masterpiece of small scale engineering.

The wagons in this group are fitted with super detail Die Cast underframes with Dummy Brake Gear and new Floating Axle Suspension.

T.T.R. WELTROL WAGONS

Perfect reproductions of the B.R. prototype sharp super detail castings, 7 in. long

AMERICAN FREIGHT CARS

Fine reproductions of principal types in use on the great American and Canadian Railroad systems.

662	Tarpaulin Wagon	7/9
637	Coal Wagon, High Side	5/9
638	Ballast Wagon	5/9
639	Container Wagon	8/6
634	Open High Side	4/9
632	Open Low Side	4/6
630	3-Plank	4/3
644	Tank Wagon-Shell	7/9
641	Tank Wagon-Esso	7/9

677	WELTROL, without load	13/6
678	„ with Marine Boiler	20/-
679	„ with Transformer	20/-
680	„ with Cable Drum	20/-
671	BOGIE BOLSTER WAGON	10/6
673	„ Timber Loaded Wagon	12/-
675	„ Brick Wagon	10/6
676	„ High Capacity	10/6

681	Flat Car	9/6
682	Lumber Empty	10/6
683	Lumber Loaded	12/-
684	Gondola Car	10/6
685	Box Car	13/-

686	Refrigerator Car	13/-
687	Fruit Car	13/-
688	Union Tank Car	14/6
689	Texaco Tank Car (illus.)	14/6
690	Caboose Car	16/3

636 Cattle Wagon 5/3   651 Goods Brake 5/6

GAMAGES, HOLBORN, LONDON, E.C.I. HOLborn 8484   *Open Thursdays until 7 p.m.*

40

Picture taken from the 1959 Gamages catalogue.

This listing is taken from a Wells price list of 1969. Prices shown are Wells' suggested retail price in shillings and pre-decimal pence. We would welcome more information.

A. WELLS & CO. LTD & BRIMTOY LTD
Head Office: Progress Works, Kingsland, Holyhead, Anglesey, North Wales.
Telephone: 0407-2391 (3 lines)
Cables: "Welsotoy", Holyhead, N.Wales

TRAIN SETS

Price List - 1969

Code No.	Description	Suggested Customer Price

No.969 **'OO' Gauge train set**, plastic engine, metal chassis, two passenger coaches, six curved rails, packed in display box. (Clockwork)..17s.11d.

No.967 **'OO' Gauge train set**, plastic engine freight van, guards van, tunnel, double arm signal, eight curved rails, packed in display box. (Clockwork). ....33s.9d.

No.942 **'O' Gauge metal Diesel Engine**, one passenger coach, six curved rails, packed in display box. (Clockwork)....22s.11d.

No.943 **'O' Gauge metal Diesel Engine**, two coaches, six curved and two straight rails, packed in display box. (Clockwork). ....29s.11d.

No.947 **'O' Gauge Electric Type Loco**, one passenger coach, six curved rails and two straight rails, packed in display box. ....26s.11d.

No.948 **'O' Gauge Electric Type Loco**, two coaches, six curved rails and two straight rails, double arm signal, tunnel, packed in display box..40s.11d.

No.981 **'OO' Gauge 'Super-Power' Electric Type Loco**, two passenger coaches, eight curved rails, packed in display box 32s.11d.

No.982 **'OO' Gauge 'Super-Power' Electric Type Loco**, one open goods truck, one oil tanker, eight curved rails, packed in display box..32s.11d.

No.457 **Railway Bridge**, makes two different types of bridge, fits both 'O' and 'OO' Gauge sets....................................5s.9d.

No.186 **Cherokee Turnabout Locomotive**: All metal fitted with novelty clockwork which turns loco at both ends of track. 'Western' style engine. Individually boxed. Size: 11" x 2" x 2". ....9s.11d.

No.275 **Magic Shunting Train**: All metal engine and goods wagon, operates on figure eight track. Size: 18" x 8" x 2"..17s.11d.

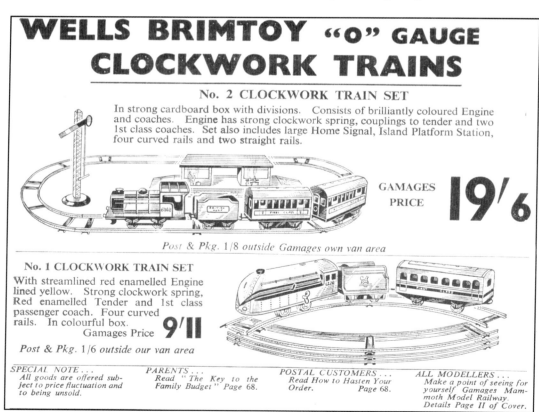

THE CORGI HERITAGE CENTRE
53 YORK STREET, HEYWOOD, NR. ROCHDALE, LANCS OL10 4NR
TEL: 01706 365812 FAX: 01706 627811
A CORGI CLASSICS VENTURE IN CO-OPERATION WITH CHRIS BRIERLEY MODELS

VISIT THE NEW CORGI HERITAGE CENTRE

- The complete range of Corgi Classics
- Selected obsolete Corgi Models
- Worldwide Mail Order Service
- Standing order facilities
- Discounts for Corgi Collector Club members
- Regular Corgi Collector Club presence, facilities for joining the Club on the spot & Club merchandise available
- Free Admission

MUSEUM OF CORGI MODELS
PAST & PRESENT

- Discover the fascinating history of Corgi models through exhibits and graphic displays, original point of sale and catalogues
- See how your Corgi model is made - stage by stage
- A Hornby Railway display complementing the Corgi Original Omnibus vehicles
- The Corgi Heritage Centre offers you the chance to discover the fascinating history of Corgi diecast model vehicles. It's a collector's heaven, and one visit will inspire you to add some 'Classic' pieces to the collection you already have, begin a collection for a relative or a friend, or even start collecting for the very first time.

(Closed Tuesday and Sunday at present)

The Corgi Heritage Centre, 53 York Street, Heywood, Nr Rochdale, Lancs. OL10 4NR.
Tel: 01706 365 812 Fax: 01706 627 811
email: corgi@zen.co.uk
http://www.zen.co.uk/home/page/corgi/

Disabled access. Free car park at rear.
Easy to get to by road and rail.

Index of Model Manufacturers

Bachmann..183
Bassett-Lowke.................26, 27, 29-32, 39, 77-84, 200
Bing....27, 30, 31, 33, 39, 75, 77-80, 84, 107, 181, 190
Brimtoy...190, 203
Carette.......................................27, 30, 33, 84
Chad Valley 190
Dinky Toys 81, 186, 191
Graham-Farish.............................26, 175, 177, 180
Hornby Trains 9, 12, 26, 27, 29, 31, 37, 39, 40,
51-53, 56-71, 74-77, 80-84, 190, 191
Hornby Dublo......26, 27, 31, 38, 39, 87-112, 126, 165,
171, 173, 176, 177, 179-181, 186, 188, 189
Leeds Model Company 26, 27, 72, 74
Lone Star..................................28, 186, 190, 191
Lima 175, 180, 181
Lines Brothers.......................................26, 27, 71, 126

Mainline 104, 109, 175, 177, 178, 180
Marklin 26, 32, 77-80, 84, 107, 108
Marx 26, 80, 190
Master Models 195-197
Mettoy 27, 190, 198, 199
Millbro...26, 27, 74
Playcraft..199
Rovex 26, 126
Trackmaster 26, 126
Tri-ang 9, 12, 26, 27, 71, 100, 101, 126-152
Tri-ang TT...153, 154
Trix Twin Railways 26, 27, 30, 31, 106, 107,
176-181, 200, 201
Wells..27, 190, 205
Wrenn 9, 12, 26, 126, 165-174, 176, 179,
181-183, 185

WHEN REPLYING TO ADVERTISEMENTS PLEASE MENTION JOHN RAMSAY'S CATALOGUE